W9-DJJ-223

theory of
ARITHMETIC

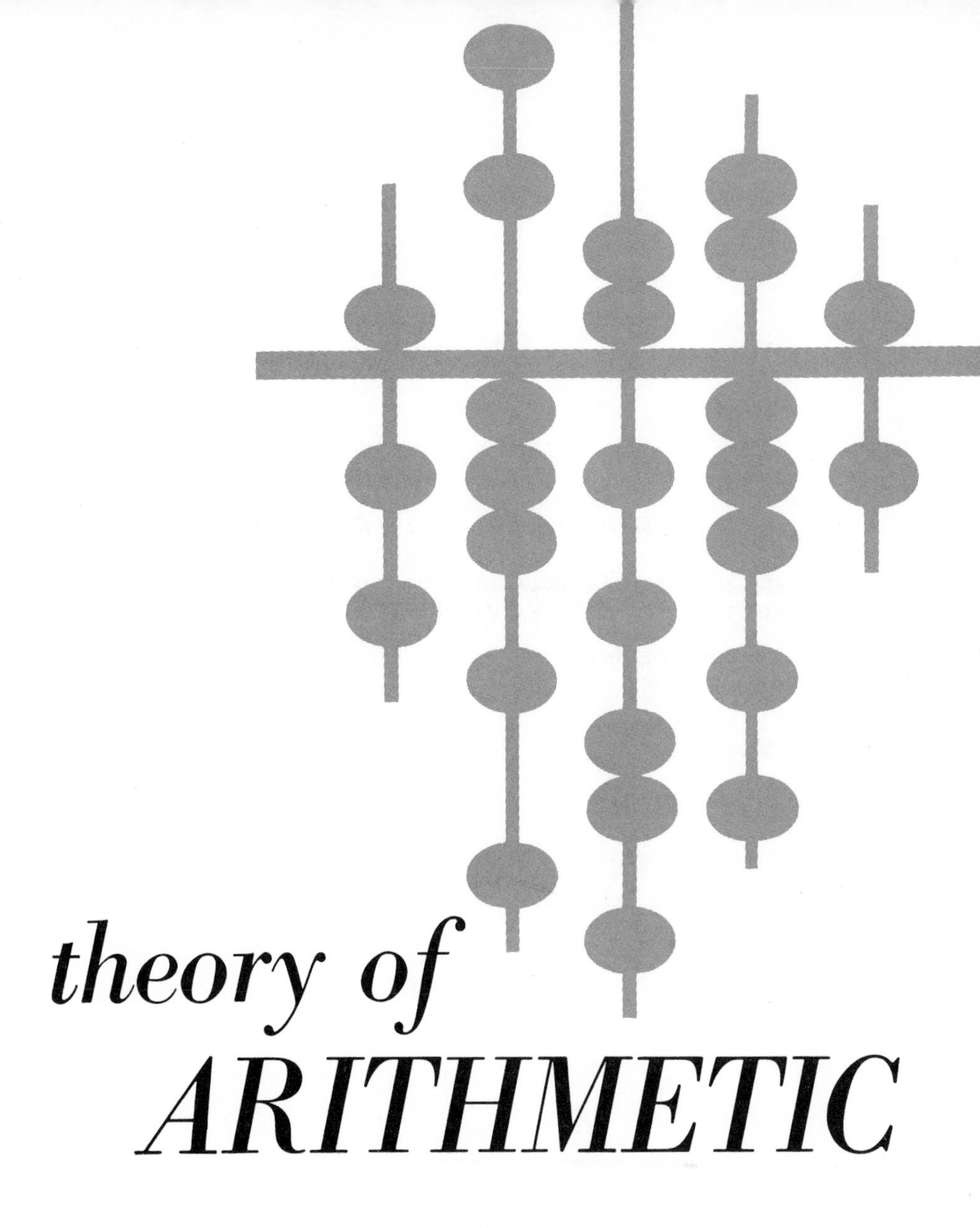

theory of *ARITHMETIC*

JOHN A. PETERSON
Assistant Professor of Mathematics, Montana State University

JOSEPH HASHISAKI
Professor of Mathematics, Western Washington State College

JOHN WILEY & SONS, INC., NEW YORK • LONDON

Library of Congress Catalog Card Number: 63-11445
Printed in the United States of America

SECOND PRINTING, JULY, 1963

Preface

This textbook is the result of six years of experimenting with mathematics training for teachers of elementary school arithmetic. The primary objective has been to provide them with the background necessary to teach what the authors anticipate will be included in the elementary school arithmetic curriculum during the next few years.

Recently more mathematicians have become actively interested in participating in the extremely important task of training elementary teachers. In general, they consider that *accurate knowledge of the subject matter is an essential prerequisite to teaching arithmetic.* It is with this point of view that *Theory of Arithmetic* was designed for a course to be taught in the department of mathematics. It is intended as a textbook for a background material course for students preparing to teach at the elementary or junior high school levels. The emphasis is on the "why" in the procedures of arithmetic computation. *Special attention was given to the formulation of precise definitions and to the simple, accurate presentation of fundamental ideas.* "Techniques" have been kept to a minimum, for these are usually taught in "methods" courses.

The book starts with the traditional historical material but quickly introduces the notions of sets and relations. These concepts are presented as a natural beginning of a course in arithmetic—not simply because they are of current interest. The book emphasizes the structure of the number systems, and the binary operations become "objects" of study. *The integration of the properties of a system of numeration with the structure of the number systems is used to clarify the procedures of arith-*

metic computation. The concepts of relations and properties of relations are introduced informally through many examples and exercises. After these concepts have been made precise, equivalence relations and equivalence classes are introduced. These ideas are used in the treatment of the system of rational numbers. Order has been carefully introduced in each of the number systems so that the concepts of *denseness* and *completeness* can be presented and made precise. The real numbers are treated in terms of least upper bounds and as infinite decimals, both consistent with sound mathematical concepts. *This is a unique feature of the book.*

The materials included have been successfully used in preparing teachers to teach in so-called "new approaches" to arithmetic. We have observed that teachers who took the course taught from this book have had no difficulty in using any of the newer textbooks in arithmetic. It was our good fortune to have taught in one of the first eleven National Science Foundation In-Service Institutes for teachers of elementary school arithmetic during the academic year, 1959–60. This experience, and the experience and insight gained in working with potential teachers, has been invaluable in helping us select those materials of greatest interest and help to the teachers. The attitudes of the experienced teachers have provided encouragement and guidance. Many asked why the course taught from this material was not available to them sooner.

The book is written in a language and style designed to appeal to a wide range of students, students differing both in ability and in mathematical maturity. The simplicity of the language, numerous examples, and exercises designed to promote understanding, have proved it an effective teaching instrument. It is being used in a formal course at the university level. It was designed so that it can be used at colleges of education and junior colleges, as well as for in-service training programs. Undergraduates and graduates have found it readable and challenging. Liberal arts students take the course as an introduction to mathematics.

The material is presented in sufficient detail so that it can be taught to students who have had the usual college preparatory mathematics. Chapters 2 through 8 include the key ideas in the development of this material and should serve as the core of any course for which this book is used as a text. Under the quarter system the first eight chapters, minus a few selected topics, have proven adequate for a 5-hour, one-quarter course. Time allotted to the topics, including time for review and examination, has been essentially as follows:

Hours 1–4. Chapters 1 and 2, with most of the time spent on the language of sets.

Hours 5–10. Chapter 3, with a careful treatment of relations and their properties.

Hours 11–15. Chapter 4, with emphasis on the development of a complete understanding of the place-value system of numeration.

Hours 16–23. Chapter 5, introduction to operations and the first development of a number system.

Hours 24–33. Chapter 6, extension of the concepts of the previous chapter to the set of integers with careful consideration of prime factorization, the division algorithm, the Euclidean algorithm, and related topics.

Hours 34–42. Chapter 7, with emphasis on understanding the rational number as an element of the rational number system, rational numbers as equivalence classes, the concept of denseness, and the usual interpretations of rational numbers.

Hours 43–48. Chapter 8, with emphasis on decimal approximations, the real numbers as infinite decimals, completeness, the real line, and the approximation of square roots.

By careful consideration of all topics of the first eight chapters and inclusion of Chapter 9 this could be extended to a 3-hour, two-quarter sequence. Under the semester system, the material is adequate for a 4- or 5-hour, one-semester course.

In regard to the arrangement of the material in the text, each chapter consists of several sections and possibly subsections. These are identified by a number followed by a period, then a number or a combination of a number and a letter. The first number identifies the chapter and the one following the period identifies the section or subsection. For example, the symbol 5.7 is used to identify Chapter 5, Section 7; the symbol 5.7a identifies the first subsection of that section. Definitions and exercises are numbered in a similar manner for easy reference. Definition 5.5a is the first definition of Section 5, Chapter 5. References to other material mentioned briefly in the context are listed completely in alphabetical order at the end of each chapter. Answers to selected exercises appear at the end of the book.

We wish to acknowledge the constructive criticism and suggestions of Dr. W. R. Ballard of the Department of Mathematics, Montana State University, and the reviewers of the publishers, in particular, Dr. Roy Dubisch, Department of Mathematics, University of Washington. We wish to express our appreciation to the publishers for their helpful assistance and guidance and to the many students who over the years have assisted in the development of this material. We also wish to express our appreciation to the School of Education, Montana State University, and in particular to Dr. Frances Hanson, for their cooperation with the Department of Mathematics in the development of the mathematics program for the elementary teaching major.

Missoula, Montana
Bellingham, Washington
December, 1962

JOHN A. PETERSON
JOSEPH HASHISAKI

Contents

one * *The Origin of Numerals and Systems of Numeration, 1*

1.1 Introduction 1.2 The Hindu-Arabic Symbols 1.3 Systems of Numeration 1.4 Additive Systems of Numeration 1.5 Multiplicative Systems of Numeration 1.6 Place-Value Systems of Numeration 1.7 Summary 1.8 The Counting Board 1.9 The Abacus

two * *Sets, 20*

2.1 Introduction 2.2 Sets 2.3 Subsets 2.4 New Sets from Old 2.5 The Complement of a Set 2.6 The Cartesian Product of Sets

three * *Relations and Their Properties, 37*

3.1 Introduction 3.2 The Inclusion Relation 3.3 The Reflexive Property of Relations 3.4 The Transitive Property of Relations 3.5 The Sameness Relation 3.6 Properties of the "Sameness" (Equals) Relation for Sets 3.7 The Symmetric Property of Relations 3.8 The "Divides" Relation 3.9 The "R, S, T" Properties 3.10 One-to-One Correspondence 3.11 The Matching Relation 3.12 An Equivalence Relation 3.13 The Cardinal Number of a Set 3.14 More on Relations in General 3.15 Relations as Sets 3.16 Order *four* * *Systems of Numeration, 59*

4.1 Exponents 4.2 The Hindu-Arabic System 4.3 The Decimal Point 4.4 Expanding and Reading Large Numbers 4.5 Other Bases for Counting 4.6 Finger Counting 4.7 Changing Bases of Numerals 4.8 Counting Systems in Other Bases 4.9 Computation in Other Bases

five * *The System of Whole Numbers, 81*

5.1 Introduction 5.2 Ordinal and Cardinal Use of Natural Numbers 5.3 The Set of Whole Numbers 5.4 Systems of Numeration and Number Systems 5.5 Binary Operations 5.6 Addition in W 5.7 Multiplication in W 5.8 The Distributive Law 5.9 Special Properties of Zero and One 5.10 The System of Whole Numbers 5.11 The Algorithms 5.12 Order Relations for the Whole Numbers

six * *The System of Integers, 112*

6.1 Introduction 6.2 The Set of Integers 6.3 Properties of the Set of Integers 6.4 The System of Integers 6.5 The Cancellation Laws 6.6 Prime Numbers and Composite Numbers 6.7 Prime Factorization 6.8 The Division Algorithm 6.9 The Greatest Common Divisor 6.10 The Least Common Multiple 6.11 Order Relations for the Integers 6.12 The Number Line for the Integers 6.13 Clock Arithmetic (Optional) 6.14 The Congruence Relation

seven * *The System of Rational Numbers, 151*

7.1 Introduction 7.2 Interpretation of Number Pairs 7.3 The Set of Rational Numbers 7.4 Equivalence Relation for Ordered Pairs of Integers 7.5 Equivalence Classes of Ordered Pairs of Integers 7.6 Rational Numbers as Equivalence Classes 7.7 Addition of Rational Numbers 7.8 Multiplication of Rational Numbers 7.9 Naming of Classes (Reducing Fractions) 7.10 The System of Rational Numbers 7.11 Interpretations of Rational Numbers 7.12 Order in the Rational Numbers 7.13 Introduction to Irrational Numbers

eight * *The System of Real Numbers, 193*

8.1 Introduction 8.2 The Number Line 8.3 The Set of Real Numbers 8.4 Decimal Fractions 8.5 Approximations 8.6 Decimal Approximations of Rational Numbers 8.7 Real Numbers as Infinite Decimals 8.8 The Real Line 8.9 Order Relations in the Reals 8.10 The System of Real Numbers

8.11 Repeating Decimals 8.12 Rounding Off Decimal Approximations 8.13 Decimal Approximations of Irrational Numbers 8.14 Square Roots

nine * *Topics from Geometry, 226*

9.1 Introduction 9.2 Lengths of Line Segments 9.3 Areas 9.4 Volumes and Surface Area 9.5 Similar Plane Figures 9.6 The Pythagorean Theorem 9.7 The Number π 9.8 Introduction to Coordinate Geometry

Answers to Selected Exercises, 271

Index, 299

Table of Symbols

$\in$	is an element of, membership, 22
$\notin$	is not an element of, 22
$=$	is a name for, 22
A	$= \{x \| x$ has a certain property$\}$, 23
$\subseteq$	inclusion, 25
$\subset$	proper inclusion, 25
$\emptyset$	empty set, null set, 26
U	universal set, 26
$\cup$	union, 29
$\cap$	intersection, 29
A'	complement of, 31
$\times$	Cartesian product, 33
Ⓡ	relation, 39
$\mid$	divides, 43
$\nmid$	does not divide, 43
1-1	one-to-one correspondence, 46
$[a]$	equivalence class, 47, 145
$n(S)$	cardinal of S, 50
$<$	less than, 54
$\leqq$	less than or equal, 54
$*$	binary operation, 87
^{-}n	additive inverse, 144
$\|m\|$	absolute value, 140

J_{12}	145
$\equiv$	congruence, 144
$\doteq$	equivalent, 155
$\left[\frac{m}{n}\right]$	equivalence class, 157
$\%$	percent, 183
N	set of natural numbers, 23, 43, 84
W	set of whole numbers, 84
J	set of integers, 114
R	set of rational numbers, 171

*
*
*

CHAPTER ONE

The Origin of Numerals and Systems of Numeration

1.1 INTRODUCTION

In the study of arithmetic we shall be concerned with fundamental concepts and their relation to procedures and techniques in current use. None could be more fundamental than the concepts of "number" and "numeral." The distinction between these is consistently overlooked because the term "number" is commonly used in reference to either concept. The number "names" are called *numerals*. They are what we write or say when we refer to the abstract concept of *number*. In what follows we make this distinction whenever it adds to the clarity of the presentation.

We begin our study with a brief summary of the history of numerals and systems of numeration. These are "tools of the trade" of the arithmetician, and some knowledge of their origin leads to better understanding of their use. We are interested not so much in computation in other systems as in the principles that underlie the systems so that we may understand and appreciate our own.

Statements regarding the origin of the concept of number must necessarily be conjectural in nature. It seems logical to assume that man always had some intuitive notion of "more than" and "less than." In the development of civilization, the quantitative aspects of the environment dictated the development of some means of answering the question, "How many?" This can be done without numerals. Some sort of tally system is all that is needed to answer this question. The tally system might involve pebbles in a bag, sticks tied in a bundle, notches cut in a stick, knots tied in a rope, or marks in the sand. Whatever the type of device used to form the reference set, the principle involved is the same, namely, a matching between the objects being counted and the reference set. The set consisting of the fingers of the hands was, and for some purposes still is, the most convenient reference set. From this man developed a set of words to use as a more convenient reference set for keeping track of "how many." The next step was from the oral words to written words, then to symbols and the development of systems of numeration. Ancient records support this line of reasoning.

1.2 THE HINDU-ARABIC SYMBOLS

The symbols we use in our present-day arithmetic are referred to as Hindu-Arabic, Hindu because they were probably originated by the Hindus and Arabic because they came to Europe in the Arabic language. The earliest preserved examples of our present numerals are found on some stone columns in India dating from about 250 B.C. Other early examples are found among records cut about 100 B.C. on the walls of a cave in a hill near Poona, India, and in some inscriptions of about A.D. 200 carved in the caves at Nasik, India. These early examples contain no zero and do not employ place value. Place value, however, and also zero, must have been introduced before A.D. 800, for the Persian mathematician al-Khowârizmî describes such a completed system in a book dated A.D. 825. Just how the new numerals were transmitted to Europe is not historically clear. Probably they were transmitted by traders and travelers. The Arabs invaded the Iberian Peninsula in A.D. 711 and, no doubt, introduced the new symbols to the Spaniards. In a book written in Spain, dated A.D. 976, the following set of symbols was recorded:

9 8 7 6 5 4 3 2 1

Changes in the shape of the symbols from the earliest known form to those in use today can be attributed primarily to the scribes who did the copy work. With the advent of the printing press at about the middle of the fifteenth century the symbols were fairly well standardized, only slight changes in form having occurred since then.

Considering the individual symbols, it is quite clear that the symbol for "one," 1, was a natural outgrowth of such things as one tally, one stick, etc. The symbol for "two" probably began as || or $=$. The former followed a rather natural evolution from || to N to ٢, which is the present-day symbol for two used by the Mohammedan people. Similarly, the latter symbol = may have changed from = to Z, and then to 2, which is the symbol we use. The symbol for "three" possibly changed from ||| to W to ʌʌʌ to ٣, which is again the present-day symbol used by the Mohammedan people, or from ≡ to ≷ to 3, our present-day symbol. To conjecture the origin of the symbol we use for "four" is much more difficult. The Arabic symbol for four, ٤ , is the only symbol involving four joined straight lines for the number four. Little is known or conjectured about the origin of the other symbols. The table on page 454 of Vol. I, Newman, gives an interesting comparison of the shapes of the Hindu-Arabic symbols from the twelfth century to the advent of the printing press in the fifteenth.

1.3 SYSTEMS OF NUMERATION

By a *system of numeration* we mean a set of symbols that is used according to some scheme for assigning numerals, or number symbols, to numbers. In order to understand better and appreciate our own system of numeration, we shall investigate some other systems that have been or are now used. We shall be interested not so much in the particular symbolism of each system as in the principles and concepts involved.

All the systems of numeration have certain characteristics in common. The number of symbols is finite, varying from as few as two in some systems to thirty or more in others. Since the number of symbols is finite, it is necessary at times to use the same symbol more than once in the representation of a number. This is true with every system. Every system possesses a symbol for the number "one." In some systems subsequent numbers are written by repeated use of this symbol (the repetitive principle) until the collection becomes not readily recognizable or inconvenient because of sheer bulk; then a new symbol is introduced to replace the collection of "one-symbols." In other systems distinct single-character symbols are used to represent subsequent numbers up to a certain number, then a symbol of two or more characters is introduced. This number that marks the changeover is what is commonly referred to as the *base of the system.* In most cases this number is ten. This compounding of the previous symbols was early recognized as a powerful way to represent large numbers with an economy of symbols.

In addition, there are underlying principles that play varying roles in different systems and certain concepts that occur in some and not in others. The concepts and principles are important and, once understood, allow us to invent new symbols and to construct other systems of numeration. These principles form our basis for classifying the systems of numeration. We consider several systems with these thoughts in mind.

1.4 ADDITIVE SYSTEMS OF NUMERATION

Additive systems of numeration are characterized as those systems that rely primarily on the additive principle to determine the number represented by a given set of symbols. They have symbols for the number one, for the base, and powers of the base, and sometimes for multiples of powers of the base. The *repetitive principle,* that is, repeated use of the same symbol, is used in representing numbers between powers of the base. The number represented by a particular set of symbols is simply the sum of the numbers each symbol of the set represents. This is the *additive principle.*

To clarify these underlying principles, let us examine some examples of such systems.

1.4a The Egyptian Hieroglyphic System

The Egyptian hieroglyphic system dates back as early as 3000 B.C. and was used for some two thousand years. Table 1 is a partial list of the symbols used with the Hindu-Arabic equivalents and a word description.

TABLE 1

EGYPTIAN HIEROGLYPHICS

Hindu-Arabic or Decimal	Egyptian	Description
1	𓏺	A staff (vertical stroke)
10	𓎆	A heel bone (arch)
100	𓍢	A scroll (coiled rope)
1000	𓆼	A lotus flower
10,000	𓂭	A pointing finger
100,000	𓆐	A bourbot fish (tadpole)
1,000,000	𓁨	A man in astonishment

These symbols are used to represent a number in the same way that coins and bills are used to make up a given sum of money. The one-symbol is used repeatedly to represent the numbers one through nine. Essentially this amounts to constructing a representative set for a matching between the objects being counted and the repeated one-symbols. The other symbols represent a compounding of the previous symbols, and any number is expressed by using these symbols additively. Consider the following examples:

Example 1

means 1000 + 1000 + 100 + 10 + 10 + 1 + 1 + 1 + 1, which is 2124 as a decimal numeral.

Example 2

means 1,000,000 + 1 + 1 + 1 + 1 + 1 + 1 + 100 + 1000 + 10, which is 1,001,116 as a decimal numeral.

Example 3

means 10 + 10 + 10 + 10 + 10 + 10 + 10 + 10 + 1 + 1 + 1 + 1 + 1 + 1 + 1, which is 87 as a decimal numeral.

Note that in a simply additive system of numeration such as this, the order in which the symbols appear is immaterial.

Adding and subtracting Egyptian numerals are as easy as making change. Multiplication and division must have been something of a chore when using their cumbersome system, especially without benefit of pencil and paper. The Egyptians had methods for performing these operations (see Swain, p. 81). Also, fractions were understood and used by Egyptians (see Eves, pp. 39–40). We do not present the details of computation in the various systems here, for our interest is primarily in the properties of the systems of numeration for comparison with our own system.

To summarize, the Egyptian hieroglyphic system possesses the following properties. The symbols are hieroglyphs and as many as forty-five of six different symbols are required to represent numbers to and including 100,000. The repetitive principle is used in representing numbers between one and the base, which is ten, and between powers of the base. The additive principle applies to any set of symbols to determine the number represented.

Exercise 1.4a

1. Express the following in Egyptian numerals:

(a) 77 (b) 629 (c) 90,909
(d) 2,507,916 (e) 2124 (f) 1,001,116
(g) 808

2. Write the Hindu-Arabic equivalent of the following Egyptian numerals:

(a) (c)

(b) (d)

3. Write in Egyptian numerals

(a) the sum of (a) and (b) of problem 2.
(b) the sum of (a) and (c) of problem 2.
(c) the sum of (b) and (a) of problem 2.

1.4b The Roman System

The Roman numerals and system of numeration date from the time of the ancient Romans. These numerals were commonly used in bookkeeping in European countries until the eighteenth century, although the Hindu-Arabic numerals were generally known as early as the year 1000. The introduction of the printing press saw a rapid change to the Hindu-Arabic numerals, although the Roman numerals continued in use in some schools until about 1600. The Roman numerals are still in use to a limited extent. Examples of their present-day usage are as numerals on a clock face, as chapter numbers in a book, and as section numbers in an outline.

Much has been written relative to Roman notation. It is not our purpose to examine the system in detail but simply to look at some of the general characteristics (see Newman, pp. 447–449).

As now used, the symbols for Roman numerals are summarized in Table 2.

TABLE 2

ROMAN NUMERALS

Decimal	1		10		100		1000
Roman	I		X		C		M
Decimal		5		50		500	
Roman		V		L		D	

The Roman system is also essentially an additive system of numeration in that a number designated by a set of symbols is simply the sum of the numbers represented by each of the symbols in the set. A symbol with a bar above it indicates the number represented by that symbol multiplied by 1000. A double bar means multiplication by one thousand thousand or 1,000,000. This is an example of the *multiplicative principle.*

Example 1

$$\text{MDCCCLXII} = 1000 + 500 + 100 + 100 + 100 + 50 + 10 + 1 + 1$$
$$= 1862 \text{ in the Hindu-Arabic system.}$$

With so few symbols in an additive system, a great deal of repetition is necessary to express some large numbers. For example, the Hindu-Arabic numeral 387 is written CCCLXXXVII. How many symbols would be necessary to designate the number that in Hindu-Arabic is symbolized 8888?

Present-day use of the Roman system also involves the *subtractive principle.* This principle states that if a symbol of a smaller number precedes a symbol of a larger number, the two are considered as a pair. The number represented by the pair is the larger number minus the smaller number. Present-day usage has this principle restricted to the numerals for four and nine, forty and ninety, four hundred and nine hundred, and so forth. Table 3 summarizes this property.

TABLE 3

ROMAN NUMERAL SUBTRACTIVE PRINCIPLE

IV = IIII	XL = XXXX	CD = CCCC
IX = VIIII	XC = LXXXX	CM = DCCCC

Any extension of the use of this principle to more than pairs of symbols could lead to ambiguous results, for example, IXC could be interpreted as 100 − 9, or as 100 − 10 − 1, resulting in a designation for 91 or 89, depending on the interpretation. Note that the subtractive principle necessitates *ordering* of the symbols for proper interpretation.

In summary, the Roman system possesses the following properties. The symbols are, at present, letters of the alphabet and as many as twenty of six different symbols along with the multiplicative principle are required to represent numbers to and including 100,000. The repetitive principle is used in representing numbers between those for which distinct symbols are available. This system is what might be called a modified base ten system in that intermediate symbols are introduced for five, fifty, and five hundred. The additive principle applies, as does the subtractive principle. The multiplicative principle applies in representing large numbers.

Exercise 1.4b

1. Express the following in Roman numerals:

(a) 26	(b) 39	(c) 49
(d) 342	(e) 431	(f) 449
(g) 1551	(h) 1961	(i) 2409

2. Express each of the following in Hindu-Arabic numerals:

(a) XXXVII	(b) XLIX	(c) XCIV
(d) CCCLXII	(e) CDLVII	(f) DCXLIV
(g) MCLI	(h) MCMXLV	(i) MMCMXCIX

3. State some advantages of the Roman system over the Egyptian system.

4. For numbers less than one thousand, the addition facts for the Roman system consist of the following:

IIIII = V	VV = X
XXXXX = L	LL = C
CCCCC = D	DD = M

(a) Add: MDCCCLXII + CXLIV
(*Note:* Here it is helpful to write CXLIV as CXXXXIIII.)
(b) Add: MDXII + DCVII
(c) Subtract: MCCVI − DCLXIII

1.4c The Ionic Greek System

The Ionic Greek numeral system was also a system of this type but with a more complicated set of symbols. The set of symbols consisted of the twenty-four letters of the Greek alphabet, plus three additional for the obsolete digamma, sampi, and koppa. Initially capital letters were used, later the small letters. The system necessitated memorizing the set of symbols given in Table 4.

TABLE 4

IONIC GREEK NUMERALS

1	α	alpha	10	ι	iota	100	ρ	rho
2	β	beta	20	κ	kappa	200	σ	sigma
3	γ	gamma	30	λ	lambda	300	τ	tau
4	δ	delta	40	μ	mu	400	υ	upsilon
5	ϵ	epsilon	50	ν	nu	500	ϕ	phi
6	obsolete digamma		60	ξ	xi	600	χ	chi
7	ζ	zeta	70	o	omicron	700	ψ	psi
8	η	eta	80	π	pi	800	ω	omega
9	θ	theta	90	obsolete koppa		900	obsolete sampi	

With this system numbers could be written in a more compact form, although still of the additive type, for example,

$$\lambda\gamma = 33 \quad \chi\xi\epsilon = 665 \quad \pi\eta = 88$$

For the multiples of 1000, the first nine symbols were used with a "prime" thus, $\alpha' = 1000$, $\beta' = 2000$, etc. For 10,000 M was used, and the multiplicative principle was applied for larger numbers, for example, $\beta M = 20{,}000$. $\varsigma M\beta'\upsilon\nu\beta = 72{,}452$.

You will note that there are advantages and disadvantages in the Ionic Greek system over the other systems we have discussed. The principal advantage is in the economy of symbols. For numbers up to one thousand the number of symbols required to express a number is the same as in the Hindu-Arabic system of numeration. The principal disadvantages are that there are so many symbols to memorize and that they are letters of the alphabet and may be confused with words.

Characterization of this system includes the following facts. The symbols are letters of an early Greek alphabet, twenty-seven in number, and as many as seven of these along with the multiplicative principle are required to represent numbers up to and including 100,000. This is a base ten system, and the additive principle applies.

Exercise 1.4c

In the following, use *d* for digamma, *k* for koppa and *s* for sampi.

1. Express the following Hindu-Arabic numerals in the Ionic Greek system:

(a) 36	(b) 39	(c) 49
(d) 342	(e) 431	(f) 449
(g) 1551	(h) 1961	(i) 2409

2. Express the following Ionic Greek numerals in Hindu-Arabic notation:

(a) $\mu\delta$	(b) $\pi\varsigma$	(c) $\chi\nu\gamma$
(d) $\sigma\delta$	(e) $\rho o\beta$	(f) $\rho\iota\gamma$
(g) $d'\upsilon\lambda\epsilon$	(h) $\theta'\psi\kappa\epsilon$	(i) $\epsilon M\delta'\phi\xi\varsigma$

3. State some advantages and disadvantages, in addition to those mentioned above, of the Ionic Greek system as compared to the Roman and Egyptian systems of numeration.

1.5 MULTIPLICATIVE SYSTEMS OF NUMERATION

In these systems symbols are chosen for one, two, three, etc., up to the base, and another set chosen to represent powers of the base. These symbols are then used with the multiplicative and additive principles to represent any number.

1.5a Chinese-Japanese System

The traditional Chinese-Japanese numeral system is of this type. A partial list of symbols with an example follows:

1 一	10 十	2,345
2 二	100 百	二
3 三	1000 千	千
4 四		三
5 五		百
6 六		四
7 七		十
8 八		五
9 九		

Exercise 1.5a

1. Express the following Hindu-Arabic numerals in the Japanese system:

(a) 42	(b) 54	(c) 36
(d) 125	(e) 246	(f) 782
(g) 2146	(h) 1984	(i) 5469

2. Express the following Japanese numerals in Hindu-Arabic symbols:

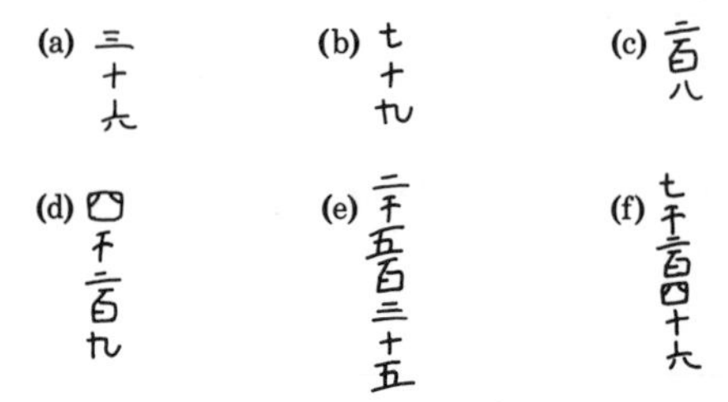

3. List some of the advantages and disadvantages of the Japanese system as compared to the systems previously mentioned.

4. Compare the Japanese system with the Hindu-Arabic system.

5. Construct the tables of elementary facts for addition and multiplication for the Japanese system of numeration.

1.6 PLACE-VALUE SYSTEMS OF NUMERATION

This is the type of system of numeration with which we are most familiar, for "our" system, the Hindu-Arabic, is a place-value system. In this type of system symbols are chosen for zero, one, two, etc., up to, but not including, the base. In the decimal system these symbols are referred to as *digits*. For a system of base "b" there are "b" such symbols. Then any number can be expressed uniquely as a sum of terms, each of which is one of the basic symbols times a *power* of the base. The power of the base by which each of the basic symbols is to be multiplied is determined by its placement in relation to a reference point. In the decimal system this is called the *decimal point*.

1.6a The Hindu-Arabic System

The Hindu-Arabic system has the ten symbols, 0, 1, 2, 3, 4, 5, 6, 7, 8, 9, and this includes a symbol for zero. It has base ten and is a place-value system. Any number may be expressed as a sequence of symbols and is interpreted as a sum of terms made up of these symbols times the appropriate power of ten. The power of ten is determined by the "position" or "place" the symbol occupies with reference to the decimal point. If the decimal point is omitted, as is usually the case with whole numbers, it is understood that the reference point is immediately to the right of the sequence of digits, for example, the symbols "241" and "241." represent the same number.

Table 5 is an abbreviated table of place values for whole numbers in the Hindu-Arabic system.

TABLE 5

HINDU-ARABIC PLACE VALUES

10^9	1,000,000,000	billions
10^8	100,000,000	hundred millions
10^7	10,000,000	ten millions
10^6	1,000,000	millions
10^5	100,000	hundred thousands
10^4	10,000	ten thousands
10^3	1000	thousands
10^2	100	hundreds
10^1	10	tens
10^0	1	units

A symbol such as 2145 is interpreted as

$$\begin{aligned} 2145 &= 2\cdot 10^3 + 1\cdot 10^2 + 4\cdot 10^1 + 5\cdot 10^0 \\ &= 2(1000) + 1(100) + 4(10) + 5(1). \end{aligned}$$

In words, two thousands, one hundred, four tens, and five units, or, two thousand, one hundred, forty-five.

The chief advantage in the Hindu-Arabic system of numeration is its economy of symbols and its adaptability to computation (see Chapter 4).

1.6b The Mayan System

Some of us may have been led to believe that our system, the Hindu-Arabic, is the only place-value system ever used. This is not the case. Of interest is the system used by the Mayans. Theirs was a vigesimal (base twenty) system. A replica of the set of symbols follows:

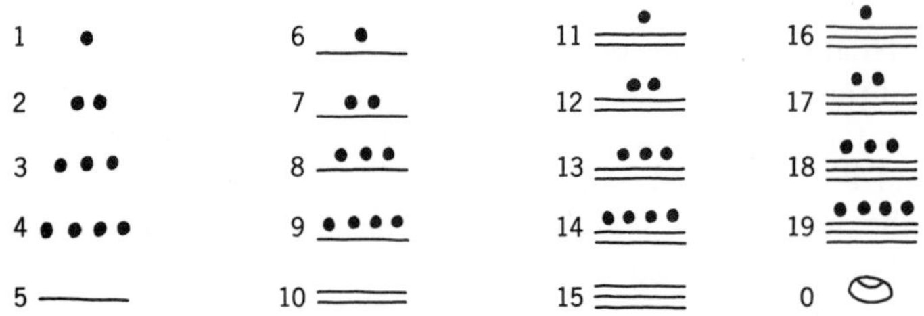

1 6 11 16

2 7 12 17

3 8 13 18

4 9 14 19

5 10 15 0

(For reasons unrelated to this discussion, instead of being consistent with base twenty, the Mayans used (18)(20) instead of $(20)^2$; $(18)(20)^2$ instead of $(20)^3$, etc.)

The Mayans, like the Chinese and Japanese, used the vertical form of writing. An example of a numeral in their system is as follows:

Example 1

In the decimal system this is

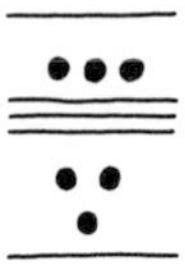

$$5[(18)(20)^2] + 18[(18)(20)] + 2(20) + 6 = 36{,}000 + 6480 + 40 + 6 = 42{,}526.$$

Example 2

In the decimal system this is

$$1[(18)(20)^3] + 15[(18)(20)^2] + 12[(18)(20)] + 9(20) + 0 = 144{,}000 + 108{,}000 + 4320 + 180 = 256{,}500.$$

1.6c Babylonian System

The Babylonians used a modified place-value system dating even further back in history. The base for their system was sixty. It was not a true place-value system, for there was no symbol for zero, and they employed only two symbols, a symbol for one, |, and a symbol for ten, $<$. These were used repetitively to represent numbers up to sixty. Because there was no symbol for zero, their system sometimes led to ambiguity. An example of a large number in their system is ||| <<|| <<<||| <<<<||||, which, in the Hindu-Arabic notation, would be written as

$$3(60)^3 + 22(60)^2 + 33(60)^1 + 44 = 729{,}224.$$

1.7 SUMMARY

It is interesting to note that the Hindu-Arabic, or decimal, system is a place-value system, but it is not the only one. It is a system with base ten, but it is not the only one. It is a system using the additive property, but all systems use this. It is a system employing just ten symbols, and here, as far as is known, it is unique.

Exercise 1.7

1. Use the symbols I, ▱, △, and ◇ to represent the decimal numbers 1, 4, 16, and 64 respectively, and let the symbols O, I, L, and F represent the decimal numbers 0, 1, 2, and 3. Use whatever symbols are necessary to write the decimal numbers 25, 100, and 197 in
   (a) an additive system.
   (b) a multiplicative system.
   (c) a place-value system.
2. (a) In an additive system, base five, let 1, 5, 5^2, and 5^3 be represented by I, L, F, and E. Express the numbers 360, 252, 78, and 33 in this system.
   (b) In a place-value system, base 5, let 0, 1, 2, 3, 4, be represented by O, I, L, F, E. Express the numbers 360, 252, 78, and 33 in this system.
3. The great pyramid of Gizeh was erected about 2900 B.C. In order to appreciate some of the engineering and mathematical problems which had to be solved using the hieroglyphic numerals, write a report on the pyramids and in particular include some statistics on the largest.

1.8 THE COUNTING BOARD

Initially man knew but one use for numbers, namely, for counting objects. The development of addition, subtraction, and multiplication was gradual and since the symbols were awkward to work with, special devices were invented to aid in computation.

The Romans used a counting table, or counting board, on which lines were drawn, each line representing units, tens, hundreds, and so on—with the space between lines representing fives, fifties, five-hundreds, and so on. They tallied with small round discs. By placing these on the lines and between the lines they were able to register any number they pleased, and, by adding additional discs and simplifying, they were able to carry out addition problems. A schematic diagram of their counting board would appear somewhat as in Figure 1.

The number represented in the schematic diagram would be 2837 in the Hindu-Arabic notation.

Addition on the counting board could have been carried out as shown in Figure 2.

The Roman merchants displayed and sold their goods over these counting tables. The words "counting table" were shortened to "counter." This gives us the origin of the word we use for the present-day fixtures in stores that are used to display goods and over which goods are sold.

It is interesting to note that in the use of their counting board the Romans essentially had a place-value system of numeration, but they did not recognize it as such.

1.9 THE ABACUS

The devices developed by various peoples of the world to aid in computation differed in appearance and, to some extent, in design. The most popular, however, appear to have the same underlying scheme and are classified as some form of the abacus. Basically the scheme was that lines, grooves, or rods were used to represent units and the powers of the base. Counters or beads were then placed on the lines, grooves, or rods to designate how many of each of the units and powers of the base were to be used in representing a number. These counters

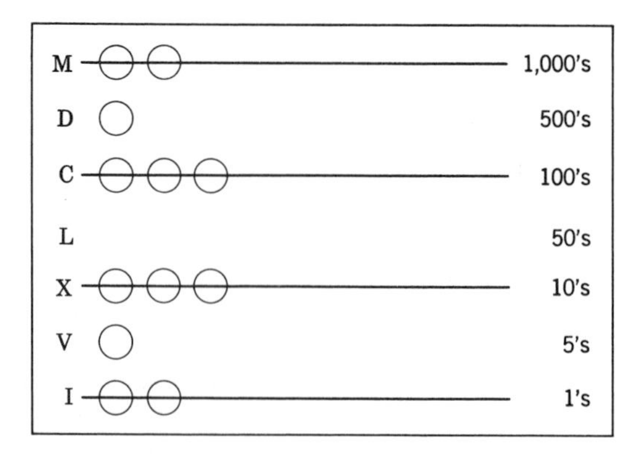

Figure 1. Roman counting board.

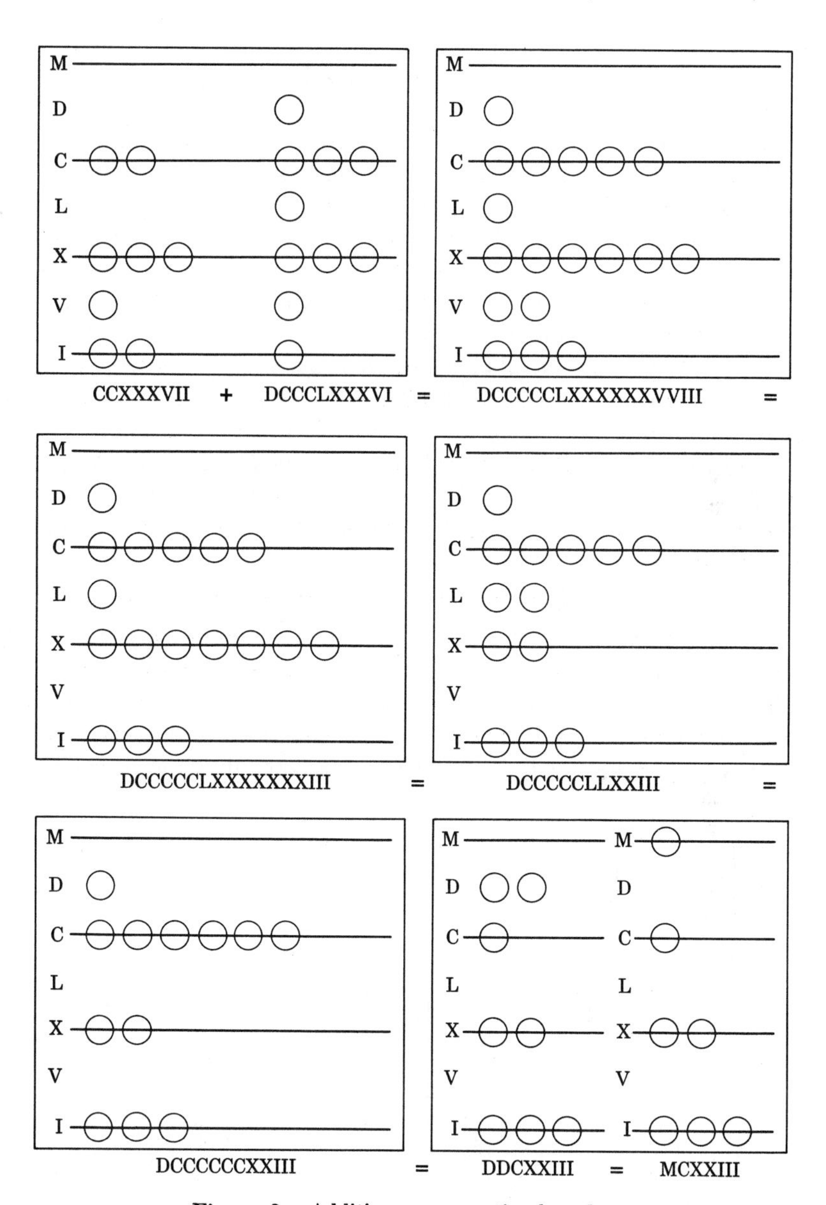

Figure 2. Addition on a counting board.

were not removed from the device. Instead their position indicated whether they were to be counted or not in the representation of a number.

The Roman abacus was a bronze or wood board. Grooves were cut in the board and small round pebbles placed in these grooves to represent numbers. These pebbles were called calculi, which is the plural of calculus. This tells us the origin of the word "calculate" and of the word "calculus" when it designates a mathematical discipline.

A schematic diagram of the Roman abacus is given in Figure 3. In this diagram a symbol with a bar above it indicates the number represented by that symbol multiplied by 1000. The double bar indicates multiplication by 1,000,000. Beads placed at the bottom of the groove, toward the operator, were in the neutral position and were not to be counted. Beads placed at the top of the groove were in the "active" position and were to be counted. The number, in our system of numeration, indicated by the position of the beads in Figure 3 would be

$$1000 + 500 + 200 + 50 + 20 + 3 + \tfrac{1}{2} + \tfrac{3}{12} = 1773\tfrac{3}{4}$$

The abacus developed by the Chinese, called the *suan pan*, was of the rod and bead variety. A dividing bar separated sets of two beads and five beads on each bar. Each bead above the bar had associated with it a value five times that of a bead below the bar on the same rod. The active position for the beads was toward the dividing bar. Beads

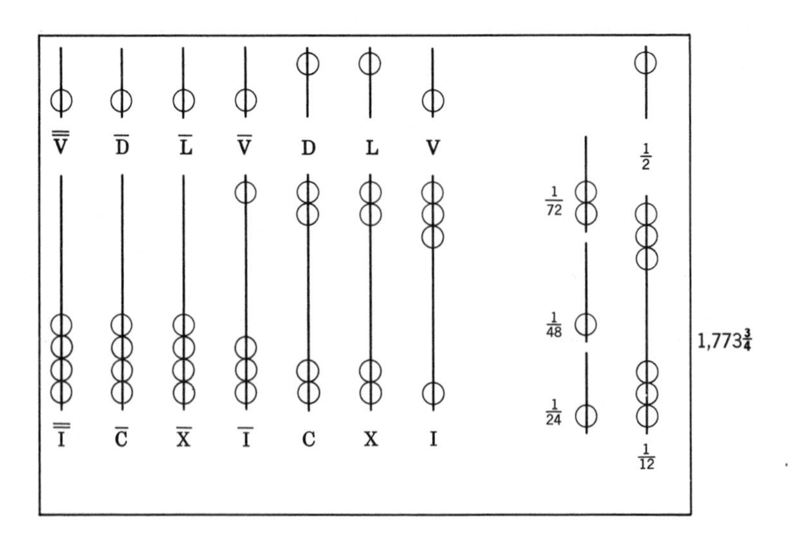

Figure 3. Roman abacus.

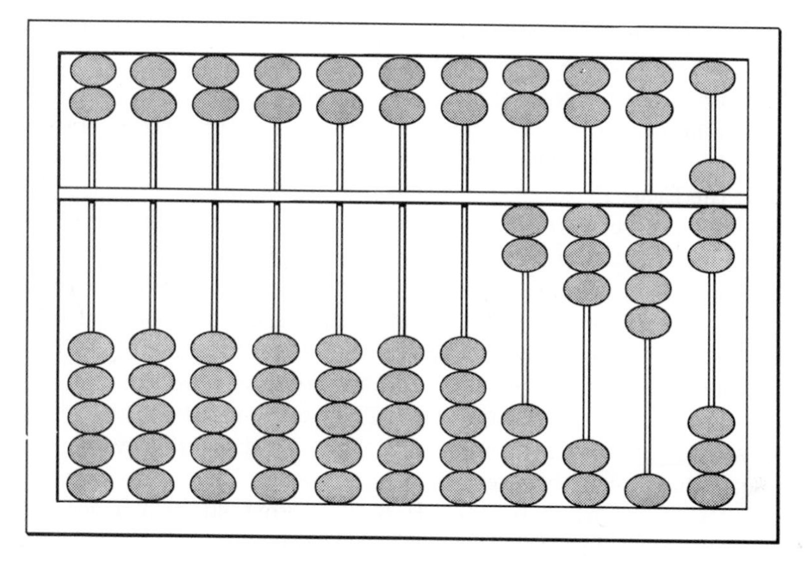

Figure 4. Chinese abacus.

toward the outside were in the passive or neutral position. Figure 4 shows a typical arrangement for the *suan pan* with the number 2347 designated by the beads.

It is interesting to note that the *suan pan* is still in general use by the Chinese.

The abacus developed by the Japanese, called the *soroban,* is very similar to that of the Chinese except that instead of the five-two bead arrangement on each rod, the Japanese model is generally of the four-one or five-one bead arrangement. Figure 5 shows a typical arrangement with the number 27,483 indicated.

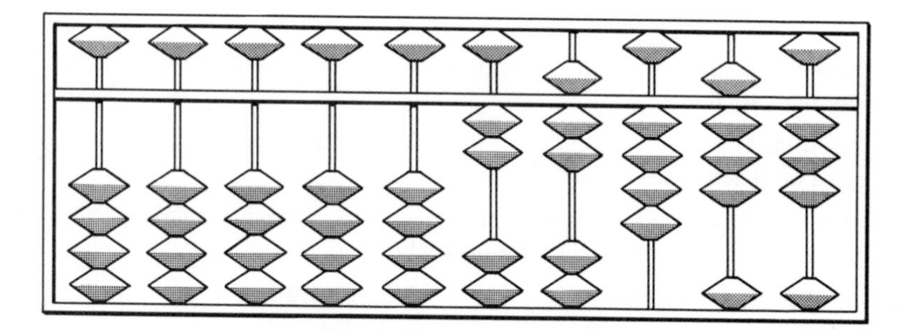

Figure 5. Japanese abacus.

The *soroban* is also in current use by the Japanese. Both the Chinese and Japanese become very adept in the use of the abacus. An expert in the use of the abacus can compute with speed and accuracy that will compare favorably with results obtained by an experienced operator of the desk calculator. One of the authors witnessed a demonstration of this at the Ernie Pyle Theater in Tokyo in 1946.

Most of us, when we think of the abacus, associate it primarily with the Orient. Actually the abacus, in one form or another, was used throughout Europe and Asia until people became acquainted with and accepted the Hindu-Arabic system of numeration and associated methods of computation. This change did not take place rapidly. There were those who favored the use of other systems of numeration and the use of the abacus in computation. They were called the "abacists." Opposed to these were the advocates of the Hindu-Arabic system with its algorithms, or procedures, for computation. They were called the "algorists" (see Swain, p. 23). It took approximately 500 years for the algorists to gain general acceptance of their techniques in computation. But by the year 1600 they had achieved their goal and had established the arithmetic techniques which have remained in general use up to the present time.

The abacus was then placed in a semiretired status, but this ancient device is finding its way back into the classrooms of today. Teachers are finding it a real aid in the teaching of place value, addition, and subtraction. With the advancements made in recent years in the field of computers, it may be interesting to note that the abacus may be classified as one of the first "digital computers" (see Mueller, pp. 9–11, and Newman, pp. 456–464).

Exercise 1.9

1. Write 385 and 583 in

(a) Egyptian hieroglyphics
(b) Babylonian cuneiform
(c) Ionic Greek
(d) Traditional Japanese
(e) Mayan

2. How many different symbols must one memorize in order to write numbers less than 1000 in

(a) Ionic Greek?
(b) Egyptian hieroglyphics?
(c) Babylonian cuneiform?

3. Systems of numeration can be characterized to a certain extent by whether or not they possess the following properties:

(a) Additive property
(b) Symbol for zero
(c) Subtractive property
(d) Multiplicative property
(e) Place value
(f) Repetition

They may be further characterized by

(a) Number of symbols (b) Type of symbols
(c) Base

Give the characteristics of the systems listed in Exercise 1.

4. (a) In a place-value system, base two, let 0 denote zero and 1 denote one. Write the first twenty-five numbers in this system.
(b) What are the decimal numerals of the numbers written as follows in the base two system?

10101, 10001000, 1110011, 1001101

Special Problems

1. A visiting lecturer told of a congressman who proudly proclaimed that he was one-twelfth Indian. The audience consisted of scientists who were quite amused. What amused the scientists?

2. A man weighing 200 lb and his two sons who weigh 75 lb and 125 lb wish to cross a river in a boat. The boat has a capacity of just 200 lb. Can they?

REFERENCES

Eves, Howard, *An Introduction to the History of Mathematics*, Rinehart and Co., New York, 1953.
Mueller, Francis J., *Arithmetic, Its Structure and Concepts*, Prentice-Hall, Englewood Cliffs, N.J., 1956.
Newman, James R., *The World of Mathematics*, Simon and Schuster, New York, 1956.
Swain, Robert L., *Understanding Arithmetic*, Rinehart and Co., New York, 1952.

*
*
*

CHAPTER TWO

Sets

2.1 INTRODUCTION

There is much in arithmetic that is clear and concise, simple and easy to understand, interesting and intriguing. At the same time, as it is usually taught, there is much that is not clearly understood by the teachers and difficult for them to explain and, unfortunately, widely accepted as being difficult to master. Many people would be reluctant to confess that they did poorly in English or history but readily admit that they never could do arithmetic. This attitude is due primarily to vague and incorrect presentation of fundamental concepts. We hope to promote understanding and interest by being reasonably precise in the presentation of the concepts and by replacing vagueness with clarity. We begin with a fundamental notion in mathematics, the idea of a set.

2.2 SETS

In everyday life one uses such words as collection, class, group, set:

a collection of stamps or coins
a set of dishes
a group of boys
the class of '63

These words are used intuitively and freely without any thought of defining them. They are used synonymously, and the same word may be used in a variety of situations. It is in this spirit that the mathematician uses the word "set." The word *set* will be used to speak of a collection of objects that we shall call *elements* of the set.

In a set of crayons, each crayon is an *element* of the *set* of crayons. In a set of dishes, each dish is an *element* of the *set* of dishes. In a set of positive integers, each integer is an *element* of the *set* of positive integers. In a set of ideas, each idea is an *element* of the *set* of ideas.

The notion of a set of elements is a creation of the mind. (Do you call this an idea?) The mind unconsciously organizes objects into sets. The process starts at a very early age. A child is shown a picture of a horse or sees a horse, and as soon as the animal has been given the name *horse*, all similar animals are soon distinguished and identified as horses. The word *horses* then can be thought of as the name of a very large set. Each *element* of this *set* is a particular horse. Different sets with different elements will be brought to mind by such words as *cows*, *cars*, *people*, *schools*, *students*, etc. As soon as the words are spoken or read, *particular elements* of each *set* come to mind. One can speak of a rancher in Montana, a professional baseball player, a teacher. Each is an arbitrary element of a set, and it is the generic element that is the object of interest. In other situations one might speak of *the* people in Montana, *the* professional baseball players, *the* school teachers. In each of these, the *set* is the object of interest.

Individuals see sets in different ways. Thus when a botanist drives along a road for the first time, his mind unconsciously checks off various plants as belonging to this genus or that genus (sets of particular kinds of plants). What happens when he encounters a plant he has never seen before? He immediately starts checking the plant to see if it is in this or that genus, that is, he is looking at this particular element to see if it satisfies the criteria of belonging to a particular set with which he might be familiar. If it does not "belong" to any that he knows about and if later he encounters another plant like it, his mind creates a new set, namely, the set of plants like the one he saw beside the road. Similarly, if you see the numbers 1, 17, 26, 3, 6, 19, 9, 101, 12, 4, 15, 2, 4, 8, 16, . . . you may sort these numbers in various ways; some are even numbers, some are odd numbers, some are prime numbers, and so forth.

The decision as to membership, that is, as to whether or not a particular element belongs to a set, is quite easy to make for some sets. For others it is much more difficult. As an example, suppose we were discussing the set of even natural numbers (consisting of 2, 4, 6, 8, and so on). Given a particular object, it is easy to decide whether or not it is an element of the set of even natural numbers. Given $\frac{1}{2}$, we would say that it does not belong because it is not a natural number. (The set consisting of 1, 2, 3, 4, and so on.) Given -5, again we would say that it does not belong because it is not a natural number. Given 7,

not fractions
" minus values

again we say "No," but this time because it is not an *even* natural number. Given 8, we would say that it *does* "belong to," or is an element of, the set under consideration. The set of even natural numbers, then, is one of the type that leads to easy decisions as to whether a given object belongs to it.

As an example of the other type, consider the set of all people in Chicago who are ill. Even if we knew all the people in Chicago and were qualified as a doctor of medicine we might have difficulty in making decisions as to whether a certain resident of Chicago belonged to the set under discussion or not.

In mathematics we can usually be quite precise in establishing the criterion for belonging when we speak of sets. It is well to bear in mind, however, that there are sets for which deciding membership is difficult. If you are discussing a set with someone else, be sure that you both have the same criterion for making your decisions as to membership.

2.2a Set Notation

Let us adopt the convention of using capital letters to represent sets and small letters to represent elements of a set. Thus we may refer to the set X consisting of the elements which we might label a, b, c, and so forth. The symbol

$$a \in X$$

shall mean "the object a is a member of the set X," or "the object a belongs to the set X," or simply "a is in X." We shall also read this as "a is an element of the set X." The symbol

$$a \notin X$$

represents the negation "a is not an element of X."

A set might be specified by listing its elements. Thus the pictured set A (see Figure 1) consists of an apple, an orange, a pencil, and a table. The pictured set B consists of four books. This method of specifying a set is expressed by the notation used in the following examples:

$$A = \{2, 4, 6, 8\}.$$

This is interpreted, "A is a name for the set consisting of the elements 2, 4, 6, 8." This is also read "the set A is composed of the elements 2, 4, 6, and 8." (Note that the symbol = is used in the sense of "is a name for.")

$$B = \{x, y, z\}.$$

B is a name for the set consisting of the elements x, y, and z.

$$C = \{1, 2, 3, \ldots, 20\}.$$

Set A

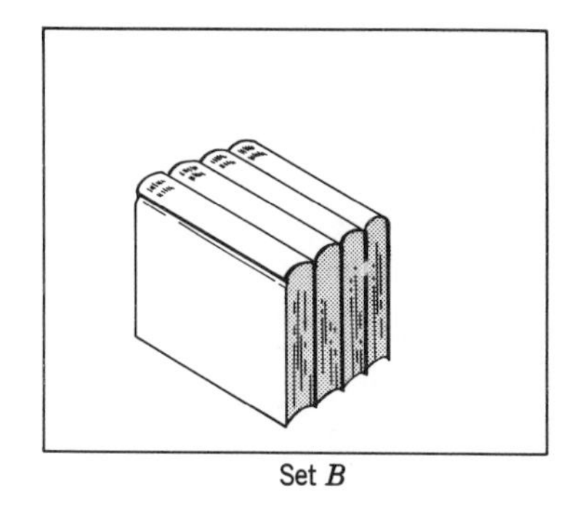
Set B

Figure 1

C is a name for the set consisting of the first twenty natural numbers. The dots in the set C mean that the sequence of natural numbers is to continue to and including 20.

A set might also be specified by giving a criterion for belonging to the set. This is usually done by describing a common property of the elements, for example: the set X consists of the set of all red-haired people; the set Y consists of all red-haired men; the set Z consists of the set of all red-haired men in Montana. Notice that by increasing the number of conditions or properties that an element must have in order to be a member of a set tends to decrease the size of the set. The once popular game of "20 questions" operated on this principle. In this game the players were concerned with identifying a particular object by asking questions which could be answered Yes or No. Each question determined whether or not the object to be identified possessed a certain property. The objective was to identify the object through the use of twenty, or fewer, questions.

We also use the following "set builder" notation to indicate sets.

$$A = \{x|x \text{ has a certain property}\}.$$

We read this "A is the set of *all* x such that x has a certain property." (Here we have shortened "is a name for" to "is.")

Example 1

$N = \{n|n \text{ is a natural number}\}$
N is the set of all n such that n is a natural number
$Z = \{n|n \text{ is an even natural number}\}$
$F = \{n|n \text{ is a natural number divisible by } 4\}$
$R = \{n|n = 32\}$
$S = \{n|n \text{ is an even natural number between } 30 \text{ and } 34\}$

Notice in Example 1 that R and S are both sets which consist of the same element, 32. (This is sometimes read as "singleton 32.") We have indicated two ways of specifying sets. It may happen that the same set may be specified in several different ways. We need some criterion for determining whether a set specified in one way is the same, or distinct from, a set specified in another way.

DEFINITION 2.2. Two sets, A and B, are the same if every element of A is an element of B and every element of B is an element of A. We denote this $A = B$.

According to this criterion, the sets R and S of Example 1 are the same: $R = S$.

Example 2

Let $A = \{1, 2\}$ and $B = \{1, 1, 2\}$. Then $A = B$.

Exercise 2.2

1. Consider the set of all quadrilaterals. Which of the following statements express object properties and which express set properties?
   (a) There are infinitely many quadrilaterals.
   (b) Every quadrilateral has four sides.
   (c) All squares are quadrilaterals.
   (d) A quadrilateral is a polygon.
   (e) The set of quadrilaterals is contained in the set of polygons.
2. In what respect or respects does a given apple differ from the set consisting of the given apple? For example, which would you say is edible?
3. For some of the sets below it is easy to make a decision as to membership (i.e., the set is clearly specified or well defined), whereas for others it is not. Classify each set as being well defined or not well defined, and tabulate the elements of the set if possible.
   (a) All months of the year that have exactly 30 days.
   (b) All months of the year that have exactly 29 days.
   (c) All even integers greater than 43.
   (d) All integers that are perfect squares and less than 61.
   (e) All numbers whose squares are zero.
   (f) The five students not attending the University of Montana who learned the most in high school.
   (g) All good boys.
   (h) All fractions between zero and one.
   (i) All healthy men in Chicago.

2.3 SUBSETS

Referring to Example 1, Section 2.2, notice that the elements of F are elements of Z and that the elements of Z are elements of N. We call F a *subset* of Z and Z a *subset* of N.

DEFINITION 2.3a. The set A is a *subset* of the set B if every element of A is an element of B.

We use the symbol $A \subseteq B$ to denote this. This can also be written $B \supseteq A$. We read this "the set B contains the subset A."

Example 1

Let $A = \{1, 2, 3, 4, 5, 6\}$ and $B = \{1, 2, 3, 4, 5, 6, 7, 8, 9\}$; then A is a subset of B, for every element of A is an element of B.

$$\overbrace{\underbrace{1, 2, 3, 4, 5, 6}_{A}, 7, 8, 9}^{B}$$

Example 2

Let A be the set consisting of all people in the United States and let B be the set consisting of all the students in the first grades in the United States. B is a subset of A. If we let C be the set consisting of the girls in the first grades in the United States, then C is a subset of B. Notice also that C is a subset of A.

Notice that according to our definition, every set A is a subset of itself.

DEFINITION 2.3b. The set A is a *proper subset* of B if every element of A is an element of B, but *not* every element of B is an element of A.

We use the symbol $A \subset B$ to denote this. This is read "A is properly contained in B," or "A is properly included in B." This can also be written $B \supset A$ and is read "B properly contains A" or "B properly includes A."

The word *animals* refers to a set of living objects. The word *horses* refers to another set of living objects. The statement that every horse is an animal is the same as the statement that the set of horses is a subset of the set of animals. Figure 2 will help you visualize these sets.

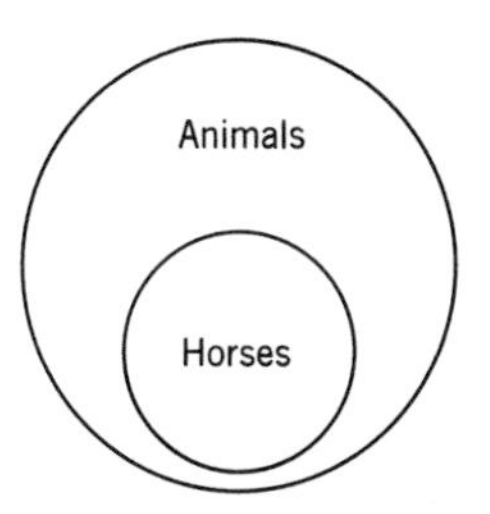

Figure 2

Notice that this is a *pairing* of the terms "animals" and "horses" in a particular way, that is, the set of horses is related to the set of animals. The set of horses is "included" in the set of animals. We say that the set of horses is related to the set of animals by inclusion, and we use the notation

$$\{\text{horses}\} \subset \{\text{animals}\}.$$

Inclusion is a relation between sets in the same way that "is a relative of" is a relation between people.

2.3a The Empty Set

It will be useful to introduce a new set called the *empty set* (or void set), which we denote by $\emptyset$. The empty set $\emptyset$ is the set that has no elements. Its occurrence seems natural and convenient if we consider the following examples.

Example 1

Let $A = \{\text{students under 21 years of age}\}$
and $B = \{\text{students over 21 years of age}\}$.

The set of elements common to both A and B is empty, that is, there is no student who is both under 21 years of age and over 21 years of age.

Example 2

Let $A = \{a, b, c\}$ and $B = \{1, 2, 3\}$.
The set of elements common to both A and B is empty.

Example 3

Let $A = \{0, 1, 2, 3\}$ and $B = \{0, 4, 5, 6\}$.
The set of elements common to both A and B is $\{0\}$. It is not the empty set. It is the set containing zero.

Two sets, X and Y, which have no elements in common are said to be *disjoint* (see Definition 2.4c).

2.3b The Universal Set

In discussions with sets we will have in mind some fixed class of objects to which the discussion is limited, and the sets we mention will be sets of elements from this fixed class. The fixed class will be referred to as the *universal set* or the *universe*. The universal set is not the same for all problems. When discussing sets consisting of natural numbers, the universal set could be the set of all natural numbers. In other problems the universal set may be the set of all people, the set of all students, the set of all real numbers, and so on. We shall designate the universal set by the symbol U.

2.3c Counting Subsets

Counting is not always as easy as it may appear. Some problems involving counting may be difficult because of the extremely large numbers involved, whereas other problems involving counting may be difficult because the "things" being counted may be hard to distinguish.

The man who, in return for a favor to the king, modestly asked for 1 grain of wheat on the first square of a checker board, 2 grains on the second, 4 on the third, each time doubling the amount on the previous square for the 64 squares on the checker board, posed a problem of the first type.

Counting subsets of a given set could be a problem of the second type without some helpful hints. It is particularly useful to observe the following principle.

If an event can occur in M ways and after it has occurred in any one of these ways, a second event can occur in N ways, then the two successive events can occur in $M \cdot N$ ways.

Example 1

If there are 2 routes from city A to city B and 3 routes from city B to city C, then there are 6 routes from A to C.

List all six routes by number and letter (see Figure 3).

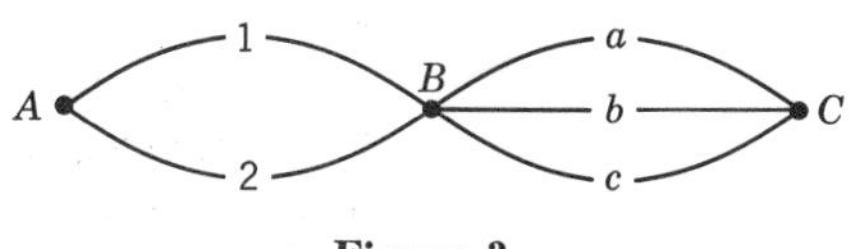

Figure 3

In counting subsets of a set with n elements, an "event" will be "placing an element." This event can occur in two ways; either place the element in a subset or do not place an element in a subset. After the first element has been disposed of, the second element is *placed.* This can also be done in two ways. Since there are n elements, there are

$$\underbrace{2 \cdot 2 \cdots 2}_{n \text{ factors}} = 2^n$$

ways of forming subsets of a set with n elements. If the choice "do not place" is made for each of the elements of the set, the resulting set is the empty set. If the choice "place" is made for each of the elements of the set, the resulting set is the set itself. Hence when we say there are 2^n subsets of a set of n elements, this includes the empty set and the set itself.

Exercise 2.3

1. Using the sets N, Z, F, R, and S of Example 1, Section 2.2, indicate which sets are subsets of other sets in the set. Which are *proper* subsets?
2. If A denotes a set, is A a subset of A? Explain. Is A a proper subset of A?
3. Let X denote the set consisting of the numbers 1, 2, and 3. List all possible subsets of X. Which are proper subsets?
4. How many committees can you form if you have 3 people to choose from?

5. Consider the set $S = \{0, 1, 2, 3, 4, 5, 6, 7, 8\}$.

(a) Select a subset of S so that each number in the subset is even; odd.
(b) Select a subset of S that contains all the numbers in S that are multiples of 3; of 1.
(c) Select a subset of S that contains all the numbers in S that added to 3 give 5; that added to 3 give 2; that added to 3 give a number in S; that added to 0 give a number in S; that added to 4 give a number not in S.
(d) Select a subset of S so that twice each number in the subset is not in S; three times each number in the subset is in S.
(e) Select a subset of S so that five more than twice each number in the subset is in S.

6. Let S be the set of all even numbers and T the set of all odd numbers. Use the set-builder notation to specify the sets S and T.

7. Let Q denote the set of all quadrilaterals in plane geometry. Express symbolically the relation of membership in the set Q for the following individual figures.

(a) A square, s
(b) A triangle, t
(c) A trapezoid, z
(d) A parallelogram, p
(e) A hexagon, h
(f) A figure eight, e
(g) A rhombus, b
(h) A rectangle, r
(i) A pentagon, f
(j) A decagon, d

8. (a) Is $0 \in \emptyset$?
(b) Is $\emptyset \in \emptyset$?
(c) If A is a set, is $\emptyset$ a subset of A?
(d) Is $\emptyset$ a subset of $\emptyset$?

9. (a) Specify the singleton set {George Washington} in three different ways.
(b) Specify the set $\{2, 4, 6, 8\}$ in two different ways.
(c) Specify the set $\{4, 2, 8, 6\}$ in two different ways.
(d) What can you say about the set consisting of the girls who are graduates of West Point Military Academy?
(e) Is the set, whose only element is the empty set, empty? That is, is $\{\emptyset\} = \emptyset$?

2.4 NEW SETS FROM OLD

It is because we can do more than just discuss them that sets are of mathematical interest. We shall see how to construct new sets in terms of given sets, thereby defining "operations" involving sets.

2.4a Union of Sets

DEFINITION 2.4a. The *union* of two sets, A and B, is the set of all elements that are in A, *or* in B, *or* in both.

We denote this $A \cup B$. (Note that this is the *inclusive* use of "or.") An element will belong to $A \cup B$ if the element belongs to A, or B, or both. In our set-builder notation

$$A \cup B = \{x|x \text{ is an element of } A \text{ } or \text{ } B \text{ } or \text{ both}\}.$$

Example 1

Let $A = \{a, b, c\}$ and $B = \{1, 5, a, x, y\}$; then
$A \cup B = \{a, b, c, 1, 5, x, y\}$.

Example 2

Let $A = \{x|x \text{ is a student in the freshman class}\}$, and
$B = \{x|x \text{ is a freshman boy}\}$; then
$A \cup B = \{x|x \text{ is a student in the freshman class}\}$.

2.4b Intersection of Sets

DEFINITION 2.4b. The *intersection* of two sets, A and B, is the set of all elements that are in both A and B.

We denote this $A \cap B$. An element will belong to $A \cap B$ if it belongs to both A and B. In our set-builder notation

$$A \cap B = \{x|x \text{ is an element of } A \text{ } and \text{ } B\}.$$

In Example 1, Section 2.4a, $A \cap B = \{a\}$. In Example 2, $A \cap B = B$, which denotes that the intersection of the set which consists of all the freshman boys with the set consisting of all the freshmen is the set of all freshman boys.

DEFINITION 2.4c. Two sets, X and Y, whose intersection is the empty set are said to be *disjoint*. The sets X and Y are disjoint if $X \cap Y = \emptyset$.

Example 1

Let $A = \{1, 2, 3, 4, 5\}$, $B = \{3, 4, 5, 6, 7, 8, 9\}$, and $C = \{11, 12\}$; then $A \cap B = \{3, 4, 5\}$, $A \cap C = \emptyset$, and $B \cap C = \emptyset$. A and C are disjoint. B and C are disjoint.

Example 2

In the diagrams in Figure 4 let A be the set of all points inside and on the circle marked A; let B be the set of all points inside and on the circle marked B; and let C be the set of all points inside and on the circle marked C.

These diagrams are called *Venn diagrams*. The sets corresponding to the intersection and union of the various sets are shaded and marked.

Exercise 2.4

Draw Venn diagrams as in Figure 4 and shade the areas corresponding to the following unions and intersections. Label each diagram.

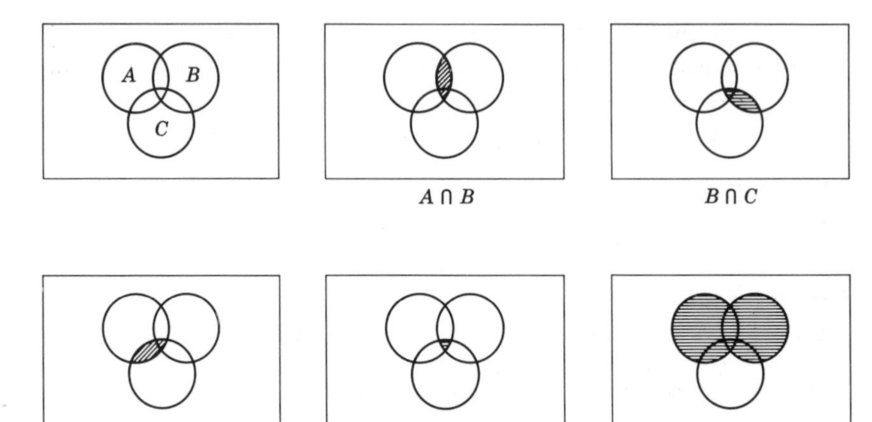

Figure 4

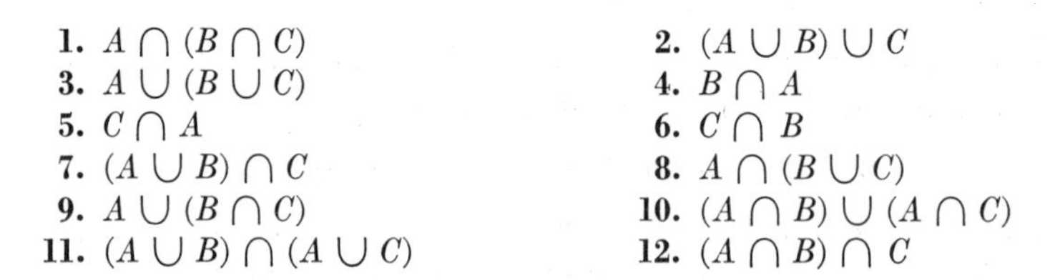

1. $A \cap (B \cap C)$
2. $(A \cup B) \cup C$
3. $A \cup (B \cup C)$
4. $B \cap A$
5. $C \cap A$
6. $C \cap B$
7. $(A \cup B) \cap C$
8. $A \cap (B \cup C)$
9. $A \cup (B \cap C)$
10. $(A \cap B) \cup (A \cap C)$
11. $(A \cup B) \cap (A \cup C)$
12. $(A \cap B) \cap C$

13. In planning for a birthday party for her daughter, Mrs. Jones made a list of the children according to their preferences in refreshments. It was as follows:

Ice Cream	*Cake*	*Apples*
Tom	Ted	Sue
Jim	Tim	Ted
Joan	John	Jill
Sam	Jill	Sara
Ted	Tobe	Jack
Jack	Jane	John
June	Sono	June
Tim	Jan	Tim

There were no two children with the same name.

(a) List the names of the children who like both ice cream and cake.
(b) List the names of the children who like both ice cream and apples.
(c) List the names of the children who like both cake and apples.
(d) List the names of the children who like all three.

2.5 THE COMPLEMENT OF A SET

DEFINITION 2.5. If A is a subset of the universal set U, the set of all elements of the universe that are not in A is called the *complement* of A.

We use the symbol A' to signify the complement of A.

Example 1

If U is the set of students in the University and M is the subset consisting of the men students, then M' is the set of women students.

Example 2

Let $U = \{a, b, c, d, e\}$, and
$A = \{a, e, c\}$; then
$A' = \{b, d\}$.

In general, if

$$A \cup B = U, \text{ and}$$
$$A \cap B = \emptyset,$$

then A and B are *complementary sets*, and

$$A' = B, \text{ and}$$
$$B' = A.$$

In particular,

$$U' = \emptyset, \text{ and}$$
$$\emptyset' = U.$$

Exercise 2.5

1. Translate the following into verbal statements:
   (a) $A \cup A = A$, $A \cup \emptyset = A$, and $A \cup U = U$.
   (b) $A \cup B \supseteq A$ and $A \cup B \supseteq B$.
   (c) If $C \subset A$ and $C \subset B$, then $C \subset A \cup B$.
   (d) $A \cup B = A$ if and only if $A \supseteq B$.
   (e) $A \cap A = A$, $A \cap U = A$, and $A \cap \emptyset = \emptyset$.
   (f) $A \cap B \subseteq A$ and $A \cap B \subseteq B$.
   (g) If $C \subset A$ and $C \subset B$, then $C \subset A \cap B$.
   (h) $A \cap B = A$ if and only if $A \subseteq B$.

2. Find the union and the intersection for each of the following pairs of sets:
   (a) $A = \{1, 3, 5\}$, $B = \{2, 4\}$
   (b) $A = \{1, 3, 5\}$, $B = \{1, 3, 5\}$
   (c) $A = \{1, 3, 5\}$, $B = \{1, 2, 3\}$
   (d) $A = \{2, 3, 4\}$, $B = \{2, 4\}$
   (e) $A = \{2, 3\}$, $B = \{1, 2, 3\}$
   (f) $A = \{2, 4, 6\}$, $B = \{2, 3, 5\}$

3. Let U be the set of natural numbers $\{1, 2, 3, 4, \ldots\}$, E the set of even natural numbers, A the set of odd natural numbers, and B the set $\{1, 2, 3, 4, 5, 6\}$. Perform the following set calculations giving each result in two ways: by *tabulation* (perhaps incomplete) and by *description.*

(a) $E \cup U$ (b) $E \cup A$ (c) $A \cup B$
(d) $E \cup B$ (e) $E \cap U$ (f) $E \cap A$
(g) $A \cap B$ (h) $E \cap B$ (i) $(A \cup B) \cap E$
(j) $A \cup (B \cap E)$ (k) $(E \cap A) \cup B$ (l) $E \cap (A \cup B)$

4. What is $A \cap B$ if

(a) A and B are disjoint? (b) A and B are identical?
(c) $A \subset B$? (d) $A \supset B$?
(e) A and B overlap?

5. What is $A \cup B$ if

(a) A and B are disjoint? (b) A and B are identical?
(c) $A \subset B$? (d) $A \supset B$?
(e) A and B overlap?

6. Let $U = \{1, 2, 3, 4, 5\}$, $C = \{1, 3\}$, and A and B be nonempty sets. Find A in each of the following:

(a) $A \cup B = U$, $A \cap B = \emptyset$, and $B = \{1\}$.
(b) $A \subset B$ and $A \cup B = \{4, 5\}$.
(c) $A \cap B = \{3\}$, $A \cup B = \{2, 3, 4\}$, and $B \cup C = \{1, 2, 3\}$.
(d) A and B are disjoint, B and C are disjoint, and the union of A and B is the set $\{1, 2\}$.

7. In the diagram below, let U be the set of all points inside and on the rectangle and let A, B, and C denote the points inside and on the circles as marked.

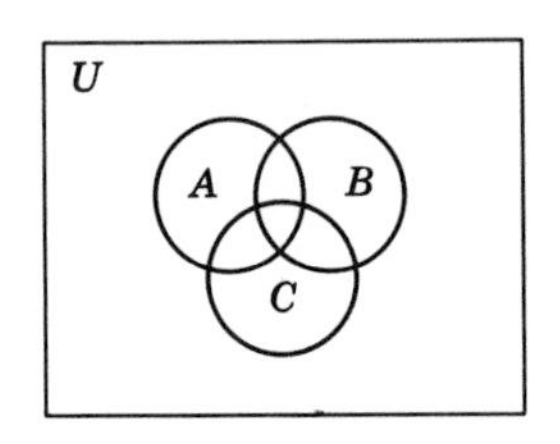

Use slanted lines to indicate the set A'; use lines slanted in another direction to indicate the set B'. Now draw a similar figure and shade the set $(A \cup B)'$. Verify that

(a) $(A \cup B)' = A' \cap B'$ (b) $(A \cup C)' = A' \cap C'$.

8. Follow the instructions of problem 7, and diagram $(A \cap B)'$ and A' and B'. How are $(A \cap B)'$, A' and B' related? What is $(A \cup B \cup C)'$?

9. How many subsets can a set with 5 elements have? How many proper subsets?

2.6 THE CARTESIAN PRODUCT OF SETS

The *Cartesian product* of two sets A and B is quite unlike the sets $A \cup B$ and $A \cap B$. The elements of the Cartesian product are not elements from A nor elements from B but rather what we call *ordered pairs.*

Ordered pairs occur quite naturally. One encounters ordered pairs when locating places on maps. Highway maps usually have a sequence of numerals spaced equally along one border of the map, say the bottom border, and a sequence of letters equally spaced along one of the vertical borders. A list of the towns will have after each name a number and a letter. For instance, on a map of Montana we find Missoula . . . 4-D. Following along the lower border until we find the numeral 4, we then move along a vertical line until we are opposite the letter D on the vertical border. Missoula is located in this way by the pair, $(4, D)$. The 4 is called the first component of the ordered pair, and D is called the second component. On road maps, letters and numerals are used to strengthen the concept of the ordered pair. The labels on the borders of military maps are usually numerals. Thus a hill may be designated by the ordered pair (705, 600). It is understood that one reads the first component along the horizontal edge and the second component along the vertical edge. In this way the ordered pair locates a single point. If the pair (705, 600) were not understood to be an ordered pair, one would have to check the pair (600, 705) as a possibility for locating the hill.

DEFINITION 2.6a. The *Cartesian product* of the sets A and B is the set of all ordered pairs (a, b) where the element in the first place, a, is an element of A and the element in the second place, b, is an element of B.

In order to distinguish the elements of the Cartesian product from one another and to avoid duplication, we must establish a criterion for "sameness." When are two elements the same?

DEFINITION 2.6b. Ordered pairs of the Cartesian product are the same, and we write $(a, b) = (c, d)$ if and only if $a = c$ and $b = d$.

We denote the Cartesian product of sets A and B by the symbol $A \times B$, and we read this as "the Cartesian product of A and B" or simply as "A cross B". In our notation

$$A \times B = \{(a, b) | a \text{ is in } A \text{ and } b \text{ is in } B\}.$$

Example 1

Let $A = \{a, b\}$ and let $B = \{0, 1, 2\}$. Some elements of the set $A \times B$ are $(b, 2)$, $(a, 1)$, and $(b, 0)$. Is the ordered pair $(1, a)$ an element of $A \times B$? The answer is No, because the first place element 1 is not in A nor is the second place element a in B. Does (a, a) belong to $A \times B$? No, because the second place member of the ordered pair does not belong to B. Can you write a complete list of the elements of $A \times B$?

Example 2

Let A be the set consisting of the digits 1 through 9. What are some elements of the Cartesian product $A \times A$? Is (1, 1) an element of $A \times A$? Yes, in fact

$$A \times A = \{(n, m) | n \text{ can be any of } 1, 2, 3, 4, 5, 6, 7, 8, 9, \text{ and } m \text{ can be any of } 1, 2, 3, 4, 5, 6, 7, 8, 9\}.$$

Example 3

One sees the following type of question on tests. Draw a line from each word in the column labeled A to a word with the opposite meaning in the column labeled B.

A	B
good	small
large	light
dark	bad
	up
	smooth

In this question, one is simply specifying certain elements of the Cartesian product of A and B such as (good, bad), (large, small), (dark, light).

The Cartesian product of any two sets may be represented pictorially, using perpendicular lines and the same scheme used by map makers. Along the horizontal axis we label equally spaced points with the elements of the first set and equally spaced points along the vertical line with elements of the second set. Following the usual convention, we read along the horizontal axis first and then along the vertical axis. The Cartesian product of the sets $A = \{a, b, c\}$ and $B = \{1, 5, 6, 9\}$ would be the points whose addresses or coordinates are the ordered pairs of $A \times B$.

$A \times B$

9	$(a, 9)$	$(b, 9)$	$(c, 9)$
6	$(a, 6)$	$(b, 6)$	$(c, 6)$
5	$(a, 5)$	$(b, 5)$	$(c, 5)$
1	$(a, 1)$	$(b, 1)$	$(c, 1)$
	a	b	c

Exercise 2.6

1. Find the Cartesian product $A \times B$ of sets A and B of Example 1, Section 2.6.

   For problems 2 and 3 consider the sets listed below.

   $A = \{a, b, c, d, e\}$ $\qquad D = \{1, 2, 3, 4, 5, 6, 7, 8, 9, 0\}$
   $B = \{1, a, 2, b, 3, c\}$ $\qquad E = \{0, 1\}$
   $C = \{1, 3, 5, 7, 9\}$ $\qquad F = \{2, 3, 4\}$

2. List the subsets of E and F.

3. Specify the following sets by listing the members in each of the sets.

(a) $A \cup B$ (b) $A \cap B$ (c) $B \cup C$
(d) $B \cap A$ (e) $A \cap C$ (f) $(B \cap C) \cap D$
(g) $B \cap (C \cap D)$ (h) $E \cup F$ (i) $E \cap F$
(j) $E \times F$ (k) $(B \cup C) \cap D$ (l) $(B \cap D) \cup (B \cap D)$
(m) $(B \cap C) \cup D$ (n) $(B \cup D) \cap (C \cup D)$

4. Let the sets, A, B, and C be the points inside and on the circle as in Example 2, Section 2.4b. Draw Venn diagrams of the following sets:

(a) $A \cap B$ (b) $A \cap B \cap C$
(c) $A \cup (B \cap C)$ (d) $(A \cap B) \cup (A \cap C)$

5. Let $A = \{a, b, c, d\}$. How many subsets has $A \times A$?

6. Let $A = \{1, 2, 3\}$, $B = \{2, 3, 4\}$, $C = \{3, 4, 5\}$, and $D = \{4, 5, 6\}$. Tabulate each of the following sets:

(a) $A \cap B$ (b) $B \cap C$
(c) $A \cap C$ (d) $A \cap B \cap C$
(e) $(A \cap B) \cap (C \cap D)$ (f) $(A \times A) \cap (B \times B)$
(g) $(A \times A) \cap (C \times C)$ (h) $(C \times C) \cap (D \times D)$

7. What does $A \cap (B \cup C)$ equal if

(a) A and B are disjoint? (b) B is identical to C?
(c) $A \subset C$? (d) $A \supset B$? $(A \cap C \neq \emptyset.)$
(e) C is the empty set?

8. Let $X = \{a, b, c\}$, $A = \{a\}$, $B = \{b\}$, $C = \{c\}$, $D = \{a, b\}$, $E = \{a, c\}$, and $F = \{b, c\}$. Then $S = \{\emptyset, A, B, C, D, E, F, X\}$ is the family of all subsets of X. Insert the correct element of S in each square of the following tables.

$\cup$	$\emptyset$	A	B	C	D	E	F	X
$\emptyset$								
A								
B								
C								
D								
E								
F								
X								

$\cap$	$\emptyset$	A	B	C	D	E	F	X
$\emptyset$								
A								
B								
C								
D								
E								
F								
X								

9. Illustrate that $A \cap (B \cup C) = (A \cap B) \cup (A \cap C)$ by the use of Venn diagrams such as in Figure 4.

10. In problem 13, Exercise 2.4, let I denote the children who like ice cream, C denote the children who like cake, and A denote the children who like apples. Describe each of the following sets by listing the names in each.

(a) $I \cap A$ (b) $C \cap A$
(c) $C \cap I$ (d) $I \cup A$
(e) $I \cap A \cap C$ (f) $C \cup A$
(g) $I \cup A \cup C$

How many children attended the party?

11. You, as a representative of a company selling soft drinks, are interested in putting soft-drink dispensers in the Student Union. The company is interested in finding out how many people like orange soda, grape soda, and strawberry soda. You hire a boy for $50 to poll 1000 students. He is to count only those who indicate a liking for at least one of the drinks. You observe your helper and see him drinking coffee in the lounge most of the time. Later he comes to you with the results of his poll as follows:

Orange	596
Grape	710
Strawberry	427
Strawberry and Orange	274
Orange and Grape	430
Grape and Strawberry	309
All three	212

You have serious doubts about how he obtained these figures, but you are willing to pay him the $50 if the figures "add up." Would you pay him?

REFERENCES

Banks, J. Houston, *Elements of Mathematics*, Allyn and Bacon, Boston, 1956, pp. 233–246.

Christian, Robert R., *Introduction to Logic and Sets*, Ginn and Co., New York, 1958, pp. 33–70.

Hafstrom, John E., *Basic Concepts in Modern Mathematics*, Addison-Wesley Publishing Co., Reading, Mass., 1961, ch. 3.

Hartung, Van Engen, and Trimble, *Seeing Through Mathematics I*, Scott, Foresman and Company, Chicago, 1961 (preliminary edition).

Mathematical Association of America, CUP, *Elementary Mathematics of Sets with Applications*, Mathematical Association of America, 1955, ch. I.

*
*
*

CHAPTER THREE

Relations and Their Properties

3.1 INTRODUCTION

Objects and ideas are seldom thought of or spoken of alone. They occur in thought and in speech with other objects or other ideas. Consciously or unconsciously we associate these objects or ideas with others, that is, we think or speak of these objects in the light of relations they bear to others of like or different kinds.

We may say of two things that one "is the same shape as" the other, or one "is heavier than" the other, or one "is lighter than" the other, and so on. We may say of two ideas that one "led to" the other, or one "is essentially the same as" the other, or that one "precedes historically" the other, and so on. Everyone is familiar with relationships—legal, blood-line, and other—that people bear to one another: "is a sister of," "is a friend of," "is the wife of," "is the mother of," and so forth.

Mathematics has a genuine concern with relations, the relations objects in mathematical systems bear to one another, for example, in the investigation of the system of natural numbers, a mathematician may be concerned with such relations as "is a successor of," "is greater than," "is divisible by," "divides," "is a factor of," "is relatively prime to," and so on.

In plane geometry the mathematician is concerned with such relations as "is parallel to," "is congruent to," "is perpendicular to." The reader could supply many more examples of "relations."

3.2 THE INCLUSION RELATION

In dealing with sets we have already mentioned a mathematical relation. In Section 2.3 we mentioned that inclusion is a relation between sets. The statement "A is a subset of B" pairs the sets A and B in a particular way. Notice that the pair, A and B, is an ordered pair in the sense that "B is a subset of A" has a different meaning from "A is a subset of B." A is a subset of B means that every element of A is an element of B, whereas B is a subset of A means that every element of B is an element of A.

Example 1

Let B be the set consisting of all four-legged animals and let A be the set consisting of all horses. Certainly in this case, with the exception of certain freaks, we can agree that A is a subset of B. Every horse has four legs but not all four-legged animals are horses, that is, B is not a subset of A.

Example 2

Consider the following sets:

$A = \{1, 2, 3, 4, 5, 6, 7, 8, 9\}$
$B = \{a, b, c, d, e, f, g, h, i\}$
$C = \{1, 5\}$
$D = \{a, c, e, f, h\}$
$E = \{a, e\}$
$F = \{1, a, 5, e\}$
$G = \{9, 3, 6, 7, 2, 5, 4, 8, 1\}$
$H = \{x | x \text{ is a letter of the alphabet.}\}$
$I = \emptyset$
$J = \{a, e, 5, 1\}$
$K = \{c, h, e, a, f\}$
$L = \{2, 4, 6, 8, 1, 3, 5, 7, 9\}$

In this example some sets are related to other sets. If we ask which ones are related, several ways of answering are possible. One way would be to indicate the sets in pairs, such as "C and A," or "E and D," but this tells us nothing about *how* they are related. Without any convention or agreement on what we mean when we write "C and A," all we would know is that they are somehow related. It would be somewhat like saying "ham and eggs." The relation is not obvious. If we wanted to be precise, we would need to say, for example, "C is contained in A."

DEFINITION 3.2. A set A is related to a set B by *inclusion* if A is a subset of B.

Recall that a set A "is a subset of" a set B if every element of A is an element of B.

We symbolize the relation "is included in" or "inclusion" as follows: $A \subseteq B$.

We can now ask which of the first six sets of Example 2 are related by inclusion. The answer would be, $C \subseteq A$, $E \subseteq D$, $D \subseteq B$, $E \subseteq B$, $C \subseteq F$, and $E \subseteq F$. The first set of symbols would be read "C is related to A by inclusion." This can also be read as "C is a subset of A," or "C is included in A." This determines a *relation* in the collection of sets, the relationship holding between members of particular ordered pairs, depending on the criterion given above. Because relations deal with ordered pairs, they are often defined in terms of subsets of the Cartesian product. This approach to the definition of relation will be presented in more detail in Section 3.15.

Exercise 3.2

State in words the relation suggested by each of the following:

1. The set of pairs of names: {(Martha, George), (Ann, Abe), (Jacqueline, John), (Mary, Joseph), (Eleanor, Franklin), (Blondie, Dagwood)}.
2. The set of pairs of words: {(good, bad), (large, small), (wet, dry), (hot, cold)}.
3. The set of pairs of numbers: $\{(2, 5), (3, 7), (9, 10), (4, 100), (37, 38)\}$.
4. The set of pairs: $\{(2, 2), (3 + 2, 5), (6 - 2, 4), (17, 17), (4 + 4, 8)\}$.
5. The set of pairs: {(Helena, Montana), (Eugene, Oregon), (Springfield, Illinois), (Austin, Texas), (Albany, New York), (Atlanta, Georgia), (Sacramento, California)}.

3.3 THE REFLEXIVE PROPERTY OF RELATIONS

Look at the sets in Example 2, Section 3.2, again. Are there any other pairs that are related by inclusion? Is C related to C? Remembering the definition of a subset, we see that C certainly is a subset of C. So C is related to itself by inclusion: $C \subseteq C$. In fact, every set is related to itself by inclusion. That every set is related to itself is a property of the inclusion relation. We call this property the *reflexive* property, and we say the inclusion relation is *reflexive.*

Let us use symbols, such as Ⓡ, Ⓗ, Ⓣ, to represent an arbitrary relation defined in a set S.

DEFINITION 3.3. We say that the relation Ⓡ is *reflexive* if it is true that each element x of the set S in which the relation is defined is related to itself, that is, Ⓡ is reflexive if x Ⓡ x for all x in S.

Example 1

Let us define a relation Ⓗ in the set consisting of the students in a class in the following way. A student in a class, whom we may call x, will bear this relation to a student, y, if they are the same height. Here we might encounter ambiguity in interpretation, that is, what do we mean by "same height?" To avoid such complications let us say that heights shall be expressed to the nearest half inch. We may symbolize our relation, x Ⓗ y. We can readily see from the definition of this relation that for any student x, x Ⓗ x. The relation as defined is reflexive or the relation Ⓗ possesses the reflexive property.

Example 2

Not all relations possess this property, for example, let the set S be the students in a particular class. Let the relation be "is taller than" and let Ⓣ represent this relation. We will say that student x is related to student y if student x is taller than student y, and write x Ⓣ y. This relation, Ⓣ, is not *reflexive* because it is *not* true that a student is taller than himself, that is, x Ⓣ x is not true.

3.4 THE TRANSITIVE PROPERTY OF RELATIONS

The inclusion relation has another property, which we call the *transitive* property. This property is demonstrated by the sets E, D, and B of Example 2, Section 3.2. Notice that E is related to D by inclusion, $E \subseteq D$, and D is related to B by inclusion, $D \subseteq B$. It is easy to see that E is also related to B, $E \subseteq B$. In our notation we have $E \subseteq D$, $D \subseteq B$, so $E \subseteq B$. If some other set, say K, was related to D by inclusion, what could be said about K and B? These remarks illustrate the transitive property of the inclusion relation.

DEFINITION 3.4. A relation Ⓡ is said to be *transitive* if the hypothesis that a Ⓡ b and b Ⓡ c leads to the conclusion that a Ⓡ c.

Example 1

Let us consider Example 2, Section 3.3, again. Is the relation Ⓣ a transitive relation? If we are given that x Ⓣ y and y Ⓣ z, can we say that x Ⓣ z? That is, if student x is taller than student y, and student y is taller than student z, can we say that student x is taller than student z? Obviously we can, so intuitively we may conclude the relation Ⓣ is transitive.

Example 2

Let us define a relation, call it Ⓦ, in the following way. A student in a class, whom we may call x, will bear this relation to a student, y, if their weights differ by less than half a pound. We symbolize this relation x Ⓦ y. We can readily see from the definition of this relation that it is a reflexive relation. Is it a transitive relation? That is, for students, x, y, and z, if x Ⓦ y and y Ⓦ z, is x Ⓦ z? A simple numerical example is sufficient to show that the relation *as defined* is not necessarily transitive. Suppose x weighs 150 lb, y weighs $150\frac{3}{8}$ lb, and z weighs $150\frac{3}{4}$ lb. The difference between the weight of x and the weight of z is $\frac{3}{4}$ lb, which is beyond the limitation of the relation as defined. Hence the relation Ⓦ is not transitive.

3.5 THE SAMENESS RELATION

We have indicated two ways of specifying sets. It may happen that the same set may be specified in several different ways. We need some criterion for determining whether a set specified in one way is the same, or distinct from, a set specified in another way. We distinguish sets by defining a *relation,* which we might call *equals,* but which, at this time, we prefer to call *sameness.*

DEFINITION 3.5. Two sets, A and B, will be related by "sameness" or the set A "is the same as" the set B if every element of A is an element of B *and* every element of B is an element of A (see also Definition 2.2).

We will use the symbol "=" to denote this relation. In our set notation we would write:

$$A = B \text{ if and only if } A \subseteq B \textit{ and } B \subseteq A.$$

Example 1

Let $A = \{c, a, t, 13\}$ and $B = \{13, a, c, t\}$. Then $A = B$, for every element of A is an element of B and every element of B is an element of A.

Exercise 3.5

1. Let each of the sets A, B, and C contain the points inside and on the circle so named in the following diagram:

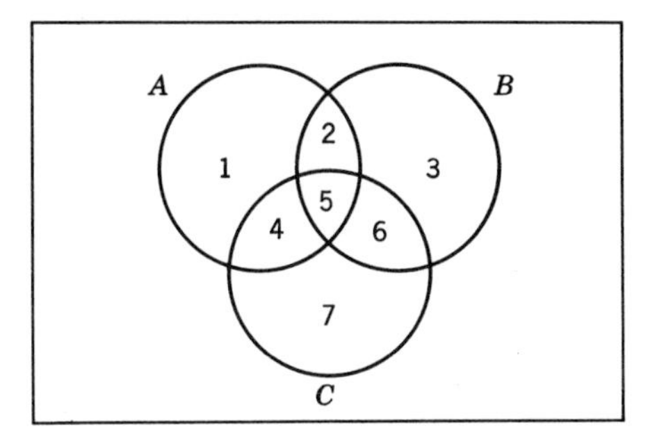

Note: The numerals are placed in the figure for convenience in identifying sets. For example, A is identified by the numerals 1, 2, 4, and 5, and we write $A = \{1, 2, 4, 5\}$, understanding that these, A and $\{1, 2, 4, 5\}$, are just different names for the set of points inside and on the circle marked A. In this way we can identify $A \cap B$ as $\{2, 5\}$ or write $A \cap B = \{2, 5\}$. Also, $A \cap (B \cup C) = \{2, 4, 5\}$.

Verify that the following pairs of sets are related by the "sameness" relation, as indicated, by listing the elements of each and checking that they satisfy the criterion stated in the definition.

(a) $A \cap B = B \cap A$
(b) $A \cup B = B \cup A$
(c) $(A \cup B) \cup C = A \cup (B \cup C)$
(d) $A \cap (B \cap C) = (A \cap B) \cap C$
(e) List other sets using A, B, and C and the operations union and intersection, which are related by the "sameness" relation.

2. Consider the following sets:

$A = \{1, 2, 3, 4, 5, 6, 7, 8, 9\}$
$B = \{a, b, c, d, e, f, g, h, i\}$
$C = \{1, 5\}$
$D = \{a, c, e, c, f, h\}$
$E = \{a, e\}$
$F = \{1, a, 5, e\}$
$G = \{9, 3, 6, 7, 2, 5, 4, 8, 1\}$
$H = \{x|x \text{ is a letter of the alphabet.}\}$
$I = \emptyset$
$J = \{a, e, 5, 1\}$
$K = \{c, h, e, a, f\}$
$L = \{2, 4, 6, 8, 1, 3, 5, 7, 9\}$

(a) Is $J = F$? $A = G$? $D = K$?
(b) Is $H = A$? $B = H$? $C = E$?
(c) Indicate other sets that are related by "sameness."

3. "Is shorter than" describes a relation that can be defined in the set of people. Is this relation reflexive? Is it transitive?

4. "Is the same age as" describes a relation that can be defined in the set of schoolchildren. Is this relation reflexive? Is it transitive?

3.6 PROPERTIES OF THE "SAMENESS" (EQUALS) RELATION FOR SETS

Notice that the "sameness" relation, $=$, holds between every set and itself, that is, $A = A$, $B = B$, and so forth. By the definition of the "sameness" relation we can say that it is a reflexive relation or the relation "is the same as" has the reflexive property.

What other properties does this relation have? Is the relation transitive? If we assume that $A = B$ and $B = C$, can we conclude that $A = C$? Consider the sets A, G, and L of Example 2, Section 3.2. Is $A = G$?

$$A = \{1, 2, 3, 4, 5, 6, 7, 8, 9\}$$
$$G = \{9, 3, 6, 7, 2, 5, 4, 8, 1\}$$

Notice that $A \subseteq G$ and $G \subseteq A$, so $A = G$. Now consider the sets G and L.

$$G = \{9, 3, 6, 7, 2, 5, 4, 8, 1\}$$
$$L = \{2, 4, 6, 8, 1, 3, 5, 7, 9\}$$

Again $G \subseteq L$ and $L \subseteq G$, so $G = L$. Do we have to test each element of A to see if it belongs to L and each element of L to see if it belongs to A? We could, but we could also use something we know about the relation of inclusion. We know that $A \subseteq G$ and $G \subseteq L$, so by the transitive property of the inclusion relation (Section 3.4) we know that $A \subseteq L$. Also, we know that $L \subseteq G$ and $G \subseteq A$, so $L \subseteq A$. Hence $A = L$ by our criterion of "sameness," that is, this sameness relation that we symbolize by "$=$" has the *transitive* property.

3.7 THE SYMMETRIC PROPERTY OF RELATIONS

Consider the sets A and G again: $A = G$ and $G = A$. Similarly, $G = L$ and $L = G$. In fact, for any ordered pair of sets (X, Y) for which the "sameness" relation holds, we have, if $X = Y$, then $Y = X$. This property of the "sameness" relation is called the *symmetric* property.

DEFINITION 3.7. A relation Ⓡ defined on a set S has the *symmetric* property if, for any elements a and b in S, whenever a Ⓡ b, then b Ⓡ a.

Notice that the inclusion relation is not symmetric. From Example 2, Section 3.2, $E \subseteq F$ but $F \nsubseteq E$. This last symbol is read "F is not related to E by inclusion" or "F is not a subset of E."

3.8 THE "DIVIDES" RELATION

We have referred to the set of natural numbers as the set $N = \{1, 2, 3, 4, 5, \ldots\}$.

DEFINITION 3.8. The relation "divides" in the set N is defined as follows: Two natural numbers, m and n, are related by the relation *divides* if there is a natural number k such that $n = m \cdot k$.

We symbolize this $m|n$, and read it "m divides n." If m does *not* divide n, we symbolize this $m \nmid n$. Notice that the relation is carefully defined and that the set under consideration is clearly specified, "the natural numbers." If $m|n$, we also say n is a *multiple* of m and m is a *factor* of n.

Example 1

12|24, for there is a natural number, 2, such that $24 = 12 \cdot 2$. In this example $n = 24$, $m = 12$, and $k = 2$.

Example 2

Similarly, 3|3, for there is a natural number, 1, such that $3 = 3 \cdot 1$. In this example $n = 3$, $m = 3$, and $k = 1$.

The relation "divides" has the reflexive property, for, in general, any natural number m divides itself, that is, $m|m$ since $m = m \cdot 1$.

The relation "divides" is *not* symmetric. One counterexample is sufficient to show this. Note that 2|6 but $6 \nmid 2$, "2 divides 6 but 6 *does not* divide 2."

The relation "divides" is transitive. This requires more than a mere statement to *prove*. The proof involves the properties of the *System of Whole Numbers* and will be left as an exercise for Chapter 5. It depends on the property that for numbers a, b, and c, $(a \cdot b) \cdot c = a \cdot (b \cdot c)$. Do you know what this property is called?

3.9 THE "R, S, T" PROPERTIES

Let us review briefly. We have examined the following relations: the inclusion relation, $\subseteq$, the sameness relation, $=$, and the divides relation, $|$. These relations are distinct and yet share certain properties. The *properties* that we have so far attributed to relations are the *reflexive property*, the *symmetric property*, and the *transitive property*. If we use the symbol Ⓡ to represent an arbitrary relation, and a, b, and c to represent generic elements of a set S, then

1. Ⓡ is reflexive if a Ⓡ a for all a in S.
2. Ⓡ is symmetric if whenever a Ⓡ b, then b Ⓡ a.
3. Ⓡ is transitive if whenever a Ⓡ b and b Ⓡ c, then a Ⓡ c.

Recall that the inclusion relation is reflexive and transitive but not symmetric. The sameness relation for sets is reflexive, symmetric, and transitive. The divides relation is reflexive and transitive but not symmetric. The ordinary equals relation that you have been using in mathematics has all three of these properties.

We shall examine other relations in Section 3.15 with a view toward determining properties they possess. In examining relations we should bear in mind the set in which the relation is defined and the definition of the relation.

Exercise 3.9

1. Let the relation Ⓣ be defined on the set of students in a particular school. Student x is related to student y by the relation Ⓣ if and only if x is taller than y. Jim Ⓣ Tom if and only if Jim is taller than Tom. Which of the "*R, S, T*" properties does the relation Ⓣ have?
2. Let the relation Ⓟ be defined on the set of natural numbers as follows: The number m is related to the number n if either both are even or both are odd. We write m Ⓟ n if and only if m and n are both even or m and n are both odd. Which of the "*R, S, T*" properties does the relation Ⓟ have?
3. Let the relation Ⓒ be defined on the set of people living in a particular city. Let person x be related to person y if x is a son or daughter of y. We write x Ⓒ y if and only if x is a child of y. Which of the "*R, S, T*" properties does Ⓒ have?
4. Let the relation $\equiv$ be defined on the set consisting of the natural numbers and 0 as follows: $m \equiv n$ if m and n have the same remainder when divided by 7. List the "*R, S, T*" properties of the relation $\equiv$.
5. What can you say about the numbers related to 0 in the last problem?

6. Let the relation $\equiv$ be defined on the set consisting of the natural numbers and 0 as follows: $m \equiv n$ if they have the same remainder when divided by 2. What can you say about the numbers related to 0? What can you say about the numbers related to 1? Does this look familiar?

3.10 ONE-TO-ONE CORRESPONDENCE

DEFINITION 3.10. Two sets, A and B, are said to be in *one-to-one correspondence* if each element of A can be "paired" to an element of B and each element of B can be "paired" to an element of A in such a way that distinct elements of A are paired to distinct elements of B and distinct elements of B are paired to distinct elements of A.

If A and B can be put into one-to-one correspondence in one way, they can be put into one-to-one correspondence in at least one other way unless A has fewer than two elements.

Example 1

Let $A = \{a, b, c, d, e\}$, and let $B = \{1, 5, 4, 2, 6\}$. One possible one-to-one correspondence would be: $a \leftrightarrow 1$, $b \leftrightarrow 6$, $c \leftrightarrow 2$, $d \leftrightarrow 5$, and $e \leftrightarrow 4$. Another would be: $a \leftrightarrow 5$, $b \leftrightarrow 2$, $c \leftrightarrow 1$, $d \leftrightarrow 4$, and $e \leftrightarrow 6$.

The idea of one-to-one correspondence, or "matching," probably enabled man to recognize that he had as many toes as he had fingers. No doubt this was somewhat of a surprise when he first realized it.

Exercise 3.10

1. Indicate how at least two other one-to-one correspondences could be established between the sets A and B of Example 1, Section 3.10.
2. How many one-to-one correspondences are possible between sets A and B of Example 1, Section 3.10? (*Hint:* In how many ways can a be "matched" to an element of B? After a has been matched, in how many ways can b be matched to the remaining elements of B?)
3. Using the definition of "divides," show that

   (a) $7|35$ (b) $8|72$ (c) $3|51$ (d) $9|9$

4. Give a counterexample different from the one in Section 3.9 to show that the relation "divides" is not symmetric.
5. Let $N = \{1, 2, 3, 4, 5, \ldots, n, \ldots\}$ and $E = \{2, 4, 6, 8, \ldots, 2n, \ldots\}$. Recall that the dots are to indicate the sequence is to go on and on. Define a one-to-one correspondence for these two sets.
6. Let the set A consist of the letters of the word "marbles." Describe a one-to-one correspondence of the set A with itself so that the resultant set again constitutes a word.
7. How many one-to-one correspondences are possible between the set in problem 6 and itself? (Each such correspondence is called a *permutation*.)

8. If we allow ten seconds to write down a permutation different from all previously written permutations of the first 15 letters of the alphabet, how long would it take to write down all possible permutations of the 15 letters? (Try to estimate the time required before you carry out the computation.)

3.11 THE MATCHING RELATION

DEFINITION 3.11. Two sets A and B are "matched,"* or satisfy the matching relation, if they can be placed in one-to-one correspondence.

We shall use the symbol "1–1" to stand for "one-to-one correspondence."

This matching process is of fundamental importance in mathematics and is introduced in the first year of a child's formal education. You may recall from your own experience pictures containing, for example, three rabbits and three children. The child is asked to show how to distribute the rabbits so that each child has just one rabbit by drawing lines from each rabbit to a child. This is a 1–1 process.

In ancient times the shepherd picked up a stone and put it in a skin bag for each sheep that went out to the pasture in the morning. In the evening he took a stone out of the bag for each one that returned. If no stones were left over, he was confident as many sheep returned as went out. He had, in fact, established a one-to-one correspondence.

The matching relation is reflexive, symmetric, and transitive. The student is asked to verify that such is the case.

3.12 AN EQUIVALENCE RELATION

We have examined some relations that have *all three* of the properties we have discussed. The ordinary equals relation, the sameness relation, and the matching relation are examples. They are each reflexive, symmetric, and transitive. In general, there are many other relations that exhibit these same properties. Because of the role such relations play in mathematics, they have been given a special name.

DEFINITION 3.12a. Any relation Ⓡ that is reflexive, symmetric, and transitive is called an *equivalence relation.*

Example 1

Let us consider the set S consisting of all the school children in the Lincoln Grade School (grades one through eight). Let us define a relation in this set in the following way.

A student x is related to a student y, and we will use the language "x is a

* Some authors use the term "equivalent" where we use the term "matched." We believe that the term "matched" is more suggestive and more appropriate at this time.

classmate of y" if x and y are in the same grade. It is to be understood that every student is a classmate of himself, and no student can be listed as belonging to more than one grade.

The relation, "is a classmate of," is an equivalence relation. This relation is reflexive because every student is related to himself by the definition. If x "is a classmate of" y, then certainly y "is a classmate of" x, for they are both in the same grade. So the relation is symmetric. Finally, if x "is a classmate of" y and y "is a classmate of" z, then x "is a classmate of" z, for they are in the same grade.

This relation partitions the pupils into classes which, in this case, are the grades one through eight.

Any equivalence relation Ⓡ defined in a set S has the effect of partitioning the set into disjoint subsets, or classes, which are called *equivalence classes.* In the last example the equivalence classes are the grades.

DEFINITION 3.12b. If Ⓡ is an equivalence relation in a set S and a is in S, the *equivalence class* of a is defined to be $[a] = \{x \in S | x \text{ Ⓡ } a\}$.

Also, $[a] = \{x \text{ in } S | a \text{ Ⓡ } x\}$, since an equivalence relation is symmetric.

Example 2

The relation in problem 6, Exercise 3.9, is an equivalence relation. It is the same relation as the one defined in problem 2 of the same section. The class to which 5 belongs is [5]. The class to which 4 belongs is [4]. Notice that 5 is also in the class [1], that is, [1] = [5]. There are really only two classes, the even numbers [0] and the odd numbers [1].

Example 3

The relation in Example 1 of this section is an equivalence relation. If Jane is in the third grade, [Jane] is the equivalence class to which Jane belongs. [Jane] is the third grade.

Notice that a is in $[a]$, since a Ⓡ a because an equivalence relation is reflexive.

Notice also that if a is in $[b]$, then b is in $[a]$ because an equivalence relation is symmetric.

Finally, note that if c belongs to both $[a]$ and $[b]$, then, since a Ⓡ c and c Ⓡ b, it would follow that a Ⓡ b by the transitivity of an equivalence relation. This implies that $[a] = [b]$.

Thus, if $[a]$ and $[b]$ are equivalence classes, either $[a] = [b]$ or $[a]$ and $[b]$ are disjoint, that is, $[a] \cap [b] = \emptyset$.

Example 4

The relation of problem 4, Exercise 3.9, ($n \equiv m$ if m and n have the same remainder when divided by 7), is an equivalence relation. We use this example to illustrate the effect of an equivalence relation defined on a set. We write the natural numbers and zero in an array as follows:

$$\begin{array}{l} 0,\ 7,\ 14,\ 21,\ 28,\ \ldots \\ 1,\ 8,\ 15,\ 22,\ 29,\ \ldots \\ 2,\ 9,\ 16,\ 23,\ 30,\ \ldots \\ 3,\ 10,\ 17,\ 24,\ 31,\ \ldots \\ 4,\ 11,\ 18,\ 25,\ 32,\ \ldots \\ 5,\ 12,\ 19,\ 26,\ 33,\ \ldots \\ 6,\ 13,\ 20,\ 27,\ 34,\ \ldots \end{array}$$

Notice that all the numbers in each row are related to each other, that is, each row is an equivalence class. Notice that there are exactly seven classes, for there are only seven possible remainders when a natural number is divided by 7. Notice that every number is accounted for so that every number belongs to some class. Notice also that the classes are disjoint in pairs. This is what we mean by a *partition* of a set.

Hence we see, as stated above, that an equivalence relation has the effect of partitioning a set into disjoint subsets. The converse is also true, namely, that any partition of a set into disjoint subsets determines a relation that is an equivalence relation. This fact will not be exploited at this time.

Exercise 3.12

1. Verify that the matching relation is an equivalence relation.
2. Let S be the students in the Lincoln Grade School. Let the relation be "same age as," and, again, it is to be understood that a person is the same age as himself. Also, let us agree to specify ages to the nearest year. Verify that this is an equivalence relation and describe the equivalence classes.
3. Consider the set of problem 2 and let the relation be "same sex as." Verify that this is also an equivalence relation and describe the equivalence classes.
4. Let $J = \{\ldots, -3, -2, -1, 0, 1, 2, 3, \ldots\}$, where the dots indicate that the numbers continue indefinitely in both directions. On this set let us define the relation "is a multiple of" as follows: For m and n in J, m "is a multiple of" n if there is a k in J such that $m = n \cdot k$. Assume that $0 = n \cdot 0$ for any n, and $-n = n \cdot (-1)$ for any n. Is this relation an equivalence relation?
5. On the set J of problem 4 let us define a relation as follows. If m and n are elements of J, m is related to n if their difference is a multiple of 4 (see problem 4). For example, 9 is related to 5 because $9 - 5 = 4$, and 4 is a multiple of 4. Also 25 is related to 41 because their difference is 16, and 16 is a multiple of 4. Is this relation an equivalence relation? If so, describe the equivalence classes.
6. What do you mean when you say that $1 + 1 + 1 + 1 = 4$? $2 + 2 = 4$? $1 + 3 = 4$? $1 + 3 = 3 + 1$? $\frac{8}{2} = 4$? $5 - 1 = 4$?
7. In the following you are to consider the relation, the set in which it is defined, and the symbol, then
   (a) specify a criterion for the relation.

(b) name the properties it possesses.
(c) if it is an equivalence relation, describe the equivalence classes.

Relation	*Set in which defined*	*Symbol*
Inclusion	Set whose elements are sets	$\subseteq$
Divides	Natural numbers	$\mid$
"is the daughter of"	People	®
"is the same as"	Set whose elements are sets	$=$
"is a classmate of"	Students	©
Matching	Set whose elements are sets	1–1

3.13 THE CARDINAL NUMBER OF A SET

The one-to-one correspondence or matching relation is an equivalence relation. It partitions the sets of all objects into equivalence classes. The singleton sets have the common property of "oneness." The sets with two objects have the common property of "twoness." The sets with three objects have the common property of "threeness." Thus every set has a name associated with it. This is not a profound notion. In fact, it is the idea used to teach children to count. The teacher points to pictures of sets of 3 rabbits, 3 children, 3 hats, and so forth, each time saying the word "three," and the idea of "threeness" is impressed on the child at an early age. It does not take long for a child to learn to say the words one, two, three, four, five, six, seven, eight, nine, and ten. It takes more time for a child to learn the meaning of the words.

Counting probably had its origin in keeping track of possessions, but this was possible without numerals. Pebbles in a bag, notches on a stick, and knots in a rope are some of the devices that have been used in "keeping tally" (see Newman or Hogben). The essential idea was the one-to-one correspondence between the set being counted and the objects in the representative set or counting set. Man's recognition of what 2 pebbles, 2 shells, 2 notches, 2 knots, and so on, have in common marked the real beginning of arithmetic. Certain words in our language seem to suggest that at one time man did not recognize, and give a single name to, the common property of matched sets. The words brace (of pheasants), yoke (of oxen), pair (of dice), couple, and others that convey the idea of "twoness" are examples of this.

When the significance of "twoness," "threeness," and so forth, was realized, that is, that the same identifying word or symbol could be used for all matched sets, the next step was to give names to these abstractions. The abstractions themselves are called *numbers*, while the names or symbols that we give them are called *numerals*. Thus when one counts a set of objects by calling off the number words, "one, two, three, . . . ," he is practically doing what the primitive man did when he put pebbles in the skin bag. A one-to-one correspondence is established between the counted objects and the number words.

One difference should be noted. It was immaterial which pebble was put in or taken out of the bag first, second, third, and so on, but the number words must be used in a prescribed order. One reason for this is that when we use the word "two" or the symbol 2, we are admitting that there is a one-to-one correspondence between the objects being counted and the particular set $\{1, 2\}$. When we use the word "five," or the symbol 5, we are admitting that there is a one-to-one correspondence between the objects being counted and the set $\{1, 2, 3, 4, 5\}$. When we say there are six books on a shelf, we are admitting that there is a one-to-one correspondence between the books and the set $\{1, 2, 3, 4, 5, 6\}$.

DEFINITION 3.13. A set S will have cardinal n, or cardinal number n, if and only if there exists a one-to-one correspondence between the elements in the set S and the set $\{1, 2, 3, 4, \ldots, n\}$. The empty set has cardinal 0.

If S is a set, then $n(S)$ denotes the cardinal number of S, or the cardinal of S. It is read "n of S."

Example 1

If $S = \{1, 2, 3, 4, 5, 6\}$, then $n(S) = 6$.
If $A = \{a, b, c, d, e, f, g, h, i\}$, then $n(A) = 9$.
If $B = \{a, b, c, d\}$ and $C = \{c, d, e, f\}$, then $n(B \cup C) = 6$.

We can define finiteness using these notions. We say that a set is *finite* if there is a natural number n such that the set can be put in a one-to-one correspondence with the set $\{1, 2, 3, 4, \ldots, n\}$. Otherwise we say the set is *infinite*.

The ideas presented in the last few paragraphs will be discussed more fully in Chapter 5.

Exercise 3.13

Let the sets X, Y, Z, and W be the points inside and on the circles as indicated.

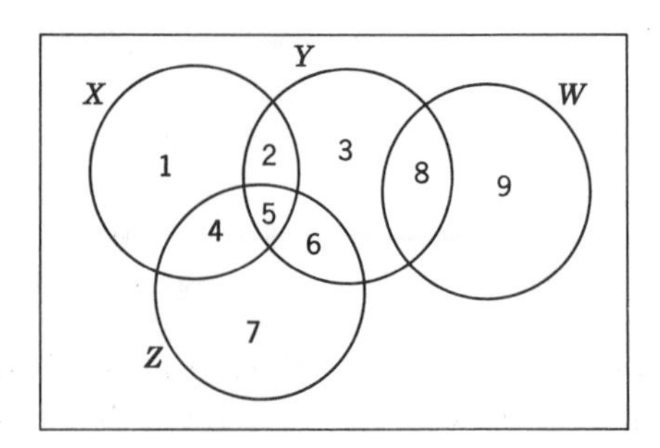

The numerals are used for convenience in identifying sets as in problem 1, Exercise 3.5, for example, $X = \{1, 2, 4, 5\}$, and $X \cup Y = \{1, 2, 3, 4, 5, 6, 8\}$.

Use the diagram above and the numerals to identify the following sets:

1. $X \cup Y$
2. $X \cap (Y \cup Z)$
3. $X \cap W$
4. $(X \cup Y) \cap (X \cup Z)$
5. $(X \cup Y) \cup Z$
6. $(X \cap Z) \cup W$
7. $(X \cap W) \cup (Y \cap W)$
8. $W \cup (X \cap Y)$
9. $Y \cup X$
10. $(X \cap Y) \cap Z$
11. $(X \cap Y) \cup (X \cap Z)$
12. $X \cup (Y \cup Z)$
13. $W \cap X$
14. $X \cap (Y \cap Z)$
15. $X \cap Y \cap Z$
16. $X \cup Y \cup Z$

In the following, let A be the set of dots inside the oval marked A, let B be the set of dots inside the oval marked B, let C be the set of dots inside the oval marked C, and let D be the set of dots inside the oval marked D.

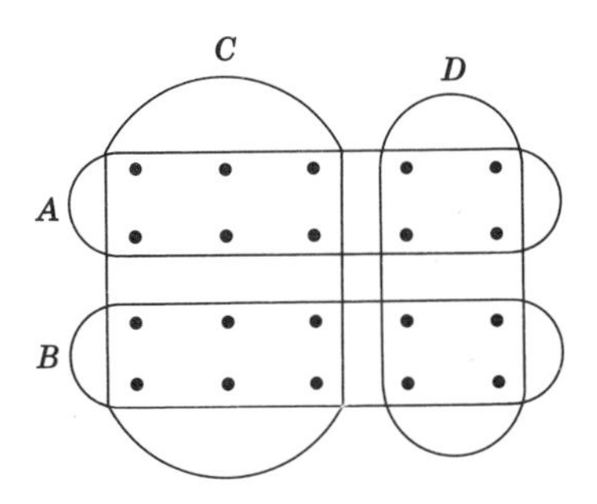

17. $n(A) = ?$
18. $n(B) = ?$
19. $n(C) = ?$
20. $n(D) = ?$
21. $n(A \cup B) = ?$
22. $n(A \cup C) = ?$
23. $n(A \cap B) = ?$
24. $n(B \cap D) = ?$
25. Verify that $n(A \cup C) = n(A) + n(C) - n(A \cap C)$.
26. Verify that $n(A \cup B) = n(A) + n(B)$.
27. Find $n(A \times B)$. Compare with $n(A) \cdot n(B)$.
28. Find $n(A \times A)$. Compare with $n(A) \cdot n(A)$.
29. A group of people were interviewed and it was found that:

25 like candy
37 like movies
12 like television
9 like candy and movies
4 like movies and television
7 like candy and television
2 like candy, television, and movies

How many were interviewed?

30. If a traveler can go from Seattle to Chicago by three distinct routes and from Chicago to New York by four distinct routes, how many distinct routes are there between Seattle and New York?
31. Use the idea in problem 30 to count the number of 1-1 correspondences from the set $\{a, b, c, d\}$ to the set $\{x, y, z, w\}$.

3.14 MORE ON RELATIONS IN GENERAL

In our treatment of relations in the previous sections, we did not attempt to define *relation* formally. Instead, we adopted an intuitive approach to the concept of relation by citing many examples of relations, each of which was a *pairing* of elements according to some specific criterion. It was noted that some relations had certain properties, other relations did not. We intentionally emphasized those properties that characterize equivalence relations. We were motivated by two main purposes:

1. The concept of an equivalence class will be especially useful in our discussion of the system of rational numbers.
2. The word "equals" is used in many different contexts and with different meanings. We hope to achieve a better understanding and appreciation of the equals relation.

Exercise 3.14

1. State the criterion for the equals relation to hold in each of the following situations:

(a) A and B are sets. $A = B$.
(b) m and n are integers. $m = n$.
(c) (a, b) and (c, d) are ordered pairs. $(a, b) = (c, d)$.

2. Explain the meaning of the word "equal" in the statement "All men are born free and equal."

3. The statement "A half plus a half is equal to a whole" is not necessarily true. Would you be willing to accept two halves of an automobile tire for a whole tire? Give other examples where the truth of the statement depends on the interpretation of the word "equals."

4. Suppose two people, both of whom like a particular cake, want to divide the cake *equally*. Cutting a cake into two *equal* parts is a difficult chore. Knowing this, the two people agree that a reasonable criterion for dividing the cake equally would be that each should be satisfied with the piece he receives. How should they divide the cake with just a single cut?

5. Referring to problem 4, how would three people cut the cake?

3.15 RELATIONS AS SETS

The emphasis on equivalence relations and the reflexive, symmetric, and transitive properties may be somewhat misleading. To dispel any notions that these are the only relations of interest or that there are no other properties of relations that are useful, we include a brief formal treatment of relations. This approach leads naturally to other useful concepts, in particular to the concept of *function*.

We indicated previously that the concept of relation involved a *pairing* of elements according to a specific criterion. Because the manner in which the elements may be paired is usually significant, the *ordered pair* is particularly well suited to a formal definition of relation.

Earlier we used the symbol Ⓡ to denote an arbitrary relation. (We used special symbols to designate relations that occur often enough to have become conventional.) We wrote a Ⓡ b to indicate that a is Ⓡ-related to b. The "pairing" of the elements can be indicated by simply writing the pairs that are related as ordered pairs. By knowing the relation, the set of all ordered pairs determined by it can be specified. This leads to the following definition.

DEFINITION 3.15a. A *relation* is a set of ordered pairs.

If we use Ⓡ to denote a relation, then Ⓡ is a set, each member of which is an ordered pair. We write interchangeably x Ⓡ y or $(x, y) \in$ Ⓡ. Either symbol is read "x is Ⓡ-related to y." We shall continue to write x Ⓡ y.

DEFINITION 3.15b. The set of all first components of members of a relation is called the *domain* of the relation.

DEFINITION 3.15c. The set of all second components of members of a relation is called the *range* of the relation.

In general, the domain and the range of a relation are distinct sets. The domain of the marriage relation, "is the wife of," is the set of married women. The range of "is the wife of" is the set of married men.

DEFINITION 3.15d. A relation with domain and range in the same set A is said to be *defined in* A.

A relation with domain A and range B is quite frequently defined as a subset of the Cartesian product, $A \times B$. A relation in a set A is a subset of $A \times A$.

We saw earlier that the number of subsets of a given set is quite large. If the set A has four elements, that is, if $n(A) = 4$, then there are 2^4 subsets of A. How many subsets has $A \times A$? According to our definition, each such subset defines a relation. Most of these relations are quite uninteresting. We will be interested in only those few that have certain desirable properties. In addition to the properties with which we are familiar, one or two other properties may give some indication of the power and scope of the relation concept.

Every relation has an inverse.

DEFINITION 3.15e. The *inverse* of a relation Ⓡ is the set of all ordered pairs (y, x) for which (x, y) is in Ⓡ. We use the notation Ⓡ$^{-1}$ to denote the inverse relation.

Example 1

If $\circledR$ is the relation $<$, then $\circledR^{-1}$ is the relation $>$.

$$3 < 5 \qquad\qquad 5 > 3$$
$$(3, 5) \in \circledR \qquad\qquad (5, 3) \in \circledR^{-1}$$

Example 2

If $\circledR$ is the relation "is a factor of" in the set of natural numbers, then $\circledR^{-1}$ is the relation "is a multiple of."

2 is a factor of 6, $(2, 6) \in \circledR$
6 is a multiple of 2, $(6, 2) \in \circledR^{-1}$

DEFINITION 3.15f. A relation $\circledR$ is *single valued* if no two distinct members of $\circledR$ have the same first component, that is, $x \circledR y$ and $x \circledR z$ cannot happen unless $y = z$.

DEFINITION 3.15g. Single-valued relations are called *functions*.

Functions play a central role in mathematics. For relations that are functions, single letters are used. Such relations are usually referred to as the function f, the function g, and so on.

We reiterate: a function is a single-valued relation. A relation involves two sets called the domain and range and a pairing of elements of the domain to elements of the range.

3.16 ORDER

Another type of relation that will be of particular interest to us later is the order relation.

DEFINITION 3.16. A relation that is transitive is called an *order relation*.

We use the symbol $<$ (less than) to denote the order relation if the relation is not reflexive. We use the symbol $\leqq$ (less than or equal to) to denote the order relation if it is reflexive, that is, we write $x \leqq y$ to mean either $x < y$ or $x = y$ (identical). (The relations symbolized by $<$ and $\leqq$ are also called *inequalities*.)

Example 1

$$3 < 5$$
$$9 < 30$$

It is not true that $3 < 3$, that is, the "less than" relation is not reflexive.

Example 2

$3 \leqq 5$	since	$3 < 5$
$9 \leqq 30$	since	$9 < 30$
$3 \leqq 3$	since	$3 = 3$
$9 \leqq 9$	since	$9 = 9$

The "less than or equal to" relation is reflexive.

At this time we appeal to the intuitive interpretation of "less than" or "equal." These relations will be defined for each of the number systems as they are introduced.

Example 3

Consider the set $A = \{1, 2, 3, 4\}$. Then the set $A \times A$ is given by the following table.

$A \times A$

4	(1, 4)	(2, 4)	(3, 4)	(4, 4)
3	(1, 3)	(2, 3)	(3, 3)	(4, 3)
2	(1, 2)	(2, 2)	(3, 2)	(4, 2)
1	(1, 1)	(2, 1)	(3, 1)	(4, 1)
	1	2	3	4

From the set $A \times A$ consider the subset consisting of

$$\{(1, 1), (2, 2), (3, 3), (4, 4)\}.$$

4	(1, 4)	(2, 4)	(3, 4)	**(4, 4)**
3	(1, 3)	(2, 3)	**(3, 3)**	(4, 3)
2	(1, 2)	**(2, 2)**	(3, 2)	(4, 2)
1	**(1, 1)**	(2, 1)	(3, 1)	(4, 1)
	1	2	3	4

Suppose you were told that these pairs were selected because the first component bears a special relation to the second and that only these ordered pairs of the set $A \times A$ have this relation. Certainly you would conclude that the relation described is the "equals" relation.

Consider the subset $\{(1, 4), (1, 3), (1, 2), (2, 4), (2, 3), (3, 4)\}$.

4	**(1, 4)**	**(2, 4)**	**(3, 4)**	(4, 4)
3	**(1, 3)**	**(2, 3)**	(3, 3)	(4, 3)
2	**(1, 2)**	(2, 2)	(3, 2)	(4, 2)
1	(1, 1)	(2, 1)	(3, 1)	(4, 1)
	1	2	3	4

This subset also defines a relation. After examining the ordered pairs in the set, you should see they describe the relation "is less than."

Consider the subset $\{(1, 1), (1, 2), (1, 3), (1, 4), (2, 2), (2, 4), (3, 3), (4, 4)\}$.

4	**(1, 4)**	**(2, 4)**	(3, 4)	**(4, 4)**
3	**(1, 3)**	(2, 3)	**(3, 3)**	(4, 3)
2	**(1, 2)**	**(2, 2)**	(3, 2)	(4, 2)
1	**(1, 1)**	(2, 1)	(3, 1)	(4, 1)
	1	2	3	4

This subset defines the relation "divides" in the set A. The relation "divides" is a subset of the Cartesian product $A \times A$.

Notice that if the subset of $A \times A$ contains the diagonal elements, that is, (1, 1), (2, 2), (3, 3), (4, 4), whatever the remaining elements of the subset may be, we must conclude that the relation defined by the subset is *reflexive*. Can similar statements be made with reference to the symmetric and transitive properties of relations?

We repeat: A relation with domain A and range B is quite frequently defined as a subset of the Cartesian product, $A \times B$. A relation in a set A is a subset of $A \times A$.

Exercise 3.16

1. Let $A = \{$Boise, Helena, Olympia, Salem$\}$.
$B = \{$Idaho, Montana, Washington, Oregon$\}$.

(a) Construct $A \times B$.
(b) Indicate the subset defined by the relation "is the capital of."
(c) Indicate the subset defined by the inverse of the relation in (b).

2. If f is a function, the inverse of f is a relation. When is the inverse of f a function?

3. What is the difference in meaning between the symbols

(a) (a, b) and (b, a)?
(b) (a, b) and $\{a, b\}$?

4. (a) Which of the relations described by the following graphs are functions of either x or y?
(b) State the domain and range of each relation that is a function.

y	1	2	3	4
4	·	·	·	⊙
3	·	·	·	⊙
2	·	·	·	⊙
1	·	·	·	⊙

(a)

y	1	2	3	4
4	·	·	⊙	·
3	·	·	·	⊙
2	·	⊙	·	·
1	·	·	·	·

(b)

y	1	2	3	4
4	·	⊙	·	·
3	·	⊙	⊙	·
2	⊙	⊙	·	⊙
1	·	·	⊙	·

(c)

y	1	2	3	4
4	·	·	·	·
3	·	⊙	⊙	·
2	·	·	·	·
1	⊙	·	·	⊙

(d)

5. Define an order relation in the set consisting of the pupils at Garfield Elementary School.

REVIEW EXERCISES

1. Let 0 represent zero, I represent one, L represent two, and a, b, c, d represent 3, 3^2, 3^3, 3^4, respectively. Make a table as follows and, using the necessary symbols from this set, represent the given decimal numbers in (a) an additive system of numeration, (b) a multiplicative system of numeration, and (c) a place-value system of numeration, where the respective place values are units, threes, nines, twenty-sevens, eighty-ones, and so on.

	Additive	*Multiplicative*	*Place-Value*
9	________	________	________
25	________	________	________
109	________	________	________

2. Let I denote the set of all people.
M denote the set of all male people.
W denote the set of all female people.
R denote the set of all red-haired people.
T denote the set of all people 21 or more years of age.

Describe the following subsets of I in words. (For example, $W \cap R$ is the set of all red-haired females.)

(a) $M \cap R$
(b) $R \cup T$
(c) $M \cap W$
(d) $M \cup T$

3. Let $A = \{1, 2, 3, 4\}$, $B = \{a, b, c\}$.

(a) Make the table of $A \times B$.
(b) Make the table of $A \times A$.
(c) Pick the subset of $A \times A$ such that the numbers of the ordered pairs are related by "less than."

4. Given the set $A = \{1, 2, 3, 4, 5, 6\}$, produce a set equivalent to A, that is, one that is related to A by the "matching" relation.

5. Given the set $M = \{1, 2, 3, 4\}$ and $N = \{a, b, c, d\}$,

(a) establish a one-to-one correspondence between M and N.
(b) How many such correspondences are there?

6. Given $M = \{1, 2, 3\}$,

(a) list all subsets of M.
(b) How many subsets are there of a set of five elements?

7. Consider $U = \{1, 2, 3, 4, 5, 6, 7\}$;

$A = \{1, 2, 3, 7\}$; $B = \{3, 4, 6, 7\}$; $C = \{4, 5\}$.

(a) Draw a Venn diagram of the sets U, A, B, and C.
(b) Describe the following sets by listing the elements:

(1) $A \cap B$
(2) $A \cup (B \cup C)$
(3) $A \cup B$
(4) $A \cap (B \cup C)$
(5) $A \cap (B \cap C)$
(6) $A \cup (B \cap C)$

8. List the properties (i.e., reflexive, symmetric, transitive) possessed by each of the following relations defined on the specified sets:

	SET	*RELATION*
(a)	The natural numbers	"is greater than"
(b)	The natural numbers	"divides"
(c)	Straight lines in a plane	"is parallel to"
(d)	Pupils at Paxon School	"is in the same grade as"
(e)	Animals	"is the same specie as"

(f) Which of the above relations are equivalence relations?

9. Define the following:
(a) The union of two sets.
(b) The intersection of two sets.
(c) The empty set.
(d) The Cartesian product of two sets.
(e) Subset.
(f) Equivalence relation.
(g) Function.
(h) Order relation.

10. Let $A = \{1, 2, 3\}$, $B = \{1, 2, 3, 4\}$, and $C = \{4, 5, 6, 7\}$.
(a) Find $n(A)$, $n(C)$, $n(A \cup C)$, and $n(A \cap C)$. Write $n(A \cup C)$ in terms of $n(A)$, $n(C)$, and $n(A \cap C)$.
(b) Find $n(A)$, $n(B)$, and $n(A \times B)$. Write $n(A \times B)$ in terms of $n(A)$ and $n(B)$.
(c) Find $n(C \times B)$ and write it in terms of $n(C)$ and $n(B)$.
(d) Find $n((A \cup C) \times B)$ and write it in terms of $n(A)$, $n(B)$, and $n(C)$.

REFERENCES

Banks, J. Houston, *Elements of Mathematics*, Allyn and Bacon, Boston, 1956, ch. VI.

Hafstrom, John E., *Basic Concepts in Modern Mathematics*, Addison-Wesley Publishing Co., Reading, Mass., 1961, ch. VI.

Hamilton, Norman T. and Joseph Landin, *Set Theory, the Structure of Arithmetic*, Allyn and Bacon, Boston, 1961, pp. 46–73.

Kelley, John L., *An Introduction to Modern Algebra*, D. Van Nostrand and Co., Princeton, N.J., 1960.

Schaaf, William L., *Basic Concepts of Elementary Mathematics*, John Wiley and Sons, New York, 1960, pp. 22–23 and ch. IX.

* * *

CHAPTER FOUR

Systems of Numeration

4.1 EXPONENTS

You may recall that the idea of exponent is a convention in notation that we adopted by definition. Just as it is easier to write $5n$ instead of $n + n + n + n + n$, so also we agreed to write 10^3 instead of $10 \cdot 10 \cdot 10$. The numeral "3" is called the *exponent* and the numeral "10" is called the *base*. In general, b^n means $b \cdot b \cdot b \cdot b \ldots$ to n factors. The superscript "n" is called the *exponent* and the "b" is called the *base*. The whole symbol, "b^n," is called a *power of the base, b.*

For convenience we review briefly some simple consequences of our convention of writing b^n instead of $b \cdot b \cdot b \cdot b \ldots$ to n factors. Rather than prove the results, which requires the use of mathematical induction and the associative law for multiplication, we simply state the results without proof and cite a few examples to make the general statements seem plausible. (In the following $a \neq 0$.)

1. $$a^m \cdot a^n = a^{m+n}.$$

2. $$(a^m)^n = a^{m \cdot n}.$$

If we define

$$a^0 = 1,$$

and

$$a^{-n} = \frac{1}{a^n},$$

then 3.

$$\frac{a^m}{a^n} = a^{m-n}.$$

Example 1

$$3^2 \cdot 3^3 = (3 \cdot 3)(3 \cdot 3 \cdot 3) = (3 \cdot 3 \cdot 3 \cdot 3 \cdot 3) = 3^5.$$

Example 2

$$(2^3)^2 = (2^3)(2^3) = (2\cdot 2\cdot 2)(2\cdot 2\cdot 2) = (2\cdot 2\cdot 2\cdot 2\cdot 2\cdot 2) = 2^6.$$

Example 3

Case 1. If m is greater than n,

$$\frac{a^5}{a^3} = \frac{a\cdot a\cdot a\cdot a\cdot a}{a\cdot a\cdot a} = a\cdot a = a^2 = a^{5-3}.$$

Case 2. If $m = n$,

$$\frac{a^3}{a^3} = \frac{a\cdot a\cdot a}{a\cdot a\cdot a} = 1 = a^{3-3} = a^0.$$

Case 3. If m is less than n,

$$\frac{a^2}{a^3} = \frac{a\cdot a}{a\cdot a\cdot a} = \frac{1}{a} = a^{2-3} = a^{-1}.$$

Cases 2 and 3 of Example 3 illustrate the desirability of the definitions that for any nonzero a, $a^0 = 1$ and $a^{-n} = 1/a^n$.

4.2 HINDU-ARABIC SYSTEM

The Hindu-Arabic system of numeration might be called an exponential-positional system because it embodies powers of the base (exponential) and place value (positional). Such systems are usually referred to as place-value systems but the term exponential-positional more accurately describes the system. We shall use these two terms interchangeably.

Any numeral in an exponential-positional system represents a sum of multiples of powers of the base. When place-value systems were first devised, no symbolism for powers existed. Powers of the base were implicit in the system. Symbols such as 2^4 or 10^3 would have meant nothing to the early users of the Hindu-Arabic system of numeration. It is interesting to note that the place-value principle is embodied in the abacus. Failure to recognize this and to write numbers as they appeared on the abacus was an unfortunate accident of history.

The Hindu-Arabic system of numeration is a base ten system. There are ten symbols, which we call digits, 1, 2, 3, 4, 5, 6, 7, 8, 9, 0. These are the numerals for the first nine natural numbers and the number zero. These digits are used to express the multiples of the powers of the base. The system also embodies the additive property and place value. In order to speak of the position a digit occupies in a numeral, a reference position needs to be specified. If any of the digits occurs alone, we will say that it indicates the multiple of the base raised to the exponent zero (recall that $10^0 = 1$).

The numeral 6 in our language of arithmetic represents 6 units. We could write this as $6 \cdot 1$, and since $10^0 = 1$, we mean the same thing by writing $6 \cdot 10^0$. Henceforth, when symbolizing the "value" of the first place in our system, we shall use 10^0. Remember, 10^0 is the same as "one" or "unit."

Let us use the place with 10^0 as its place value as the reference place for determining the position a digit occupies in a numeral. The positions, in order, to the left of the 10^0 (units) position will correspond to the successive powers of the base, ten (see Table 5, Section 1.6).

hundred thousands	ten thousands	thousands	hundreds	tens	units
100,000	10,000	1000	100	10	1
10^5	10^4	10^3	10^2	10^1	10^0
		3	0	8	6

Thus the position a digit occupies has implicitly associated with it a power of the base, for example, the numeral 3086 is read "three thousand eighty-six" and means 3 thousands, 0 hundreds, 8 tens, and 6 units or $3000 + 80 + 6$. Using the properties of the system, this could be written as $3 \cdot 10^3 + 0 \cdot 10^2 + 8 \cdot 10^1 + 6 \cdot 10^0$. This last expression will be called the *expanded form.*

Exercise 4.2

1. Write 1,020,304 in expanded form.
2. Write 12 in expanded form.
3. Write 10 in expanded form.
4. Write 10,000 in expanded form.
5. What is the meaning attached to the digit 3 in the numeral

   345? 435? 453?

6. Simplify each of the following:

   (a) $2^3 \cdot 2^6$ (b) $5^p \cdot 5^q$
   (c) $(a^2)^4$ (d) $(x^3)^2 \cdot (x^4)^3$
   (e) $\frac{m^7}{m^5}$, $m \neq 0$ (f) $b^{3x} \div b^x$, $b \neq 0$
   (g) $x^2 \div x^6$, $x \neq 0$

7. Find the value of

   (a) $10^3 \cdot 10^2$ (b) $3^2 \cdot 2^3$
   (c) $2^3 - 2^0$ (d) $3^2 \cdot 6^{-2}$
   (f) $(5^{-4})^{-1}$ (g) $5^{2x} \cdot 5^{-2x}$
   (h) $8^{-1} \cdot 2^0$ (i) $a^{-3} \div a^0$, $a \neq 0$

4.3 THE DECIMAL POINT

When we see the numeral 386 we recognize that the 6 is in the units position and the place it occupies becomes the reference place for determining the place values associated with the other digits. Another way of indicating the reference point or reference position is to put a dot immediately after the 6, that is 386., which serves to identify the units position. The numerals "386" and "386." are names for the same number. The dot actually serves two purposes. The first purpose, as mentioned above, is to indicate the units position. The other purpose will be discussed in Section 8.4. This dot is called the *decimal point.* It is used in the United States and England, but the English write it higher in the line of print than we do. In other European countries a comma is used instead.

4.4 EXPANDING AND READING LARGE NUMBERS

Example 1

$$56{,}146{,}929 = 5\cdot10^7 + 6\cdot10^6 + 1\cdot10^5 + 4\cdot10^4 + 6\cdot10^3 + 9\cdot10^2 + 2\cdot10^1 + 9\cdot10^0.$$

$$3{,}050{,}060{,}992 = 3\cdot10^9 + 0\cdot10^8 + 5\cdot10^7 + 0\cdot10^6 + 0\cdot10^5 + 6\cdot10^4 + 0\cdot10^3 + 9\cdot10^2 + 9\cdot10^1 + 2\cdot10^0.$$

The first number in Example 1 is read "fifty-six million, one hundred forty-six thousand, nine hundred twenty-nine." The commas are used to mark off groups of three digits. These groups of three digits are called "*periods*." This grouping facilitates reading of the numbers. Starting with the first group on the right and reading toward the left, we have hundreds, thousands, millions, billions, trillions, quadrillions, quintillions, and so forth.

Very large and very small numbers are usually written in what is called the "scientific notation." In this notation the numbers are expressed as some number greater than or equal to one but less than ten, times the appropriate power of ten. For example, 1,000,000 could be written as $1\cdot10^6$. 23,000,000,000 is simply $2.3\cdot10^{10}$. The speed of light is approximately $3\cdot10^{10}$ cm/sec. This would be read "three times ten to the tenth centimeters per second."

The following are given as examples of physical constants presented in scientific notation:

Velocity of light	$2.99776\cdot10^{10}$ cm/sec
Avogadro number	$6.0228\cdot10^{23}$/mole
Velocity of sound	$3.3\cdot10^4$ cm/sec (approx.)
An Angstrom unit	10^{-8} cm
Constant of gravitation	$6.673\cdot10^{-8}$ dyne
Electronic charge	$4.803\cdot10^{-10}$ esu
Mass of electron	$9.107\cdot10^{-28}$ grams
Mass of hydrogen atom	$1.673\cdot10^{-24}$ grams

Exercise 4.4

1. Write the following numbers in expanded form:

(a) 12 (b) 121
(c) 302 (d) 10,504
(e) 10,000 (f) 9090
(g) 11 (h) 1,001,001

2. Write the following in two different forms:
Example: $10^1 \cdot 10^2 = 10^{1+2} = 10^3$ or $10^1 \cdot 10^2 = 10 \cdot 100 = 1000$.

(a) $10^2 \cdot 10^3$ (b) $10^0 \cdot 10^0$
(c) $10^3 \cdot 10^7$ (d) $10^1 \cdot 10^1$
(e) $2^5 \cdot 2^2$ (f) $2^2 \cdot 2^2$
(g) $2^0 \cdot 2^1$ (h) $2^{10} \cdot 2^{10}$

3. Write the numbers given in problem 1 in

(a) the Roman system of numeration.
(b) the Egyptian system of numeration.
(c) the Ionic Greek system of numeration.

4. The sum of the digits of a two-digit number is 10. If the digits are interchanged, the number thus formed is 54 less than the original number. Find the number.

5. In a two-digit number, the units digit is three times the tens digit. If the digits are interchanged, the number is increased by 18. Find the number.

6. Carry out the following calculations in scientific notation:

(a) $(3 \cdot 10^5)(2 \cdot 10^7) = ?$
(b) $(8 \cdot 10^8) \div (2 \cdot 10^6) = ?$
(c) $(6 \cdot 10^{23})(3 \cdot 10^{-18}) = ?$
(d) Using the speed of light as approximately $3 \cdot 10^{10}$ cm/sec and 1 mile as approximately $1.6 \cdot 10^5$ cm, determine the speed of light in miles per second.

7. Write the following numbers, using scientific notation:

(a) 0.0000065 (b) 0.000000087
(c) eight billionths (d) 5,700,000,000,000
(e) 6,000,000,000,000 (f) twenty-one trillionths

8. Write the following numbers in standard notation:

(a) $8.7 \cdot 10^9$ (b) $6.23 \cdot 10^{-6}$
(c) $8.7 \cdot 10^{-8}$ (d) $6.02 \cdot 10^{23}$
(e) $5 \cdot 10^{-9}$ (f) $1.08 \cdot 10^{-7}$

9. Multiply the following, expressing the product in scientific notation and in standard form:

(a) $(10^{-3})(10^5)$ (b) $(10^{-4})(10^{-3})$
(c) $(10^{-6})(10^6)$ (d) $(3.75 \cdot 10^{-5})(2.24 \cdot 10^6)$
(e) $(7.25 \cdot 10^5)(2.16 \cdot 10^{-8})$ (f) $(6.75 \cdot 10^8)(2.42 \cdot 10^{-5})$

4.5 OTHER BASES FOR COUNTING

The choice of the number ten as the base for numeration systems probably has an anatomical basis, as mentioned earlier, in the fact that a man has ten fingers on his two hands. Some historians refer to the choice of ten as the base as a "physiological accident." But equally plausible bases on these grounds are base *five* (the digits of one hand) or base *twenty* (the digits of both hands and both feet). Once one exponential-positional system is known, other bases present no problem. In fact, many other bases have been and are being used.

Let us see how and why other bases might be used as well as base ten.

4.6 FINGER COUNTING

To introduce you to other methods of counting, let us describe a procedure we shall call "finger counting." To begin, consider the open right hand as descriptive of zero—we have not begun to count. As we count we fold the fingers in, beginning with the little finger. We count—"one," "two," "three," "four"—and we have run out of fingers. We could fold in the thumb and make a fist to indicate five, but then we would have no more "digits" on that hand with which to keep a record of our counting. Instead, let us use the left hand to record the "fists." Now we have one finger folded in our left hand to indicate one "fist" (five) and can open our right hand to continue the counting. Now, instead of saying "six, seven, eight," and so on, which are decimal names for numbers, let us say, "one fist and one," "one fist and two," "one fist and three," "one fist and four"—here we must stop to consider again. If we fold in the right thumb, we really have "one fist and one fist" or "two fists." We can record this by folding in a second finger on our left hand and opening our right hand. Next in our counting comes "two fists and one," "two fists and two," "two fists and three," and so on. Continuing in this manner, we soon come to "four fists and four," then "four fists and a fist," or a whole fistful of fists, and we need to look for another place to record "fistfuls of fists." We could turn to our toes as a new *place* for keeping this record, but it is rather difficult to control toes as one does fingers.

In any event, we have gone far enough with our discussion so that you should recognize that what we are really doing is counting in a system of numeration with base *five*. Using the properties of a place-value system and borrowing symbols from the decimal system, a numeral such as 12 would then mean "one fist and two," or, "one *five* and two," or, $1 \cdot 5 + 2$, or $1 \cdot 5^1 + 2 \cdot 5^0$. (Recall that $5^0 = 1$.) This is the expanded form of our numeral 12 using *base five.*

Let us compare counting in a base five system with the base ten, or decimal, system.

Base Ten		*Base Five*	
1	one	1	one
2	two	2	two
3	three	3	three
4	four	4	four
5	five	10	one five and zero
6	six	11	one five and one
7	seven	12	one five and two
8	eight	13	one five and three
9	nine	14	one five and four
10	ten	20	two fives and zero
11	eleven	21	two fives and one
12	twelve	22	two fives and two
	⋮		⋮
23	twenty-three	43	four fives and three
24	twenty-four	44	four fives and four
25	twenty-five	100	one five-fives, zero fives, and zero
	⋮		⋮
33	thirty-three	113	one five-fives, one five, and three or $1 \cdot 5^2 + 1 \cdot 5^1 + 3 \cdot 5^0$
	⋮		⋮

Since we are borrowing symbols from the decimal system of numeration, we are inclined to borrow names also, but there is a limitation. The numeral 12 is not "twelve" in the quinary (base five) system. We would read it as "one five and two," or "one-two, base five," and symbolize it $12)_5$ to distinguish it from the decimal numeral, 12. Similarly, $21)_5$ is "two fives and one" or "two-one, base five," *not* "twenty-one."

We should point out here that it is not at all necessary to use the decimal symbols in our quinary system. Our familiarity with their meaning leads us to borrow decimal symbols. We could, for instance, take five arbitrary letters such as O, E, T, F, M, and give them, respectively, the meaning we associate with zero, one, two, three, and four. Then the numerals to represent the first fifteen (decimal language) counting numbers would look like this:

Decimal: 1, 2, 3, 4, 5, 6, 7, 8, 9, 10, 11
Quinary: *E*, *T*, *F*, *M*, *EO*, *EE*, *ET*, *EF*, *EM*, *TO*, *TE*
Decimal: 12, 13, 14, 15
Quinary: *TT*, *TF*, *TM*, *FO*

In spite of occasional confusions, such as mistaking $12)_5$ for "twelve," it is easier to work with the familiar symbols 0, 1, 2, 3, 4, and we will continue to do so.

4.7 CHANGING BASES OF NUMERALS

To change from a decimal numeral to a quinary numeral and vice versa, the prime requisites are: (1) that we be familiar with the properties of a place-value system and (2) that we know the decimal value assigned to the places. For example, in a quinary system the first place to the left of our reference point (Is this a decimal point?) is the units position. This is true of all exponential-positional systems. We associate 5^0 ($5^0 = 1$) with this place as its "place value." The next place to the left represents the number of fives, ($5^1 = 5$), the next place the number of five-fives, or twenty-fives, ($5^2 = 25$), the next place the number of five (five-fives), or the one hundred twenty-fives, ($5^3 = 125$), the next the number of six hundred twenty-fives, ($5^4 = 625$), and so forth. We symbolize these place values by the powers of five, using the decimal language symbols 5^0, 5^1, 5^2, 5^3, 5^4, and so forth.

Example 1

Let us change some decimal numerals to quinary numerals. Consider $18)_{10}$, the symbol for the number called eighteen in our decimal language. Expressing this in a base five system of numeration is essentially the regrouping of a representative set S where $n(S) = 18$.

set S	set S
[xxxxxxxxxx][xxxxxxxx]	[(xxxxx) (xxxxx) (xxxxx)][xxx]
$1 \cdot 10^1 + 8 \cdot 10^0$	$3 \cdot 5^1 + 3 \cdot 5^0$

To accomplish this without the mechanics of regrouping, and using our knowledge of decimal computation, we ask ourselves, "What is the highest power of five that is less than eighteen, and what is the greatest multiple of this power that is less than eighteen?" Of course, our answers are 5^1 and $3 \cdot 5^1$. This means that in our quinary numeral we can use a "3" in the 5^1 place. But this is not enough. We have accounted for only fifteen of the eighteen. This means we need three more, so we can use a "3" in the 5^0, or units, place. Now our quinary numeral looks like this, $33)_5$. We conclude $18)_{10} = 33)_5$.

Example 2

Similarly, for $333)_{10}$, we see that

$$\begin{aligned} 333)_{10} &= 250 + 83 \\ &= 2\cdot 5^3 + 75 + 8 \\ &= 2\cdot 5^3 + 3\cdot 5^2 + 5 + 3 \\ &= 2\cdot 5^3 + 3\cdot 5^2 + 1\cdot 5^1 + 3 \\ &= 2\cdot 5^3 + 3\cdot 5^2 + 1\cdot 5^1 + 3\cdot 5^0 \\ &= 2313)_5 \end{aligned}$$

This discussion also shows us how we can change a quinary numeral to a decimal numeral.

Example 3

$$\begin{aligned} 2341)_5 &= 2\cdot 5^3 + 3\cdot 5^2 + 4\cdot 5^1 + 1\cdot 5^0 && \text{Expanded form} \\ &= 250 + 75 + 20 + 1 && \text{Decimal numerals} \\ &= 346)_{10} \end{aligned}$$

Exercise 4.7

1. Write the first fifty (decimal language) numerals as quinary numerals, borrowing the symbols from the decimal system of numeration.
2. Write each of the following in expanded form and find the decimal (base ten) equivalent:

   (a) $320)_5$ (b) $121)_5$ (c) $203)_5$

3. Change the following decimal system numerals to quinary system numerals, e.g., $27)_{10} = 102)_5$.

   (a) $14)_{10}$ (b) $140)_{10}$ (c) $327)_{10}$

4. You move to a country that has a monetary system that consists of the following coins:

Coin Name	*Coin Symbol*	*U.S. Equivalent*
sens	Ⓢ	1 ¢
fens	ⓕ	5 ¢
qens	ⓠ	25 ¢
dens	ⓓ	$1.25
mens	ⓜ	$6.25
nens	ⓝ	$31.25

You want to convert your U.S. money to the money of this new country so that you will have the least number of coins to carry. Convert the following amounts:

(a) $3.56 (b) $13.50
(c) $29.32 (d) $76.19

e.g., $5.36 would be four dens, one qens, two fens, and one sens.

ⓓ ⓓ ⓓ ⓓ ⓠ ⓕ ⓕ ⓢ

4.8 COUNTING SYSTEMS IN OTHER BASES

This notion of counting in systems with bases other than ten can be extended to any choice of base. Table 1 gives the representation for numbers in base ten (decimal), base five (quinary), base two (binary), and base twelve (duo-decimal).

TABLE 1

Symbols Base ten: 0, 1, 2, 3, 4, 5, 6, 7, 8, 9
Base five: 0, 1, 2, 3, 4
Base two: 0, 1
Base twelve: 0, 1, 2, 3, 4, 5, 6, 7, 8, 9, T, E

Base Ten (Decimal)	*Base Five* (Quinary)	*Base Two* (Binary)	*Base Twelve* (Duo-decimal)
1	1	1	1
2	2	10	2
3	3	11	3
4	4	100	4
5	10	101	5
6	11	110	6
7	12	111	7
8	13	1000	8
9	14	1001	9
10	20	1010	T
11	21	1011	E
12	22	1100	10
13	23	1101	11
14	24	1110	12
15	30	1111	13
16	31	10000	14

Note that in the last row of Table 1 we have: "one ten and six units," "three fives and one unit," "one sixteen, zero eights, zero fours, zero twos, and zero units," and "one twelve and four units," all representing the same number. Is this possible? This is as though we call John Arthur Palmer, "John," "John Arthur," "Art," or "Palmer." Each is simply a different name for the same fellow.

$$16)_{10} = 31)_5 = 10000)_2 = 14)_{12}$$

Exercise 4.8

1. Write the following numbers in the bases indicated:

(a) $2 \cdot 5^3 + 3 \cdot 5^2 + 4 \cdot 5^1 + 2 \cdot 5^0$ In "base five" and "base ten."

(b) $1 \cdot 3^2 + 0 \cdot 3^1 + 1 \cdot 3^0$ In "base three" and "base ten."

(c) $1 \cdot 2^5 + 0 \cdot 2^4 + 1 \cdot 2^3 + 1 \cdot 2^2 + 0 \cdot 2^1 + 1 \cdot 2^0$ In "base two" and "base ten."

2. Write the following as sums of powers of the base as indicated:

(a) $125)_5$ (b) $27)_8$
(c) $146)_7$ (d) $555)_{12}$

3. Write the following decimal numerals as sums of powers of two and as binary numerals:

(a) 125 (b) 27
(c) 32 (d) 555

4. Construct a counting table such as Table 1, Section 4.8 for bases ten, two, three, four, eight, and twelve through 50 (base ten).

5. In the table of problem 4 can you detect any patterns?

6. In the table of problem 4 can you detect any relationship between the base two, four, and eight numerals?

4.9 COMPUTATION IN OTHER BASES

After years of experience you are so familiar with computation in the decimal system of numeration (the base ten system) that you are unaware of the difficulties a pupil experiences in his first attempts at computation. It has been long enough so that you have forgotten the difficulties you encountered when you first learned to compute.

We would like to place you in the position of a beginner so that you may better realize the problems of learning. You are not a "beginner" with the decimal system of numeration so we will turn to some other system. It may even be profitable to look at computation in several other systems. We realize you will not quite attain the status of a beginner, for you will have the advantage of knowing something in general about systems of numeration. In particular, the ideas of place value, the symbols themselves, and the meaning of the symbols will not be strange to you. In spite of this advantage, however, you should be able to relive some of the difficulties inherent in learning to compute.

4.9a Computation in Base Five

First let us consider some computations in a base five system of numeration. You will recall that after you learned to count in the decimal system, the next step in the learning process was concerned with the elementary facts of addition and multiplication, the addition combinations and the multiplication tables. We will circumvent the necessity of memorizing these facts by presenting tables of elementary facts as follows.

+	0	1	2	3	4
0	0	1	2	3	4
1	1	2	3	4	10
2	2	3	4	10	11
3	3	4	10	11	12
4	4	10	11	12	13

	1	2	3	4
1	1	2	3	4
2	2	4	11	13
3	3	11	14	22
4	4	13	22	31

We read these tables in a manner similar to those concerned with ordered pairs of natural numbers in Chapter 3. For example, to find $2 + 4$, we go down the left-hand column until we find the numeral 2, then across that row until we are in the column headed 4, where we find the numeral 11. This means that in base five arithmetic, $2 + 4 = 11$. We read this, "Two plus four is one-one, base five." It would be incorrect to say, "Two plus four is 'eleven.'" "Eleven" is a decimal word, and we are dealing in base five, or quinary, arithmetic.

The multiplication table is used similarly. Consider the product $3 \cdot 4$. We go down the left-hand column until we find the numeral 3, then across that row until we are in the column headed 4, where we find the numeral 22. This means that in quinary arithmetic, $3 \cdot 4 = 22$. We read this, "Three times four is two-two, base five."

With the use of these tables, a little intuition, and an understanding of the place-value system of numeration, we will be able to carry out computations in base five. Let us try a few simple problems.

Example 1

Add the base five numerals, 234 and 432:

$$\begin{array}{r} {\scriptstyle 11} \\ 234 \\ \underline{432} \\ 1221 \end{array}$$

Procedure

1st column: From the table, $4 + 2 = 11$. Write 1 and carry 1 as in decimal arithmetic.

2nd column: From the table, $3 + 3 = 11$. $11 + 1$ (the carry) $= 12$. Write 2, carry 1.

3rd column: From the table, $2 + 4 = 11$. $11 + 1$ (the carry) $= 12$. Write 12.

We can easily check our result by converting the base five numerals to decimal numerals and computing in decimal arithmetic.

$$\begin{aligned} 234)_5 &= 2 \cdot 5^2 + 3 \cdot 5^1 + 4 \cdot 5^0 && \text{Expanded form} \\ &= 50 + 15 + 4 && \text{Decimal numerals} \\ &= 69)_{10} \end{aligned}$$

Similarly, $432)_5 = 117)_{10}$

$69 + 117 = 186$	Decimal arithmetic
$1221)_5 = 1 \cdot 5^3 + 2 \cdot 5^2 + 2 \cdot 5^1 + 1 \cdot 5^0$	Expanded form
$= 125 + 50 + 10 + 1$	Decimal numerals
$= 186)_{10}$	

This implies that our quinary arithmetic is correct. We obtained the same sum in both systems, and we feel quite confident that the decimal arithmetic is correct.

Example 2

Add the base five numerals 323, 413, and 343:

$$\begin{array}{r} {\scriptstyle 11} \\ 323 \\ 413 \\ \underline{343} \\ 2134 \end{array}$$

Procedure

1st column: From the table $3 + 3 = 11$; then $11 + 3 = 14$. Write 4, carry 1.

2nd column: $4 + 1 = 10$, $10 + 2 = 12$, $12 + 1 = 13$. Write 3, carry 1.

3rd column: $3 + 4 = 12$, $12 + 3 = 20$, $20 + 1 = 21$. Write 21.

Notice that in the procedure for this problem some of the additions performed in finding the sum of a column are problems in themselves. The answers are not found directly from the table. For example, $12 + 3 = 20$.

It is left to the student to check this example by converting to base ten arithmetic as in Example 1.

Example 3

Multiply the base five numerals 342 by 23:

$$\begin{array}{r} {\scriptstyle 1} \\ {\scriptstyle 21} \\ 342 \\ \underline{23} \\ 2131 \\ \underline{1234} \\ 20021 \end{array}$$

Procedure

Multiplying by 3: $3 \cdot 2 = 11$. Write 1, carry 1. $3 \cdot 4 = 22$, $22 + 1$ (the carry) $= 23$. Write 3, carry 2. $3 \cdot 3 = 14$, $14 + 2$ (the carry) $= 21$. Write 21.

Multiplying by 2: Same as for the 3 except that the 2 is in the second place, and we must set the partial products one place to the left as in decimal arithmetic.

The check by conversion to base ten:

$$342)_5 = 3 \cdot 5^2 + 4 \cdot 5^1 + 2 \cdot 5^0 = 75 + 20 + 2 = 97)_{10}$$
$$23)_5 = 2 \cdot 5^1 + 3 \cdot 5^0 = 10 + 3 = 13)_{10}$$
$$20021)_5 = 2 \cdot 5^4 + 0 \cdot 5^3 + 0 \cdot 5^2 + 2 \cdot 5^1 + 1 \cdot 5^0 = 1250 + 10 + 1$$
$$= 1261)_{10}$$
$$13 \cdot 97 = 1261 \qquad \text{Decimal arithmetic.}$$

Hence the quinary arithmetic is correct.

Subtraction and division can also be accomplished with the use of the addition and multiplication tables. The addition table answers the question $a + b = ?$ for a and b quinary digits, but it will also answer the question $a + ? = c$. For example, to find $11 - 3$ in quinary arithmetic, we consider the problem $3 + ? = 11$. To find the answer we go down the left-hand column until we find the numeral 3, then across the row until we find the numeral 11. The numeral that must be added to 3 to obtain 11 is at the top of this column. Hence $11 - 3 = 3$. Similarly, $12 - 4 = 3$, $10 - 2 = 3$, $11 - 2 = 4$, and so forth.

Example 4

Subtract 2341 from 4332 in quinary arithmetic:

$$\begin{array}{r} {}^{3}\!\!\not{4}\,{}^{1}\!\!\!\not{3}^{2}\,{}_{1}32 \\ \underline{2341} \\ 1441 \end{array}$$

Procedure

1st column: $1 + ? = 2$, $1 + \mathit{1} = 2$. Write 1.
2nd column: Borrow, then $4 + ? = 13$, $4 + \mathit{4} = 13$. Write 4.
3rd column: Borrow, then $3 + ? = 12$, $3 + \mathit{4} = 12$. Write 4.
4th column: $2 + ? = 3$, $2 + \mathit{1} = 3$. Write 1.

We can use our multiplication tables for division in the sense that the question $a \div b = ?$ can be interpreted as $b \cdot ? = a$.

Example 5

Divide 33011 by 4 in quinary arithmetic:

$$\begin{array}{r} 4224 \\ 4\overline{)33011} \\ \underline{31} \\ 20 \\ \underline{13} \\ 21 \\ \underline{13} \\ 31 \\ \underline{\underline{31}} \end{array}$$

Procedure

Same as for decimal arithmetic, using the base five multiplication tables to find the partial quotients.

E.g., $33 \div 4 = ?$; $4 \cdot ? = 33$; $4 \cdot \mathit{4} = 31$, which is as close as we can get to 33. So 4 is the first quotient figure. Multiply, subtract, bring down the next digit of the dividend, then continue as before.

We have presented the traditional approach to this division problem. It is well to point out that the modern approach involves returning to an older format, or arrangement, of the work as follows.

$$\begin{array}{r|r} 4\overline{)33011} & 4000 \\ \underline{31000} & \\ 2011 & 200 \\ \underline{1300} & \\ 211 & 20 \\ \underline{130} & \\ 31 & 4 \\ \underline{\underline{31}} & \\ \hline & 4224 \end{array}$$

This format indicates a more complete procedure. Here the partial quotients are obtained in essentially the same way as in the traditional approach, using the multiplication table to assist in making estimations. Additional material will be presented on this procedure in Chapter 5 (see Van Engen et al.).

Exercise 4.9a

1. Check foregoing Examples 2, 4, and 5 by converting the quinary numerals to decimal numerals and doing the arithmetic in the decimal system.

2. Carry out the following addition problems in base five arithmetic:

(a)	(b)	(c)
231	2342	2013
413	1341	4002
	3124	2144
		3241

3. Carry out the following multiplication problems in base five arithmetic:

(a)	(b)	(c)
2342	1341	2144
3	32	234

4. Carry out the following subtraction problems in base five arithmetic:

(a)	(b)	(c)
413	2342	3000
231	1424	2143

5. Carry out the following division problems in base five arithmetic:

(a) $4\overline{)2033}$ (b) $3\overline{)1414}$ (c) $10\overline{)204320}$

6. Check your results for problem 2 above by converting to the decimal system.

7. Construct the tables of elementary facts for base three (ternary) arithmetic and carry out the following computations.

(a) Add:		(b) Subtract:		(c) Multiply:	
212	222	212	2121	212	21022
220	111	121	212	22	2102

(d) Divide 21021 by 12. Divide 21020 by 12.

8. What is the minimum number of weights required to weigh objects weighing up to 41 oz with a two-pan balance?

4.9b Arithmetic in Base Two

In base two (binary) arithmetic we need but two symbols, and it is convenient to use the decimal symbols 0 and 1. (These symbols denote, respectively, the *additive identity* and the *multiplicative identity* for the system of natural numbers. Their properties will be discussed more fully in Chapter 5.) The elementary facts needed for computation in base two are elementary indeed! Bearing in mind the special properties of zero and one, the only other fact we need is that $1 + 1 = 10$ in base two. The tables are trivial but for clarity we shall include them.

+	0	1
0	0	1
1	1	10

·	1
1	1

Example 1

Add the binary (base two) numerals 1011 and 1100.

$$\begin{array}{r} 1011 \\ \underline{1100} \\ 10111 \end{array}$$

Procedure
1st column: $0 + 1 = 1$. Write 1.
2nd column: $0 + 1 = 1$. Write 1.
3rd column: $1 + 0 = 1$. Write 1.
4th column: $1 + 1 = 10$. Write 10.

Example 2

Add the binary numerals 1011, 1101, 1001.

$$\begin{array}{r} 1011 \\ 1101 \\ \underline{1001} \\ 100001 \end{array}$$

Procedure
1st column: $1 + 1 = 10$, $10 + 1 = 11$. Write 1, carry 1.
2nd column: $0 + 0 = 0$, $0 + 1 = 1$, $1 + 1$ (carry) $= 10$. Write 0, carry 1.
3rd column: $0 + 1 = 1$, $1 + 0 = 1$, $1 + 1 = 10$. Write 0, carry 1.
4th column: $1 + 1 = 10$, $10 + 1 = 11$, $11 + 1 = 100$. Write 100.

Again, as in quinary arithmetic, some of the additions performed in finding the sum of a column are problems in themselves. For example, $11 + 1 = 100$ is not found directly from the table.

To check this example we convert the binary numerals to decimal numerals and compute in the system with which we are familiar.

$$\begin{aligned} 1011)_2 &= 1 \cdot 2^3 + 0 \cdot 2^2 + 1 \cdot 2^1 + 1 \cdot 2^0 && \text{Expanded form} \\ &= 8 + 0 + 2 + 1 && \text{Decimal numerals} \\ &= 11)_{10} \end{aligned}$$

Similarly,

$$\begin{aligned} 1101)_2 &= 13)_{10} \\ 1001)_2 &= 9)_{10} \\ 11 + 13 + 9 &= 33 && \text{Decimal arithmetic} \\ 100001)_2 &= 33)_{10} && \text{Check} \end{aligned}$$

Hence our binary sum checks with the decimal sum.

Example 3

Multiply the binary numbers: (1011)(101)

	Procedure
1011 101 1011 10110 110111	We follow the same procedure as in decimal arithmetic. The problem of multiplying is much simpler, however. In multiplying by a 1 all we need do is copy the multiplicand in proper position.

It is left to the student to convert these binary numerals to decimal numerals and carry out the check.

Subtraction can be carried out with the use of the addition facts as in Example 4 of the preceding section.

In dividing binary numbers it is not necessary to estimate a trial quotient. Because of the nature of the system we have but two choices at each step in the division process. Either the divisor "goes" or it does not. A simple example will be sufficient to illustrate this.

Example 4

Divide the binary numerals: 1000010101 by 1101.

```
        101001
  1101)1000010101
       1101
         1110
         1101
            1101
            1101
```

It is left to the student to convert these binary numerals to decimal numerals and check the computation.

It may seem a waste of time even to consider a base two arithmetic, so you may be surprised to learn that the binary system has many useful and practical applications. Binary numbers are used in statistical investigations and in the study of probabilities, in analyzing games, and in the arithmetic units of some of the electronic computers. Whenever a situation may be described in terms of "on" or "off," "yes" or "no," "charge" or "no charge," or similar dual choices, the binary system of numeration is useful in its analysis.

4.9c Nim

As an example of how the binary system of numeration may be used to analyze games, let us consider the game of *Nim*. This is a simple game played by two players. There are three piles of objects (matches, buttons, coins, etc.), and a *move* consists of taking *at least* one object from *one* pile. Players move alternately, and the player to pick up the last object is the winner. A *favorable position* for the mover is a position such that if the mover makes all of his moves correctly, he is certain to win regardless of how his opponent makes his moves. An *unfavorable position* for the mover is a position such that if the opponent makes all of his moves correctly, then the mover is certain to lose. It can be shown mathematically that any position is either favorable or unfavorable for the mover, but not both (see Uspensky and Heaslet, pp. 15–19).

It turns out that favorable and unfavorable positions may be described in terms of binary numbers. For a given position consider the number of objects in each pile and write these numbers in the binary system. For example,

/////	5 objects in first pile		1	0	1
//////	6 objects in second pile		1	1	0
////////	8 objects in third pile	1	0	0	0
		"O"	"E"	"O"	"O"

Arrange the binary numerals as for addition, then consider the individual columns. If there is an even number (zero or two) of 1's in *each* column, then the position is *unfavorable* for the mover. If there is *at least one* column where there is an odd number (one or three) of 1's, then the position is a *favorable* position for the mover. Given a favorable position for the mover, there is a move that will yield an unfavorable position for the opponent. Given an unfavorable position for the mover, no matter what move he makes it will yield a favorable position for the opponent.

Consider the example again. This would be a favorable position for the mover, for there is "at least one" (in fact, three) column that has an odd number of 1's. Looking at the binary numbers again, we note that if the 1000 were changed to 11, that is, if the eight objects of the third pile were reduced to three, then each column would have an even number of 1's, and it would be an unfavorable position for the opponent. The piles would appear as follows.

/////	5 objects	1	0	1
//////	6 objects	1	1	0
///	3 objects		1	1
		"E"	"E"	"E"

Now, regardless of the moves the opponent might make, if the mover makes his moves correctly he can win.

To complete the game, let us picture a set of possible successive moves as follows.

Opponent takes four objects from first pile:

/	1 object			1
//////	6 objects	1	1	0
///	3 objects		1	1
		"O"	"E"	"E"

By selecting four objects from the second pile the mover can change the picture to:

/	1 object		1
//	2 objects	1	0
///	3 objects	1	1
		"E"	"E"

Suppose the opponent now takes the two objects of the second pile:

/	1 object		1
Empty			
///	3 objects	1	1
		"O"	"E"

The mover can now assure a win by taking two objects from the third pile.

Exercise 4.9b

1. Check Examples 1, 3, and 4 of Section 4.9b by converting the binary numerals to decimal numerals and carrying out the computation in decimal arithmetic.

2. Carry out the following addition problems in binary arithmetic.

(a) $101 + 111$ (b) $1101 + 1001 + 1111$
(c) $1001 + 1111 + 101$ (d) $10011 + 1001 + 100$
(e) $11011 + 11100 + 10111$ (f) $1111 + 1111 + 1111$

3. Compute in binary arithmetic

(a) $(1011)(111)$ (b) $(11010)(101)$
(c) $(11011)(1101)$ (d) $11011 - 1101$
(e) $10011 - 1010$ (f) $1100100 \div 1010$

4. Another application of binary arithmetic is involved in the following number game. Consider the following cards:

Card A		*Card B*		*Card C*		*Card D*		*Card E*	
16	24	8	24	4	20	2	18	1	17
17	25	9	25	5	21	3	19	3	19
18	26	10	26	6	22	6	22	5	21
19	27	11	27	7	23	7	23	7	23
20	28	12	28	12	28	10	26	9	25
21	29	13	29	13	29	11	27	11	27
22	30	14	30	14	30	14	30	13	29
23	31	15	31	15	31	15	31	15	31

A student is given the above cards and asked to indicate which ones have his age printed on them. He looks them over carefully and then answers that his age is printed on cards *A* and *E*. The owner of the cards quickly adds the upper left-hand numbers on these two cards and says, "You are 17 years old."

Try this with your friends. You will find the system infallible.

What is the system? Figure out the "why" behind this simple trick. As a beginning you might write the binary numerals from one to thirty-two and use these as a guide.

4.9d Duo-Decimal Arithmetic

Duo-decimal (base twelve) arithmetic can be carried out as in base five or base two. There is one difference, however, and that is that the symbols for the decimal digits will be insufficient in number. We need twelve symbols for a base twelve system of numeration, as indicated in Section 4.8. The tables of elementary facts for addition and multiplication would be as shown in Tables 2 and 3.

TABLE 2

ADDITION, BASE TWELVE

+	0	1	2	3	4	5	6	7	8	9	T	E
0	0	1	2	3	4	5	6	7	8	9	T	E
1	1	2	3	4	5	6	7	8	9	T	E	10
2	2	3	4	5	6	7	8	9	T	E	10	11
3	3	4	5	6	7	8	9	T	E	10	11	12
4	4	5	6	7	8	9	T	E	10	11	12	13
5	5	6	7	8	9	T	E	10	11	12	13	14
6	6	7	8	9	T	E	10	11	12	13	14	15
7	7	8	9	T	E	10	11	12	13	14	15	16
8	8	9	T	E	10	11	12	13	14	15	16	17
9	9	T	E	10	11	12	13	14	15	16	17	18
T	T	E	10	11	12	13	14	15	16	17	18	19
E	E	10	11	12	13	14	15	16	17	18	19	1T

In the duo-decimal system of numeration we do have some names for some of the powers of the base. For the name of the power of the base in the first place to the left of the reference point we can use "units," just as we do for the decimal system. The next place to the left could have the name "dozens," just as we say "tens" in the decimal system. The next place would be called "gross" (a dozen dozens) and the next "great gross" or "dozen gross," and so on.

TABLE 3

MULTIPLICATION, BASE TWELVE

·	1	2	3	4	5	6	7	8	9	T	E
1	1	2	3	4	5	6	7	8	9	T	E
2	2	4	6	8	T	10	12	14	16	18	1T
3	3	6	9	10	13	16	19	20	23	26	29
4	4	8	10	14	18	20	24	28	30	34	38
5	5	T	13	18	21	26	2E	34	39	42	47
6	6	10	16	20	26	30	36	40	46	50	56
7	7	12	19	24	2E	36	41	48	53	5T	65
8	8	14	20	28	34	40	48	54	60	68	74
9	9	16	23	30	39	46	53	60	69	76	83
T	T	18	26	34	42	50	5T	68	76	84	92
E	E	1T	29	38	47	56	65	74	83	92	T1

The duo-decimal system has been advocated by many people as a standard system of numeration instead of the decimal system. It has certain advantages over the decimal system, but the problem of conversion on a national or international scale would be almost insurmountable. The student will be asked in the next set of exercises to name some of the advantages of the duo-decimal system over the decimal system.

Example 1

Add the duo-decimal numerals 7ET45 and 21372:

Procedure

7ET45	1st column: 5 + 2 = 7. Write 7.
21372	2nd column: 4 + 7 = E. Write E.
T11E7	3rd column: T + 3 = 11. Write 1, carry 1.
	4th column: 1 (carry) + E = 10, 10 + 1 = 11. Write 1, carry 1.
	5th column: 1 (carry) + 7 = 8, 8 + 2 = T. Write T.

Example 2

Multiply the duo-decimal numerals T45 and 372:

Procedure

T45	Multiplying by 2: 2·5 = T. Write T. 2·4 = 8. Write 8.
372	2·T = 18. Write 18.
188T	Multiplying by 7: 7·5 = 2E. Write E, carry 2. 7·4 = 24,
606E	24 + 2 = 26. Write 6, carry 2. 7·T = 5T, 5T + 2 = 60.
2713	Write 60.
31367T	Multiplying by 3: 3·5 = 13. Write 3, carry 1. 3·4 = 10,
	10 + 1 = 11. Write 1, carry 1. 3·T = 26, 26 + 1 = 27.
	Write 27.

Subtraction and division can be carried out in a manner similar to that used for arithmetic in the other bases discussed. This type of computation will be left for the exercises.

Exercise 4.9c

1. What are some of the advantages of the binary system over the decimal system?
2. What are some of the advantages of the duo-decimal system over the decimal system?
3. If the objects in a game of *Nim* were distributed 8 – 5 – 13, would you choose to move first or second? If you decide to move first, what move would you make to ensure a win?
4. If the objects in a game of *Nim* were distributed 10 – 12 – 14, would you choose to move first or second? If you decide this is a favorable position, what move would you make to ensure a win?
5. Carry out the following computations in duo-decimal arithmetic:

(a) 3E + T4
(b) 204 + 60T
(c) 1702 + 91TE6
(d) 188TE + E7E03T
(e) 60T – T4
(f) 312 – 5T
(g) 18E8T – 5TE4
(h) 604T5 – 231E4
(i) (4T)(E3)
(j) (54)(214E)
(k) (2E4)(5467)
(l) (325)(TE41)
(m) 293 ÷ 7
(n) 11413 ÷ 5
(o) E468 ÷ 4E
(p) 12E114 ÷ 214

REFERENCES

Banks, J. Houston, *Elements of Mathematics*, Allyn and Bacon, Boston, 1956, ch. II, secs. 2.7–2.12.

Hafstrom, John E., *Basic Concepts in Modern Mathematics*, Addison-Wesley Publishing Co., Reading, Mass., 1961, ch. II, sec. 2–5.

Larsen, Harold D., *Arithmetic for Colleges*, The Macmillan Company, New York, 1958, ch. I, secs. 7, 8, and 9.

Mueller, Francis J., *Arithmetic, Its Structure and Concepts*, Prentice-Hall, Englewood Cliffs, N.J., 1956, units 4, 5, and 6.

Swain, Robert L., *Understanding Arithmetic*, Rinehart and Co., New York, 1952, ch. VI.

Uspensky, J. V. and Heaslet, M. A., *Elementary Number Theory*, McGraw-Hill Book Co., New York, 1939.

*
*
*

CHAPTER FIVE

The System of Whole Numbers

5.1 INTRODUCTION

Teaching a child to count is more than teaching him to repeat the words one, two, three, and so on. Teaching a child to count is actually teaching a child to recognize the common property of matched sets and properly labeling this abstraction, just as teaching a child the various colors involves distinguishing the colors and properly labeling them. "Number blindness" is not yet listed as a physiological disorder as is "color blindness." The matching process distinguishes sets with a precision that cannot be accomplished by the eye in distinguishing colors. The number concept should be easy to teach and interesting to learn.

In previous chapters we introduced the notion of sets, relations, and properties of relations, and we examined a few examples of relations defined on sets. Various relations were seen to have certain properties in common. Those relations that are reflexive, symmetric, and transitive occur so frequently in mathematics and play so important a role that they are designated by a special name. They are called *equivalence relations* (see Section 3.12). The effect of an equivalence relation on the set on which it is defined is to partition the set into subsets, which we have called *equivalence classes*. The matching relation defined on sets in terms of the fundamental concept of one-to-one correspondence is an equivalence relation, and the common property of the sets in an equivalence class of this matching relation is what we call a cardinal number. The names and symbols that we give to these abstractions are called numerals. Thus the symbol "1" is the numeral that represents the number which is the distinguishing feature of the equivalence class of all sets with the property of "oneness." As soon as we write down the symbol 1 we have a set that consists of the symbol 1. We denote this set $\{1\}$. The symbol "2" is the numeral that represents the number which is the distinguishing feature of the equivalence class of all sets with the property of "twoness." A representative set for this class is the set $\{1, 2\}$. In the same way we can form the sets $\{1, 2, 3\}$, $\{1, 2, 3, 4\}, \ldots, \{1, 2, 3, 4, 5, \ldots, n\}$, and $\{1, 2, 3, 4, 5, 6, 7, \ldots\}$.

Counting is simply the process of establishing a one-to-one correspondence between the set being counted and the appropriate set of numbers. We arrive at the appropriate set merely by counting. Notice that in each example above the last symbol is the numeral that represents the cardinal number of the set to which it belongs. We use zero as the cardinal number of the empty set.

In the set $\{1, 2, 3, 4, 5, 6, 7, \ldots\}$, the dots indicate that the *sequence* of numbers continues indefinitely. This set is the set of *natural numbers*. Any number in this set is the cardinal number of a *finite* set. A set is *countably infinite* if there is a one-to-one correspondence between the elements of the set and the set of *all* natural numbers. Thus the set of natural numbers is itself countably infinite.

5.2 ORDINAL AND CARDINAL USE OF NATURAL NUMBERS

When a set is being counted, the natural numbers are used in a *prescribed order* until the set being counted is exhausted. For example, the numeral 3 always precedes the numeral 4 in this prescribed order, and we implicitly indicate this when we write the numbers

$$1, 2, 3, 4, 5, 6, 7, 8, 9, \ldots,$$

in counting order.

Any use of these numbers that depends on the prescribed order is the *ordinal* use of the natural numbers. The number represented by the right-hand numeral at the top of this page is an example of the *ordinal* use of the natural numbers. It is the *82*nd page. When a number is used to designate a counted position, it is being used ordinally. The team is in *third* place in league standings. When we use a number to answer the question, "Which one?" we are making ordinal use of the natural number. He was the *first* person to enter the room.

Example 1

A person entering the bowling alley is given a slip of paper with the numeral 9 on it. It means he is the *9th* person who is waiting to bowl. This is the ordinal use of a natural number.

There is a "less than" relation between the cardinal numbers of two sets if there is a one-to-one correspondence between all the elements of one set with a proper subset of the other set. We can determine immediately that the number of students in a class is less than the number of chairs by observing the unoccupied chairs. The one-to-one correspondence is fundamental in comparing the natural numbers. Notice in our counting sets that the 3-set is a proper subset of the 4-set. We recognize this by saying 3 is less than 4 and denote this as we have done previously by $3 < 4$. This relation refers to the *cardinal* use of the natural numbers, that is, it is a quantitative aspect of the number. When we use a natural number in answer to the question, "How many?" we are making cardinal use of the natural number. When a number is used to designate the "size" of a set, it is being used cardinally.

Example 2

From Example 1, the bowler would have *8* people ahead of him on the waiting list. This is the cardinal use of a natural number.

We do not emphasize the distinction between ordinal number and cardinal number but emphasize instead the ordinal use and the cardinal use of the natural numbers. Mathematically there is a distinction between ordinal and cardinal numbers. This is particularly true for transfinite numbers but leads to a discussion that is beyond the scope of this book. For a more precise discussion of ordinal and cardinal numbers, see Hamilton and Landin.

Exercise 5.2

1. (a) What is meant by the statement, "The set A has cardinal 3, or cardinal number 3"?
(b) What is meant by the statement, "The set B has cardinal 87, or cardinal number 87"?
(c) What does it mean to say that a set is finite?
(d) What does it mean to say that a set is countably infinite?

2. Distinguish between the cardinal use and the ordinal use of the natural numbers by citing examples involving the same numbers. Use the numbers 1, 3, 5, and 7.

3. What properties does the relation "$<$" possess?

4. Use the relation "$<$" and set-builder notation to describe the following set: $\{3, 4, 5, 6, 7, 8\}$.

5. Let $A = \{n|n \text{ is a natural number and } n < 5\}$
$B = \{n|n \text{ is a natural number and } n < 20\}$
$C = \{n|n \text{ is natural numbers, } 7 < n, \textit{ and } n < 10\}$
(*Note:* $7 < n$ *and* $n < 10$ is usually written $7 < n < 10$.)

List the elements in the sets determined as follows:

(a) $A \cap B$ (b) $A \cap C$
(c) $A \cup C$ (d) $B \cap C$

5.3 THE SET OF WHOLE NUMBERS

Let us use the capital letter N to denote the set $\{1, 2, 3, 4, \ldots\}$. The set N with the prescribed order is the set of *natural numbers.* Recall that we have studied various systems and schemes of giving names and symbols to these numbers in various civilizations. The names and symbols change and are different in different places even today, but the concept of number is the same everywhere. Thus the set of natural numbers N, which we denote $N = \{1, 2, 3, 4, 5, \ldots\}$, where the dots indicate that the set is never ending, is the same regardless of the symbols we might use.

It should be obvious that the set N has the following properties: (1) N has a first element, which we denote by 1 and (2) N contains the element $k + 1$ whenever it contains the element k. This property is called the *inductive property.*

The number zero, which we denote by the symbol 0 is the cardinal number of the empty set $\emptyset$.

$$n(\emptyset) = 0.$$

Just as the symbol 7 is used to denote the number of the set with seven elements, so we use 0 as the symbol to denote the number of the set with no elements. Zero is not nothing! Zero is a number! In the future the symbol W will be used to designate the set $\{0, 1, 2, 3, 4, 5, \ldots\}$, and we shall call it the set of *whole numbers.*

5.4 SYSTEMS OF NUMERATION AND NUMBER SYSTEMS

A number as a counting concept is one thing. A number as an element of a number system is quite another thing. The harmonious integration of these two ideas comprise the fundamentals of arithmetic. For this purpose it is helpful to reiterate what we mean by a system of numeration and at the same time give a naive, intuitive definition of a number system.

A system of numeration is a set of symbols and a scheme for using these symbols to give names to all the numbers. We have examined a few of the many systems of numeration that man has developed to meet the needs of his society. These should be recalled to mind and the symbols and schemes re-examined in broad outline.

The system offering the greatest advantages from the standpoint of simplicity, economy of symbols in expressing numbers of any magnitude, and computation is the Hindu-Arabic exponential-positional system of numeration.

By a *number system* we mean, from an intuitive standpoint, a *set* of numbers, *operations* defined on the numbers in the set, and *rules* governing these operations. By changing the set of numbers we change the number system. By changing the rules, or adding new rules, we change the number system. We will examine in detail the following number systems:

The system of whole numbers
The system of integers
The system of rational numbers
The system of real numbers

We shall approach each intuitively, using the background of the reader, precise definitions, and a certain amount of work to gain insight into the structure of each system.

For the sophisticated, it is sufficient to consider a set of elements, much as one does with the chess men and the board, endow the elements with certain properties by prescribing the behavior of these elements under certain operations. The set, the operations, and the rules governing these operations constitute a mathematical system. (Recall that putting additional restrictions on a set tends to diminish the set. It is possible to specify sufficient axioms on a set to describe the real number system. See, for example, Kelley.)

Without prescribed operations and specific rules determining the behavior of the elements under these operations (axioms), the numbers would be no more interesting than a bag of marbles or a handful of checkers. In order to give a precise definition of a *number system*, we start with the set W and what we mean by the operations referred to earlier.

Exercise 5.4

1. Discuss the Egyptian system of numeration, stressing the underlying scheme.
2. Discuss the Roman and Hindu-Arabic systems of numeration, as in problem 1.
3. Using the fact that N possesses the inductive property, show that 10 is in N. Can you do the same for 1,000,000,000?
4. We define the relation "$\equiv$" on the set W as follows. For any two whole numbers m, n, $m \equiv n$ if they both give the same remainder when divided by 5, for example, $3 \equiv 8$, $12 \equiv 7$, $15 \equiv 30$, and so forth. This relation is an equivalence relation. Describe the equivalence classes by listing a set of representative elements.
5. The same as problem 4 except use 6 as divisor.

5.5 BINARY OPERATIONS

Addition is a *binary operation.* The operation of addition, which we denote by +, assigns to each *ordered pair* of numbers, say (2, 3), the number (2 + 3). We recognize this as the number 5. We acknowledge this by saying "Two plus three is five," and we write $2 + 3 = 5$.

We realize that the reader knows how to add, multiply, subtract, and divide. Some will even remember how to extract square roots. These *operations* will be reviewed and examined in such a way as to make meaningful many of the ideas learned in arithmetic by rote. In other words, the operations themselves become objects of study.

Addition is called a *binary* operation because it assigns to *two* numbers a third number. The term ordered pair is used because it is not immediately obvious to a beginning student that addition assigns to (9, 2) the same number as it does to the ordered pair (2, 9). In an application, adding 2 objects to 9 objects is *quite* a different operation from adding 9 objects to 2 objects. The reader might check the foregoing statement by asking some first grade pupil if the problem $9 + 2$ is the same as the problem $2 + 9$.

Multiplication is a *binary operation.* We denote this operation with a dot, ·. (A period that is centered in the line of print.) Multiplication assigns to the ordered pair (2, 3) the number $(2 \cdot 3)$. We say, "Two times three is equal to six." We write $2 \cdot 3 = 6$.

DEFINITION 5.5a. We say that two whole numbers, a and b, are *equal* and write $a = b$ if and only if a and b are names for the same number.

This is what we mean when we write $3 + 6 = 9$.

(3, 6)	$\xrightarrow{+}$	(3 + 6)	=	9
ordered pair	operation "plus"	the assigned number		another numeral for the same number

The relation "equals" (=) is an equivalence relation. The fact that this relation is an equivalence relation, that is, it is reflexive, symmetric, and transitive, will be referred to many times, sometimes implicitly and sometimes explicitly.

The symmetric property of equals allows us to say, if $3 + 6 = 9$, then $9 = 3 + 6$. Although you may say these are the same statement, $9 = 3 + 6$ has special implications. These you will become acquainted with as we proceed. There will be times when $3 + 6$ is a more appropriate name for the number than 9.

First graders are often heard to say, "Two and three *are* five." This probably reflects the way in which the child learned the whole numbers. Three children could well have been used as a representative set of the number three, and two other children comprised the representative set of the number two. The union of these disjoint sets is a representative set of the number five. There *are* five children in this set. However, mathematicians are more apt to say, "Two and three *is* five." When numbers are *added*, they are elements of a number system. The binary operation + assigns to the pair (2, 3) the number (2 + 3), and the symbol "2 + 3" *is* another name for the number 5.

DEFINITION 5.5b. *A binary operation*, denoted by $*$, defined on a set S assigns to each *ordered pair* (m, n) of elements of S, a *uniquely* determined element which we denote $m * n$.

That the element $m * n$ is "a uniquely determined element" means the binary operation $*$ assigns to each ordered pair of elements (m, n) *one and only one* element. The element $m * n$ may have other names. One of the tasks of arithmetic is to discover systematic procedures for finding other names of the resultant when the binary operation is addition or multiplication. This is nothing more or less than arithmetic computation. In some of the steps involved in these computations it may be more convenient to use different names for the same number, for example, we may use 3 + 4 instead of 7 or $5 \cdot 1$ instead of 5. This is a property of the "equals" relation. It is called the *substitution property of equals.* This property is implicit in our statement that the resultant of a binary operation is uniquely determined. It is stated in general as follows:

1. A number may be substituted for its equal in any expression.

As a consequence of the substitution property we also have

2. If equal numbers are added to equal numbers, their sums are equal, that is, if $a = b$ and $c = d$, then $a + c = b + d$.
3. If equal numbers are multiplied by equal numbers, their products are equal, that is, if $a = b$ and $c = d$, then $ac = bd$.

We shall use this property often in what follows and refer to it by saying either "unique products or sums" or "the substitution property."

Example 1

Addition assigns to the ordered pair (1, 0) the number which we write (1 + 0). We recognize this as the number 1. We write

$$1 + 0 = 1.$$

Since (1 + 0) and 1 are names of the same number, multiplying by 1, or adding 1, is the same as multiplying by (1 + 0) or adding (1 + 0), that is,

$$(1 + 0) \cdot 5 = 1 \cdot 5.$$

When using this step in arithmetic computation, we shall use either "uniqueness of products" or "substitution property" as our justification.

The element $m * n$ may or may not be in the set S. If $m * n$ is in S for all ordered pairs of elements of S, we say the binary operation $*$ satisfies the *Closure Law*. Another way of saying this is to say that the set S *is closed* with respect to the binary operation $*$.

Addition is a binary operation on the set W. The sum of any two elements of W is a uniquely determined element of W. To each ordered pair (a, b) of elements of W, the operation of addition $+$ assigns the number $(a + b)$, which is also an element of W. (The sum of two whole numbers is a whole number.)

Note that if we consider the set $\{1, 3, 5, 7, \ldots\}$, the set of all odd natural numbers, addition on this set does not satisfy the Closure Law.

Exercise 5.5

1. The even numbers are numbers of the form 2, 4, 6, 8, ... More precisely, an even number is a number that can be written in the form $2k$, where k is any number in W.

(a) Show that the set of even numbers is closed with respect to addition.
(b) Show that the set of even numbers is closed under the binary operation of multiplication.
(c) Show that the set of odd numbers is closed with respect to multiplication.

2. Let S denote the set of all odd numbers.

$$S = \{1, 3, 5, 7, 9, \ldots\}.$$

Let us define the binary operation "$\odot$" in the following manner. For m and n in S, let $m \odot n$ be the number you get by adding 1 to $m + n$, that is, $m \odot n = m + n + 1$, where the $+$ indicates the ordinary operation of addition.

(a) $1 \odot 3 = ?$ $1 \odot 5 = ?$ $3 \odot 7 = ?$ $5 \odot 7 = ?$
(b) Discuss whether the operation $\odot$ as defined on the set S satisfies the Closure Law.
(c) Using the fact that any two odd natural numbers may be represented as $2k - 1$ or $2m - 1$, where m and k are natural numbers, can you prove in general that the operation $\odot$ obeys the Closure Law on the set S?

3. Consider the set W and let the operation $\odot$ be defined as follows. For m and n in W, $m \odot n = m^n$, for example, $3 \odot 2 = 3^2 = 9$. Discuss closure.

4. Consider the set W and let the operation $\odot$ be defined as follows. For m and n in W, $m \odot n = m$. Discuss closure.

5. Let $m \odot n = m - n$ for m and n in W. Discuss closure.

6. We have defined the relation "$=$" for sets and "$=$" for numbers. Distinguish these two relations (i.e., how is each defined?).

7. What is a binary operation?

8. What is the justification for the following statements?

$$10 - 1 = 9.$$
$$(10 - 1)\cdot 4 = 9\cdot 4.$$

5.6 ADDITION IN W

5.6a Elementary Facts of Addition

As we proceed you will see how we can combine any two (or more) whole numbers by having knowledge of only the *elementary facts* of addition. The *elementary facts* consist of only those sums in which the components of the ordered pairs are the numbers from 0 through 9. Recall how we constructed tables for the Cartesian product? We can follow a similar pattern in the construction of a table of elementary facts of addition.

TABLE 1

ELEMENTARY FACTS OF ADDITION

Second element of the ordered pair

First element of the ordered pair	+	0	1	2	3	4	5	6	7	8	9
	0	*0*	1	2	3	4	5	6	7	8	9
	1	1	*2*	3	4	5	6	7	8	9	10
	2	2	3	*4*	5	6	7	8	9	10	11
	3	3	4	5	*6*	7	8	9	10	11	12
	4	4	5	6	7	*8*	9	10	11	12	13
	5	5	6	7	8	9	*10*	11	12	13	14
	6	6	7	8	9	10	11	*12*	13	14	15
	7	7	8	9	10	11	12	13	*14*	15	16
	8	8	9	10	11	12	13	14	15	*16*	17
	9	9	10	11	12	13	14	15	16	17	*18*

Of course we are familiar with these combinations. We present the table of elementary addition facts simply as an example of such a table.

The symbol + in the upper left corner of the table indicates that we are concerned with the operation of addition. The column on the left designates the first element of the ordered pair, while the first row designates the second element of the ordered pair. For example, to find another name for the number (6 + 2) which addition assigns to the ordered pair (6, 2), find the row beginning with "6" and the column headed "2." In the square where this row and column meet we find the numeral 8. Our table tells us

(6, 2)	$\xrightarrow{+}$	(6 + 2)	=	8
to the ordered pair (6, 2)	the operation "addition"	assigns the number (6 + 2)		which has the more common name of "8"

Later on, when working with systems with which we are not familiar, we shall find such tables indispensable. We will work with such systems in order that the reader appreciate the significance of these facts in teaching arithmetic.

There is special information incorporated in this table. Let us investigate further.

5.6b Zero in Addition

Notice that $0 + 1 = 1$, $0 + 2 = 2$, and, in general, $0 + n = n$, for any n in the set. The number 0 as an element of the number system plays a very special role. The statement $0 + n = n$ distinguishes 0 as the element of the number system which when added to any number gives a sum that is identically equal to that number. This is such an unusual and important property that it requires special recognition and consequently gets a distinct name. As an element of the number system, 0 is called the *additive identity*. This is but one of the special properties of zero.

5.6c The Commutative Law of Addition

With reference to Table 1, Section 5.6a, we note that the operation of addition assigns to the ordered pair (6, 2) the sum $(6 + 2) = 8$, that is, $(6, 2) \xrightarrow{+} (6 + 2) = 8$. Also, the operation of addition assigns to the ordered pair (2, 6) the sum 8, that is, $(2, 6) \xrightarrow{+} (2 + 6) = 8$. Thus $(6 + 2) = 8$ and $(2 + 6) = 8$. From the symmetric property of equals we can say $8 = (2 + 6)$. Now if $(6 + 2) = 8$ and $8 = (2 + 6)$, by the transitive property of equals we have $(6 + 2) = (2 + 6)$. Note also that $(8 + 3) = 11$ and $(3 + 8) = 11$. Hence $(8 + 3) = (3 + 8)$. You say that this is trivial? Everyone knows that! We agree with the latter but not the former. This is an example of a very important property of addition in our number system. It is called the *Commutative Law of Addition.*

In general, for any numbers a and b of W, $a + b = b + a$, and we say the operation of addition as defined on the set W obeys the Commutative Law.

To digress momentarily, recall the common meaning associated with the word "commute." A commuter is one who travels from home to work, from work to home. He "changes places." When two elements of a set commute with respect to an operation, they "exchange places." An application of the Commutative Law results in a change in the order of the elements.

More generally, for any binary operation $*$ defined on a set S, $*$ is said to obey the Commutative Law (or, more simply, $*$ is said to be commutative) if for any elements m and n in S, $m * n = n * m$.

Is ordinary subtraction an operation that obeys the Commutative Law?

5.6d The Associative Law of Addition

To the ordered pair (2, 5) the operation of addition assigns the number $(2 + 5)$. Here the parentheses are used to indicate that $(2 + 5)$ is *a number*. Now consider some other number, say 4. The binary operation of addition assigns to the ordered pair $((2 + 5), 4)$ the number $((2 + 5) + 4)$. Using the table, or our knowledge of the elementary facts of addition, we find $((2 + 5) + 4) = (7 + 4) = 11$. Now consider first the ordered pair (5, 4) to which the operation of addition assigns the number $(5 + 4)$, then the ordered pair $(2, (5 + 4))$ to which the operation of addition assigns the number $(2 + (5 + 4))$. Again using the table, or our knowledge of elementary facts of addition, we find $(2 + (5 + 4)) = (2 + 9) = 11$. This implies $(2 + 5) + 4 = 2 + (5 + 4)$ or that, in adding the three numbers 2, 5, and 4, it is immaterial how we group them by pairs to carry out the operation.

In general, we say a binary operation $*$ is *associative*, or obeys the *Associative Law*, if for any numbers a, b, and c in the set on which the operation is defined,

$$(a * b) * c = a * (b * c).$$

The binary operation of addition defined on W is associative. The Associative Law of Addition states that it is immaterial how the terms are grouped, the sum is the same. As a consequence we may write $(2 + 7) + 6$ as $2 + 7 + 6$, since the grouping is immaterial.

$$2 + 7 + 6 = (2 + 7) + 6 = 2 + (7 + 6).$$

A combination of the Associative and Commutative Laws makes it possible for us to group and change the order of the numbers in a sum without affecting the ultimate sum, for example, $2 + 7 + 6 = (2 + 7) + 6 = 2 + (7 + 6) = 2 + (6 + 7) = (2 + 6) + 7 = (6 + 2) + 7$, and so on.

Is ordinary subtraction an operation that obeys the Associative Law?

Exercise 5.6

The following are examples of the application of either the Commutative Law of Addition or the Associative Law of Addition. Designate which law is being applied in each example.

1. $2 + 3 = 3 + 2$
2. $(2 + 3) + 4 = 2 + (3 + 4)$
3. $a + b = b + a$
4. $x + (y + z) = (x + y) + z$
5. $(a + b) + c = (b + a) + c$
6. $2 + 3 + 5 + 7 = (2 + 3) + (5 + 7)$
7. $2 + (a + 3) + b = (2 + a) + (3 + b)$
8. Group the numbers 2, 3, 5, and 8 as a sum in several different ways; carry out the addition and compare the final sums.
9. Distinguish the cardinal use of the number 0 and 0 as an element of a number system.
10. The fact that addition is commutative can be seen by looking at the table of elementary facts. Conversely, the fact that addition is commutative makes the table have a special appearance. Discuss this.
11. The special property of 0 can be seen in the table. Discuss this.

5.7 MULTIPLICATION IN W

Multiplication is a binary operation defined on the set W. The product of any two elements of W is an element of W. To each ordered pair (a, b) of elements of W, the operation of multiplication $\cdot$ assigns the number $a \cdot b$ which is also an element of W.

5.7a The Elementary Facts of Multiplication

The elementary facts of multiplication consist of only those products where the components of the ordered pairs are the numbers from 1 through 9. Recall how we constructed the table of elementary facts for addition? We can follow a similar pattern for multiplication.

We present Table 2 as an aid in pointing out some important properties of multiplication.

The symbol $\cdot$ in the upper left corner indicates that we are concerned with the operation of multiplication. The column on the left designates the first element of the ordered pairs. The uppermost row designates the second element of the ordered pairs. To find the "standard name" for the numbers assigned to the ordered pairs by the operation of multiplication, we proceed as with the addition table. To the ordered

TABLE 2

ELEMENTARY FACTS OF MULTIPLICATION

Second element of the ordered pair

	·	1	2	3	4	5	6	7	8	9
	1	1	2	3	4	5	6	7	8	9
	2	2	4	6	8	10	12	14	16	18
First	3	3	6	9	12	15	18	21	24	27
element	4	4	8	12	16	20	24	28	32	36
of the	5	5	10	15	20	25	30	35	40	45
ordered	6	6	12	18	24	30	36	42	48	54
pair	7	7	14	21	28	35	42	49	56	63
	8	8	16	24	32	40	48	56	64	72
	9	9	18	27	36	45	54	63	72	81

pair (3, 5) the operation $\cdot$ assigns the number $(3\cdot5)$, which, from the table, is 15.

(3, 5)	$\longrightarrow$	$(3\cdot5)$	=	15
to the ordered pair (3, 5)	the operation of multiplication	assigns the number $(3\cdot5)$		which has the standard name "15"

There is special information incorporated in the table that should be emphasized.

5.7b The Multiplicative Identity

Note that for any number a of the set, $1\cdot a = a\cdot 1 = a$. This means that the number 1 also plays a special role in the number system. It is the element of the number system that when multiplied into any number gives a product identically equal to that number. As an element of the number system, 1 is called the *multiplicative identity.*

We use the symmetric property of equality again and write $a = 1\cdot a$. Thus $3 = 1\cdot3$, and $10 = 1\cdot10$. This important fact is often overlooked. It cannot be overemphasized.

Example 1

$$3a + 3 = 3\cdot a + 3\cdot 1 = 3(a + 1)$$
$$x + xy = x\cdot 1 + x\cdot y = x(1 + y)$$

5.7c The Commutative Law of Multiplication

With reference to Table 2, Section 5.7a, we note that the operation of multiplication assigns to the ordered pair (2, 6) the product 12, that is,

$(2, 6) \dot{\rightarrow} (2\cdot 6) = 12$. Also, we note from the table that to the ordered pair $(6, 2)$ is assigned the product 12, that is, $(6, 2) \dot{\rightarrow} (6\cdot 2) = 12$. Thus $(2\cdot 6) = 12$ and $(6\cdot 2) = 12$. From the symmetric property of equals we have $12 = (6\cdot 2)$. Now, if $(2\cdot 6) = 12$ and $12 = (6\cdot 2)$, by the transitive property of equals we have $(2\cdot 6) = (6\cdot 2)$. This is an example of the *Commutative Law of Multiplication.* It states that we may interchange the order of the numbers in arriving at a product without affecting the result.

In general, for any numbers a and b of W, $a\cdot b = b\cdot a$, and we say that the operation of multiplication as defined on the set W obeys the Commutative Law or, more simply, multiplication is commutative on the set W.

The fact that multiplication is commutative makes the table of elementary facts symmetric about one of the diagonals of the table. Also, the special property of 1 can be recognized from the table.

5.7d The Associative Law of Multiplication

To the ordered pair $(2, 4)$ the operation of multiplication assigns the *number* $(2\cdot 4)$. Here again the parentheses are used to indicate that $(2\cdot 4)$ is *a number.* Now consider some other number, say 5. The binary operation of multiplication assigns to the ordered pair $((2\cdot 4), 5)$ the number $((2\cdot 4)\cdot 5)$. Using the table, or our knowledge of elementary facts of multiplication, we find

$$((2\cdot 4)\cdot 5) = (8\cdot 5) = 40.$$

Now consider first the ordered pair $(4, 5)$ to which the operation of multiplication assigns the number $(4\cdot 5)$, then the ordered pair $(2, (4\cdot 5))$ to which the operation of multiplication assigns the number $(2\cdot (4\cdot 5))$. Again using the table of facts and an extension of this notion, we find

$$(2\cdot (4\cdot 5)) = (2\cdot 20) = 40.$$

This implies that $(2\cdot 4)\cdot 5 = 2\cdot (4\cdot 5)$ or that in multiplying the numbers 2, 4, and 5 it is immaterial how we group them by pairs to carry out the operation.

In general, we say that the operation of multiplication as defined on the set W is associative, or that the operation of multiplication obeys the Associative Law, and symbolize it this way.

For any numbers, a, b, and c of W

$$(a\cdot b)\cdot c = a\cdot (b\cdot c). \qquad \text{(see Figure 1)}$$

Furthermore, the Associative Law of Multiplication gives meaning

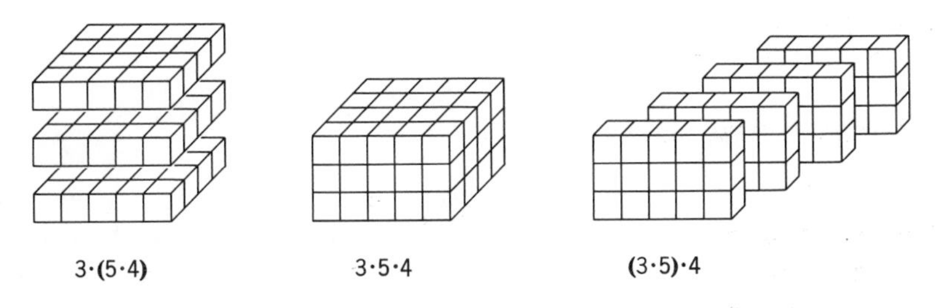

Figure 1

to an expression such as $x \cdot y \cdot z$, since it is immaterial how we *group* x, y, and z by pairs in carrying out the operation:

$$x \cdot y \cdot z = (x \cdot y) \cdot z = x \cdot (y \cdot z).$$

A combination of the Associative and Commutative Laws for Multiplication permits us to carry out the following manipulations: $a \cdot b \cdot c = (a \cdot b) \cdot c = a \cdot (b \cdot c) = a \cdot (c \cdot b) = (a \cdot c) \cdot b = (c \cdot a) \cdot b$, and so on. In particular, we can write $a \cdot a \cdot a$ or $a \cdot a \cdot a \cdot a \cdot a$, and they will have meaning even though the operation of multiplication is a *binary* operation.

Exercise 5.7

1. The following are examples of the application of either the Commutative Law of Multiplication or the Associative Law of Multiplication. Designate which law is being exemplified by each example.

(a) $5 \cdot 4 = 4 \cdot 5$
(b) $(5 \cdot 4) \cdot 8 = 5 \cdot (4 \cdot 8)$
(c) $(5 \cdot 4) \cdot 8 = 8 \cdot (5 \cdot 4)$
(d) $a \cdot b = b \cdot a$
(e) $(x \cdot y) \cdot z = x \cdot (y \cdot z)$
(f) $3 \cdot 5 \cdot 7 \cdot 4 = (3 \cdot 5) \cdot (7 \cdot 4)$

2. Group the numbers 3, 5, 7, and 4 as a product in several different ways; carry out the multiplication and compare the results.

3. The following are examples of the application of one of the laws of multiplication or addition. Identify the law exemplified by each example.

(a) $5 \cdot (3 + 7) = 5 \cdot (7 + 3)$
(b) $5 \cdot 3 + 2 = 3 \cdot 5 + 2$
(c) $5 \cdot (3 + 2) = (3 + 2) \cdot 5$
(d) $a \cdot b + a \cdot c = b \cdot a + c \cdot a$
(e) $a \cdot (b \cdot c) = (b \cdot c) \cdot a$
(f) $(a + b) \cdot (c + d) = (a + b) \cdot (d + c)$
(g) $3 \cdot (4 + 5 + 6) = 3 \cdot (4 + (5 + 6))$
(h) $(a \cdot b) \cdot c = a \cdot b \cdot c$

4. Consider the operations $\odot$ as defined on the sets in problems 2, 3, 4, and 5 of Exercise 5.5.

(a) Are these operations associative?
(b) Are these operations commutative?

5. Show that $(a \cdot b)^2 = a^2 \cdot b^2$ and justify each step.
6. Show that $(a \cdot b)^3 = a^3 \cdot b^3$ and justify each step.

5.8 THE DISTRIBUTIVE LAW

In our discussion so far we have been considering two binary operations, addition and multiplication, on the set W. We require addition and multiplication to satisfy the Associative Law and the Commutative Law. Symbolically, we require for any whole numbers a, b, and c in W:

Addition		*Multiplication*
$(a + b)$ is in W	Closure Laws	$(a \cdot b)$ is in W
$(a + b) + c = a + (b + c)$	Associative Laws	$(ab)c = a(bc)$
$a + b = b + a$	Commutative Laws	$ab = ba$

(*Note:* ab means $a \cdot b$)

The *Distributive Law* governs the behavior of the two binary operations when they are combined in an arithmetic operation. We illustrate first:

```
X X X   X X X X X
X X X   X X X X X
X X X   X X X X X
```

If we want to express the total number of X's in the diagram, it can be done in two ways. We have 3 X's in each of $(3 + 5)$ columns, or $3(3 + 5)$ X's, which is equal to 24 X's. We also have 3 rows of 3 X's and 3 rows of 5 X's or $(3 \cdot 3 + 3 \cdot 5)$ X's. But this is also 24 X's. This tells us that

$$3(3 + 5) = (3 \cdot 3) + (3 \cdot 5).$$

Notice that in the expression $3(3 + 5)$, we add first and then multiply. In the second expression, $(3 \cdot 3) + (3.5)$, we multiply first and then add. The Distributive Law tells us that, in a situation such as our example, it is immaterial whether we add first and then multiply or multiply first and then add. We arrive at the same result.

In general, if a, b, and c are elements of W, then the Distributive Law of Multiplication with respect to addition is symbolized:

$$a \cdot (b + c) = a \cdot b + a \cdot c.$$

Example 1

1. $2(3 + 4) = 2 \cdot 3 + 2 \cdot 4$
   $2 \cdot 7 = 6 + 8$
   $14 = 14$
2. $2(3 + x) = 2 \cdot 3 + 2 \cdot x = 6 + 2x$
3. $a(1 + b) = a \cdot 1 + a \cdot b = a + ab$

Recall once more that the equals relation has the property of being symmetric, among other properties. As a consequence, the Distributive Law can also be written symbolically as follows:

$$a \cdot b + a \cdot c = a(b + c).$$

In this form it reminds us that much of factoring in algebra is simply an application of the Distributive Law.

Example 2

1. $3 \cdot a + 3 \cdot b = 3(a + b)$
2. $a \cdot 10 + b \cdot 10 = (a + b) \cdot 10$
3. $3 + 3a = 3 \cdot 1 + 3 \cdot a = 3(1 + a)$
4. $3 \cdot 100 + 2 \cdot 100 = (3 + 2)100 = 5 \cdot 100$

It is worthwhile to consider these examples further. By the Commutative Law of Multiplication, we can write (1) as

$$a \cdot 3 + b \cdot 3 = (a + b)3.$$

This can be read as "a threes plus b threes is a plus b threes." We may read (2) as "a tens plus b tens is a plus b tens." We would not ordinarily read (4) as "three one-hundreds plus two one-hundreds is five one-hundreds." Instead we read this as "three hundred plus two hundred is five hundred," but this is an abbreviation of what we mean when we write

$$3 \cdot 100 + 2 \cdot 100 = 5 \cdot 100.$$

Before continuing, we remark that we will make heavy use of these laws in the discussion of the addition and multiplication algorithms and allied topics.

Some books actually have in print the preposterous statement that only "like" numbers can be added. They are referring to a situation such as

$$3 \text{ tens} + 2 \text{ tens} = 5 \text{ tens}.$$

The binary operations, addition and multiplication, assign to any and every ordered pair of numbers a particular number. The Distributive Law applies only to "like" numbers in the sense that $3 \cdot 10^2 + 2 \cdot 10^2 = 5 \cdot 10^2$, but we can certainly add $3 \cdot 10^2$ and $2 \cdot 10$. The sum can be indicated as $3 \cdot 10^2 + 2 \cdot 10$, or $3 \cdot 10^2 + 2 \cdot 10^1 + 0 \cdot 10^0 = 320$.

The Distributive Law is implicit in the ordinary addition problem

$$\begin{array}{r} 232 \\ 27 \\ 9246 \\ \hline 9505 \end{array}$$

This will be discussed in detail in the following sections.

To summarize and to generalize the statement regarding the Distributive Law in a manner similar to our general statements regarding the Associative and Commutative Laws, we make the following statement.

If $\odot$ and $\oplus$ symbolize two arbitrary operations defined on a set S, and if for any elements a, b, c of S,

$$a \odot (b \oplus c) = (a \odot b) \oplus (a \odot c),$$

the operation $\odot$ is said to be *distributive* with respect to the operation $\oplus$, or the operation $\odot$ obeys the Distributive Law with respect to the operation $\oplus$.

Multiplication is distributive with respect to addition on the set W, or the Distributive Law holds for multiplication over addition on the set W.

Exercise 5.8

Apply the Distributive Law to rename the following numbers:

1. $a(b + 2)$ **2.** $2a + ac$ **3.** $23(2 + 1)$
4. $2 \cdot 10^2 + 3 \cdot 10^2$ **5.** $30 \cdot 10 + 2 \cdot 10$
6. $(a + b)(c + d) = a(c + d) + b(c + d)$
7. $(a + b)(c + d) = (a + b)c + (a + b)d$
8. $(a + b)(a + b) = (a + b)a + (a + b)b$
9. $x(y + 2)$ **10.** $2x + bx$ **11.** $2ax + 3x$
12. $2ax + 5a$ **13.** $3 \cdot (10 \cdot 10) + 2 \cdot 10$
14. $10 \cdot 3 \cdot 10 + 2 \cdot 10$ **15.** $2xab + a$ **16.** $(20 + 3)2$

Assume that the operations symbolized by Δ and $\oplus$ are defined on a set S, and using a, b, and c as elements of S, symbolize

17. that Δ is commutative.
18. that $\oplus$ is commutative.
19. that Δ is associative.
20. that $\oplus$ is associative.
21. that Δ is distributive with respect to $\oplus$.

5.9 SPECIAL PROPERTIES OF ZERO AND ONE

Recall that 0 and 1 as elements of a number system were called the *additive identity* and the *multiplicative identity*, respectively. See Sections 5.6b and 5.7b. They are unique elements, that is, there is one and only one element of the set W that is the additive identity and one and only one element of the set W that is the multiplicative identity.

To prove *uniqueness* of the additive identity 0 let us suppose there is another whole number $0'$ which is an additive identity different from 0.

Then $0 + 0' = 0$, since $0'$ is assumed to be an additive identity.
But $0 + 0' = 0'$, since 0 is the additive identity.
This implies $0 = 0'$, by the transitive property of equals. Hence our supposition is false, and we must conclude the additive identity is unique.

It will be left to the reader to show that the multiplicative identity is unique. A similar technique can be used.

5.9a Properties of Zero in Multiplication

You are familiar with the statement:

$$0 \cdot m = m \cdot 0 = 0 \qquad \text{for any integer } m.$$

We offer the following intuitive argument to strengthen the plausibility of this statement. A proof along these lines would require the use of the principle of mathematical induction.

$1 \cdot 0 = 0$, by the definition of multiplicative identity.

$2 \cdot 0 = (1 + 1)0 = 1 \cdot 0 + 1 \cdot 0 = 0 + 0 = 0$, by the use of elementary facts, the Distributive Law, property of the multiplicative identity, and property of the additive identity.

$3 \cdot 0 = (1 + 2)0 = 1 \cdot 0 + 2 \cdot 0 = 0 + 0 = 0$, by the use of elementary facts, the Distributive Law, property of the multiplicative identity, previously proven statement, and property of the additive identity.

$4 \cdot 0 = (1 + 3)0 = 1 \cdot 0 + 3 \cdot 0 = 0 + 0 = 0$, and so on. For any integer m, assuming $m = [1 + (m - 1)]$ and $(m - 1) \cdot 0 = 0$, then

$$m \cdot 0 = (1 + (m - 1))0 = 1 \cdot 0 + (m - 1)0 = 0 + 0 = 0.$$

5.10 THE SYSTEM OF WHOLE NUMBERS

We summarize our previous statements in a formal definition.

DEFINITION 5.10a. *By the system of whole numbers* we mean the set

$$W = \{0, 1, 2, 3, 4, \ldots\},$$

the binary operations, addition $(+)$ and multiplication $(\cdot)$, and the following laws. For m, n, and k in W,

Closure Laws

1. There is a uniquely determined sum, which we write $m + n$, in W.
2. There is a uniquely determined product, which we write $m \cdot n$, in W.

Associative Laws

3. $m + (n + k) = (m + n) + k$.
4. $m \cdot (n \cdot k) = (m \cdot n) \cdot k$.

Commutative Laws

5. $m + n = n + m$.

6. $m \cdot n = n \cdot m$.

Distributive Law

7. $m \cdot (n + k) = m \cdot n + m \cdot k$.

Identities

8. There is a unique element 0 such that for any m in W, $m + 0 = 0 + m = m$.

9. There is a unique element 1 such that for any m in W, $1 \cdot m = m \cdot 1 = m$.

Exercise 5.10

1. Show that the multiplicative identity is unique. (*Hint:* Assume $1'$ is any other multiplicative identity.)
2. If we assume that $m \cdot 0 = 0$, show that $(m + 1) \cdot 0 = 0$. State the law used at each step.
3. $1 \cdot 5 = 5$ because 1 is the multiplicative identity. There are occasions when we also write $5 = 1 \cdot 5$. Give an example of a situation when it is convenient to use $1 \cdot 5$ in place of 5. (*Hint:* Write $5 + 10m$ as a multiple of 5.)
4. (a) Can you write 4 as a multiple of 0?
   (b) Can you write 0 as a multiple of 4? Explain.
5. (a) Does 5 "divide" 0? Explain.
   (b) Does 0 "divide" 5? Explain.
6. Distinguish 0 and 1 as cardinal numbers and as elements of a number system.
7. Show that $8 \cdot 0 = 0$, using the argument of Section 5.9a.
8. Show that $(a + b)(c + d) = ac + ad + bc + bd$, and justify each step.
9. Show that $(a + b)^2 = a^2 + 2ab + b^2$, and justify each step.

5.11 THE ALGORITHMS

An algorithm is simply a procedure for performing an operation, such as addition or multiplication. Whenever we perform operations with single digit numbers, we recall the necessary facts from memory or use a table of elementary facts. When faced with computation involving multiple-digit numerals, however, we turn to an algorithm. The algorithms enable us to carry out complicated computations with the use of elementary facts and a knowledge of the procedure. The place-value or exponential-positional system of numeration and the fact that the numbers are elements of a number system make the algorithm possible. The algorithms we use now are not the only possible ones. There have been changes, and possibly there will be more. Improvements in the algorithms lead to more efficient use of the system.

It will be noted as we proceed that the algorithms presented are procedures for naming the numbers determined by the binary operations of the system of whole numbers and do not depend on the *base* of the system but simply on the fact that we have a *place-value* system. This implies that the procedures will work as well in base five, base twelve, base two, or any other base, as they do in the base ten, or decimal, system.

5.11a The Addition Algorithm

First, using properties of our system of whole numbers and tables of elementary facts, we shall show that $23 + 46 = 69$. We shall then compare the complete algorithm with our usual procedure.

(a) $23 + 46 = (2 \cdot 10^1 + 3 \cdot 10^0) + (4 \cdot 10^1 + 6 \cdot 10^0)$ by our system of numeration.

(b) $(2 \cdot 10^1 + 3 \cdot 10^0) + (4 \cdot 10^1 + 6 \cdot 10^0) = 2 \cdot 10^1 + (3 \cdot 10^0 + 4 \cdot 10^1) + 6 \cdot 10^0$ by the Associative Law of Addition.

(c) $2 \cdot 10^1 + (3 \cdot 10^0 + 4 \cdot 10^1) + 6 \cdot 10^0 = 2 \cdot 10^1 + (4 \cdot 10^1 + 3 \cdot 10^0) + 6 \cdot 10^0$ by the Commutative Law of Addition.

(d) $2 \cdot 10^1 + (4 \cdot 10^1 + 3 \cdot 10^0) + 6 \cdot 10^0 = (2 \cdot 10^1 + 4 \cdot 10^1) + (3 \cdot 10^0 + 6 \cdot 10^0)$ by the Associative Law of Addition.

(e) $(2 \cdot 10^1 + 4 \cdot 10^1) + (3 \cdot 10^0 + 6 \cdot 10^0) = (2 + 4)10^1 + (3 + 6)10^0$ by the Distributive Law.

(f) $(2 + 4)10^1 + (3 + 6)10^0 = 6 \cdot 10^1 + 9 \cdot 10^0$ by the table of elementary facts.

(g) $6 \cdot 10^1 + 9 \cdot 10^0 = 69$ by our system of numeration.

(h) $23 + 46 = 69$ by the transitive property of equals.

In our usual procedure we would first write the problem in the form

$$\begin{array}{r} 23 \\ \underline{46} \end{array}$$

Steps (a), (b), (c), (d), and (e) of the complete algorithm show that we are justified in such an arrangement of work in that we will get the same result if we perform column-wise addition.

$$\begin{array}{r} 23 \\ \underline{46} \\ 69 \end{array}$$

Steps (f), (g), and (h) indicate the performance of the addition.

Let us turn to an example involving a "carry" and show how that appears in the complete algorithm. Consider the problem $46 + 38$.

(a)	$46 + 38 = (4\cdot 10^1 + 6\cdot 10^0) + (3\cdot 10^1 + 8\cdot 10^0)$	System of Num.
(b)	$= 4\cdot 10^1 + (6\cdot 10^0 + 3\cdot 10^1) + 8\cdot 10^0$	Assoc. Law of Add.
(c)	$= 4\cdot 10^1 + (3\cdot 10^1 + 6\cdot 10^0) + 8\cdot 10^0$	Com. Law of Add.
(d)	$= (4\cdot 10^1 + 3\cdot 10^1) + (6\cdot 10^0 + 8\cdot 10^0)$	Assoc. Law of Add.
(e)	$= (4 + 3)10^1 + (6 + 8)10^0$	Distributive Law
(f)	$= 7\cdot 10^1 + 14\cdot 10^0$	Table of El. Facts
(g)	$= 7\cdot 10^1 + (1\cdot 10^1 + 4\cdot 10^0)10^0$	System of Num.
(h)	$= 7\cdot 10^1 + (1\cdot 10^1)10^0 + (4\cdot 10^0)10^0$	Distributive Law
(i)	$= 7\cdot 10^1 + 1(10^1\cdot 10^0) + 4(10^0\cdot 10^0)$	Assoc. Law of Mult.
(j)	$= 7\cdot 10^1 + 1\cdot 10^1 + 4\cdot 10^0$	Laws of Exponents
(k)	$= (7\cdot 10^1 + 1\cdot 10^1) + 4\cdot 10^0$	Assoc. Law of Add.
(l)	$= (7 + 1)10^1 + 4\cdot 10^0$	Distributive Law
(m)	$= 8\cdot 10^1 + 4\cdot 10^0$	Table of El. Facts
(n)	$= 84$	System of Num.
(o)	$46 + 38 = 84$	Trans. Prop. of Equals

In this algorithm, the first five steps justify our arrangement of the problem for column-wise addition, that is, column-wise addition can be thought of as arranging the powers of the base ten so that the Distributive Law can be applied. Step (f) is an indicated addition, and if this is written as column-wise addition it would appear as follows:

$$\begin{array}{r} 46 \\ \underline{38} \\ 14 \\ \underline{70} \end{array}$$

Steps (g) through (k) justify the carry from the units to the tens position, and this is usually written as

$$\begin{array}{r} \text{carry} \rightarrow 1 \\ 46 \\ \underline{38} \\ 4 \end{array}$$

Steps (e) through (o) complete the computation and justify our writing the sum as a column sum with the appropriate carry.

The addition algorithm applies to sums of more than two numbers as you well know. In writing out the complete algorithms for such problems we simply extend the ideas used in the simpler problems.

We wish to emphasize that our addition algorithm is based on elementary facts and properties of our system of whole numbers. Each step we take in carrying out a computation can be justified in terms of one or more of the fundamental concepts.

5.11b The Multiplication Algorithm

Again, using the tables of elementary facts and the properties of our system of whole numbers, we will show that $(28)(3) = 84$.

(a)	$(28)(3) = (2\cdot10^1 + 8\cdot10^0)(3\cdot10^0)$	Sys. of Num.
(b)	$= (2\cdot10^1)(3\cdot10^0) + (8\cdot10^0)(3\cdot10^0)$	Dist. Law
(c)	$= 2(10^1\cdot3)10^0 + 8(10^0\cdot3)10^0$	Assoc. (mult.)
(d)	$= 2(3\cdot10^1)10^0 + 8(3\cdot10^0)10^0$	Com. (mult.)
(e)	$= (2\cdot3)(10^1\cdot10^0) + (8\cdot3)(10^0\cdot10^0)$	Assoc. (mult.)
(f)	$= (2\cdot3)10^1 + (8\cdot3)10^0$	Law of Exp.
(g)	$= 6\cdot10^1 + 24\cdot10^0$	Table (mult.)
(h)	$= 6\cdot10^1 + (2\cdot10^1 + 4\cdot10^0)10^0$	Sys. of Num.
(i)	$= 6\cdot10^1 + (2\cdot10^1)10^0 + (4\cdot10^0)10^0$	Dist. Law
(j)	$= 6\cdot10^1 + 2(10^1\cdot10^0) + 4(10^0\cdot10^0)$	Assoc. (mult.)
(k)	$= 6\cdot10^1 + 2\cdot10^1 + 4\cdot10^0$	Law of Exp.
(l)	$= (6 + 2)10^1 + 4\cdot10^0$	Dist. Law
(m)	$= 8\cdot10^1 + 4\cdot10^0$	Table (add.)
(n)	$= 84$	Sys. of Num.
(o)	$(28)(3) = 84$	Trans. Prop. of Equals

Step (a) is usually shortened to

$$(20 + 8)3.$$

The Distributive Law (step b) allows us to multiply 20 by 3 and 8 by 3 first and then add

$$20\cdot3 + 8\cdot3.$$

Steps (f) through (l) show why we multiply 2 by 3 first and then add the 2 carried over from the previous multiplication. This might be written in the following way, which is suggestive of what is actually taking place.

$$\begin{array}{r} 28 \\ \underline{3} \\ 24 \\ \underline{60} \\ 84 \end{array}$$

The usual practice of finding products is a much abbreviated procedure as is indicated in the following example.

Example 1

In multiplying 834 by 326 we are actually finding the sum of the following products:

(a) $(800 + 30 + 4)6 +$
(b) $(800 + 30 + 4)20 +$
(c) $(800 + 30 + 4)300$

This represents several applications of the basic laws. If we carry out this indicated addition as column-wise addition, it would appear as in I below. II and III give some indication of the actual steps that are omitted in the usual procedure.

	I	II	III
	834	834	834
	326	326	326
(a)	24		
	180		
	4800	5004	5004
(b)	80		
	600		
	16000	16680	1668
(c)	1200		
	9000		
	240000	250200	2502
	271884	271884	271884

Note in III that we "indent" the 1668 because we are actually multiplying by 20, not 2. We "indent" the 2502 two places because we are actually multiplying by 300, not 3.

Exercise 5.11

1. Use the addition algorithm to find the sum of each of the following, giving reasons for each step:

   (a) $27 + 9$ (b) $36 + 8$

2. Use the table of elementary facts in Section 4.9c and the addition algorithm to find the sum of each of the following:

   (a) 9E7 + T (b) TT + T (c) EE + E (d) TE + 9

3. Use the table of elementary facts in Section 4.9c and the multiplication algorithm to find the following products:

   (a) (EE)(9) (b) (TET)(8) (c) (7E)(T5) (d) (6T)(5E)

4. For purposes of simplicity the addition algorithm is sometimes shortened as follows:

$$\begin{aligned} 23 + 46 &= 2\cdot 10 + 3 + 4\cdot 10 + 6 \\ &= (2\cdot 10 + 4\cdot 10) + (3 + 6) \\ &= (2 + 4)10 + (3 + 6) \\ &= 6\cdot 10 + 9 \\ &= 69 \end{aligned}$$

   We remarked earlier that the numbers were rearranged in order to apply the Distributive Law so that the problem could be reduced to one involving only the elementary facts. We do this in order to stress the importance of knowing the elementary facts.

   Give the reason or reasons for each step in the shortened algorithm.

5. The second example of the addition algorithm could be shortened as follows:

$$\begin{aligned} 46 + 38 &= 4\cdot 10 + 6 + 3\cdot 10 + 8 \\ &= (4\cdot 10 + 3\cdot 10) + (6 + 8) \\ &= (4 + 3)10 + 14 \\ &= (7\cdot 10 + 1\cdot 10) + 4 \\ &= (7 + 1)10 + 4 \\ &= 8\cdot 10 + 4 \\ &= 84 \end{aligned}$$

Compare the steps given here with the previous example and give the reason or reasons for each step in the shortened algorithm.

6. For multiplication, the shortened algorithm would be written as follows:

$$\begin{aligned} (28)(3) &= (2\cdot 10 + 8)3 \\ &= (2\cdot 10)3 + 8\cdot 3 \\ &= (2\cdot 3)10 + 8\cdot 3 \\ &= 6\cdot 10 + 24 \\ &= (6\cdot 10 + 2\cdot 10) + 4 \\ &= (6 + 2)10 + 4 \\ &= 8\cdot 10 + 4 \\ &= 84 \end{aligned}$$

Again the steps have been combined in order to simplify the presentation of the algorithm. Essentially the skipped steps involve the Commutative and Associative Laws.

Compare this shortened algorithm with the same problem in Section 5.11b and supply the reason or reasons for each step in the shortened algorithm.

7. Use the shortened algorithm to find the sum of each of the following:

(a) $379 + 96$ (b) $432 + 899$

8. Use the shortened algorithm to find the product of each of the following:

(a) $(36)(9)$ (b) $(47)(8)$ (c) $(36)(45)$ (d) $(57)(92)$

9. (a) What is the effect of multiplying a number by the base of the system of numeration?

(b) Multiply the base five number $342)_5$ by the base.

(c) Multiply the base twelve number $TET7)_{12}$ by the base.

10. The following exercises illustrate additional applications of base two arithmetic.

The question of multiplication in the Egyptian hieroglyphics has undoubtedly occurred to the reader. Addition is a simple process in this system of numeration and multiplication can be thought of as addition of one of the numbers to itself as many times as indicated by the second number. Thus: $3\cdot 6 = 6 + 6 + 6$. This is the way multiplication is carried out on a desk calculator. This method was probably the way multiplication was carried out for a long time by the Egyptians. However, their writing tools and working conditions dictated a more compact multiplication process. A very ingenious process called "doubling and summing" shortened their work considerably. This process was based on the fact that any number can be expressed as a sum of powers of 2. (This is the base two idea.) The base two notation was not used, however. Let us consider an example.

Find (39)(46).

Expressing 39 as a sum of powers of 2 we get $39 = 32 + 4 + 2 + 1$, or $39 = 2^5 + 2^2 + 2^1 + 2^0$. Hence multiplying by 39 is the same as multiplying by 1, 2, 4, and 32 and summing (use of the Distributive Law).

1	....	46
2	....	92
4	....	184
8	....	368
16	....	736
32	....	1472

Note that successive numbers in each column are obtained by "doubling" the preceding number.

(a) Which numbers in the right-hand column should be added to obtain the product of 39 and 46?
(b) Multiply (27)(49) by this method.
(c) Multiply (325)(202) by this method.

A variation of this method is called "halving and doubling." The work would be laid out as follows:

39	....	46*
19	....	92*
9	....	184*
4	....	368
2	....	736
1	....	1472*

Notice that in the process of "halving" we disregard remainders. To obtain the product, (39)(46), add the numbers in the right-hand column opposite the *odd* numbers in the left-hand column, that is,

$$(39)(46) = 46 + 92 + 184 + 1472 = 1794.$$

(d) Use this method for the problems in (b) and (c) above.

Consider the procedure for halving and doubling and this time write the remainder after each "halving" as follows:

39	....	1	↑
19	....	1	│
9	....	1	│
4	....	0	│
2	....	0	│
1	....	1	│

Now write the remainders from left to right in the same order they appear from bottom to top, that is, 100111.

(e) Do you recognize this number?

5.12 ORDER RELATIONS FOR THE WHOLE NUMBERS

In much of arithmetic, in fact, in much of our everyday life, we are interested in the biggest, the smallest, the least expensive, the most profitable, and so on. In the simplest cases these comparisons are easy to make, but we do meet situations where some care is needed.

Example 1

The symbol π denotes the number which expresses the ratio of the circumference of a circle to its diameter. In computations involving this symbol one is often told to use 22/7, and at other times to use 3.1416. How do these three numbers compare? Are any two equal? If not, which is the largest and which the smallest?

We do not intend to answer the above questions at this time. It is our intention to make precise certain concepts which will in time enable the reader to answer these questions and supply sound reasons to support his answers. We begin by making precise the meaning of "less than" for the whole numbers.

We define the relation "less than" (denoted by $<$) in terms of the 1–1 correspondence relation for sets. We remarked earlier that the concept of "more than" and "less than" may have had meaning in the earliest civilizations, even in the absence of counting systems. Preschool children comprehend these concepts in terms of pieces of candy. Their idea of sharing equally takes form in the familiar "one for you and one for me," but this is the matching relation or 1–1 correspondence. If the "one for you and one for me" ends while "me" still has several unmatched pieces, the "less than" concept has dramatic meaning for one person, at least.

DEFINITION 5.12a. If A and B are finite sets and A can be matched to a *proper* subset of B under a one-to-one correspondence, we say the cardinal number, $n(A)$, of the set A is *less than* the cardinal number, $n(B)$, of the set B.

We write this

$$n(A) < n(B).$$

We can also read this as "$n(B)$ is greater than $n(A)$." This is written

$$n(B) > n(A).$$

Example 2

The cardinal number of the set $\{1, 2, 3\}$ is 3. The cardinal number of the set $\{1, 2, 3, 4, 5\}$ is 5. The set $\{1, 2, 3\}$ can be matched with a proper subset of the set $\{1, 2, 3, 4, 5\}$ so $3 < 5$. The cardinal number of the empty set is 0. The cardinal number of the set $\{1\}$ is 1. Since the empty set is vacuously a subset of $\{1\}$, we have $0 < 1$.

The "less than" relation in the set of whole numbers is trivially a transitive relation. A transitive relation is called an *order*. Additional information is needed to make comparisons. Part of the additional information needed is embodied in the *Trichotomy Law for the whole numbers*.

DEFINITION 5.12b. THE TRICHOTOMY LAW. If m and n are any two whole numbers, then one and only one of the following relations holds:

1. $m = n$.
2. $m < n$.
3. $n < m$.

This permits us to compare any two whole numbers by "size." It allows us to make comparisons of the "bigger" and "smaller" or "more than" and "less than" type. In order to make precise the idea of the "biggest" or "smallest" type we need the relation $\leqq$, which is read "less than or equal to."

DEFINITION 5.12c. If m and n are any two whole numbers, we say m is "less than or equal to" n if m is *either* less than n *or* m is equal to n.

We can now introduce the idea of a bound on sets of numbers.

DEFINITION 5.12d. Let W denote a set of whole numbers. We say that c is an *upper bound* of the set W if $a \leqq c$ for each a in W. Similarly, we say that b is a *lower bound* for the set W if $b \leqq a$ for each a in W.

Example 3

Let $A = \{2, 3, 19\}$. An upper bound of A is 20 and 1 is a lower bound of A. Also, 100 is an upper bound. Note that 19 is also an upper bound and 2 is a lower bound. Furthermore, 19 is an upper bound and is less than any other upper bound.

DEFINITION 5.12e. (1) If c is an upper bound of a set A and (2) if d is any other upper bound, $c \leqq d$, we call c the *least upper bound* of the set A, that is, c is the *smallest* of the upper bounds.

DEFINITION 5.12f. (1) If b is a lower bound of a set A and (2) if e is any other lower bound, $e \leqq b$, we call b the *greatest lower bound* of the set A, that is, b is the *largest* of the lower bounds.

A set of whole numbers may have many upper bounds but has only one least upper bound; it may have many lower bounds but has only one greatest lower bound.

It may be of interest to remark that there is no biggest *number* less than 10. We shall say more about this later. Now it is sufficient to note that there is a biggest *whole number* less than 10. It is the number 9.

Exercise 5.12

In the following, consider $n \in W$, and interpret the expression $a < n < b$ as $n > a$ *and* $n < b$.

1. (a) Let $A = \{n|3 < n < 12\}$.
List the elements in the set A. List an upper and lower bound of the set A.
(b) Let $B = \{n|0 < n < 4\}$.
List the elements of the set B. List two distinct upper bounds of the set B.

2. If $C = \{n|3 < n\}$ and $D = \{n|n < 12\}$, then $C \cap D = ?$

3. List the elements in the set $A \cap B$ for the sets A and B of problem 1.

4. List the elements in the set $A \times B$ for the sets A and B of problem 1.

5. Let $C = \{n|6 \leqq n \leqq 12\}$.
List the elements of C. What is the least upper bound of C? List the elements of $B \cup C$ (set B of problem 1).

6. List the elements in the set $B \cap C$ (set B of problem 1 and set C of problem 5).

7. Describe the sets of whole numbers satisfying the following inequalities:

(a) $3 + n < 10$.
(b) $n + 2 < 6$.
(c) $3 + n < 9$ and $2 + n < 6$.

8. If $3 < 5$, how is $3 + n$ related to $5 + n$?

9. If $3 < 5$, how is $3 \cdot n$ related to $5 \cdot n$?

10. If you have a *set* of 5 apples and someone takes the apples, you have the *empty set* left. The cardinal number of the empty set is 0.
We now rely on your familiarity with the operation of subtraction to redefine "is less than." For whole numbers m and n, $m < n$ if $n - m > 0$. If we interpret this to mean that we have an excess under the matching relation, show that if $6 < 12$, then $6 + n < 12 + n$, using this criterion.

11. Show that the order relation, $<$, is not reflexive, is not symmetric, is transitive.

12. For whole numbers a, b, and c, show that if $a = b$, then $a + c = b + c$. Is the converse true?

13. For whole numbers a, b, and c, show that if $a = b$, then $a \cdot c = b \cdot c$. Is the converse true?

14. State problems 12 and 13 in words.

15. What restriction must be placed on n of problems 8 and 9 for your conclusions to hold true?

Show that the following equalities hold by beginning with the left side and with the use of the fundamental properties of the system of whole numbers, transforming it so that it is identical with the right side. Assume the letters are to represent whole numbers, for example,
to show: $5 + 6 + a = 6 + a + 5$

$5 + 6 + a = 5 + (6 + a)$ by the Associative Law of Addition
$= (6 + a) + 5$ by the Commutative Law of Addition
$= 6 + a + 5$ by the Associative Law of Addition

Hence, by the transitive property of equals, the given equality holds.

16. $x + 2 = 2 + x$
17. $(x + 3) + (y + 2) = (2 + 3) + (x + y)$
18. $3xy = x(3y)$
19. $(3b)^2 = 9b^2$
20. $3(x + 2y) = 6y + 3x$
21. $3 \cdot 10^0 + 4 \cdot 10^0 = 7 \cdot 10^0$
22. $2 \cdot 10^2 + 8 \cdot 10^2 = 1 \cdot 10^3$
23. $13 \cdot 10^2 = 1 \cdot 10^3 + 3 \cdot 10^2$
24. $(3 + 2)(4 + 1) = 25$ (two ways)
25. $(3 + x)(2 + y) = 6 + 3y + 2x + xy$
26. $(a + b)(a + b) = a^2 + 2ab + b^2$

REVIEW EXERCISES

1. What do we mean by the statement, "The set B has cardinal 87, or cardinal number 87"?
2. Use the set-builder notation in any way you can to specify the empty set, ∅.
3. The number 0 is a unique number in many ways. List some of the ways in which 0 is unique.
4. Show that 0 is unique as an element of the system of whole numbers (i.e., show that there is one and only one additive identity in the system of whole numbers).
5. Show that $3 \cdot 0 = 0$, and justify each step.
6. If $A = \{2, 3, 5, 16\}$, what is the least upper bound of A?
7. In the indicated multiplication,

```
  372
   39
 3338
1116
14498
```

explain why the fourth row of digits is indented one place to the left before the addition is performed.

Give precise definitions of each of the following:

8. The order relation "$<$" for the whole numbers.
9. The order relation "$\leqq$" for the whole numbers.
10. The subset of a set.
11. The union of two sets.
12. The empty set.
13. The Cartesian product of two sets.
14. Equality of ordered pairs.
15. A relation: (a) intuitively, (b) in terms of sets.
16. Range of a relation.
17. The "equals" relation for numbers.
18. The cardinal of a set.

Give examples of relations possessing the following properties:

19. Reflexive and transitive, but not symmetric.
20. Transitive, but not reflexive and not symmetric.
21. Symmetric and transitive, but not reflexive.
22. Single-valued.

REFERENCES

Banks, J. Houston, *Elements of Mathematics*, Allyn and Bacon, Boston, 1956, ch. II.

Hafstrom, John E., *Basic Concepts in Modern Mathematics*, Addison-Wesley, Reading, Mass., 1961, ch. II.

Halmos, Paul R., *Naive Set Theory*, D. Van Nostrand Co., Princeton, N.J., 1960.

Hamilton, Norman T. and Joseph Landin, *Set Theory, the Structure of Arithmetic*, Allyn and Bacon, Boston, 1961, ch. II.

Jones, Burton W., *Elementary Concepts of Mathematics*, The Macmillan Co., New York, 1947, ch. II.

Kelley, John L., *An Introduction to Modern Algebra*, D. Van Nostrand Co., Princeton, N.J., 1960.

Mueller, Francis J., *Arithmetic, Its Structure and Concepts*, Prentice-Hall, Englewood Cliffs, N.J., 1956, units 8 and 10.

Schaaf, William L., *Basic Concepts of Elementary Mathematics*, John Wiley and Sons, New York, 1960, pp. 97–117.

Swain, Robert L., *Understanding Arithmetic*, Rinehart and Co., New York, 1952, ch. III.

*
*
*

CHAPTER SIX

The System of Integers

6.1 INTRODUCTION

Historically the natural numbers were invented for the purpose of counting. The rational numbers (fractions) were introduced in connection with problems of measuring. The number zero was accepted as a number only after a long, slow struggle for recognition. So, also, for negative numbers. The irrational numbers were discovered quite recently, although the incommensurability of certain line segments was known at the time of the early Greek culture. Almost the same sequence of development is followed in the teaching of numbers in our present educational system. The numbers, when introduced in this sequence, are probably learned more efficiently than in any other order because it is easy to relate each new number concept to physical experiences. The concept of a half of something is learned long before $\frac{1}{2}$ is introduced as a number. By the time $\frac{1}{2}$ is introduced as a number it is easy to relate the fact that two halves of a cake are the same as a whole cake to the fact that $\frac{1}{2} + \frac{1}{2} = 1$. These analogies must be selected carefully. Thus to say two halves of something are equal to the whole has meaning only in certain contexts. Not many people would be willing to accept two halves of an automobile tire for a whole tire.

We depart from tradition and treat the negative numbers before we treat the fractions (the rational numbers). This should present no difficulties, for this is not a first course in arithmetic. It does allow us to present the various number systems in what seems to us a reasonable order. This approach permits us to emphasize the power and limitations of each system and to gain insight into the *structure* of the various number systems. The idea of the structure of various number systems is important in the understanding of the structure of mathematics. We hope, finally, to clarify the arithmetic processes in terms of the systems of numeration and the structure of the number systems.

6.2 THE SET OF INTEGERS

Recall that the *set* N of natural numbers is the "counting numbers," $1, 2, 3, \ldots$. The *set* W of whole numbers is the set $\{0, 1, 2, 3, 4, \ldots\}$. By the *system* of whole numbers we meant the set W, the two binary operations, $+$ and $\cdot$, and the rules governing the behavior of the numbers under the binary operations.

We point out that there is a subtle difference in the nature of the question, "How many?" and "What is?" This difference reflects the difference in the nature or character of a number as a "counting number" and as an element (number) in a number system. Thus 0 as a whole number is the cardinal of the empty set. As an element of a number system it plays a more conspicuous role.

"How many" relates to the cardinal of a set.

"What is" relates to an element in the number system.

Besides the question "How many?" we have, in the system of whole numbers, a system in which we can answer the following simple questions.

First, what is the number $2 + 3$? We write this

$$2 + 3 = ?$$

or

$$2 + 3 = n,\ n = ?$$

Second, "I am thinking of a number. If I add 3 to this number, I get 5. What is the number?" We write this

$$n + 3 = 5,\ n = ?$$

(We are essentially doing subtraction.)

There are, however, severe limitations to the system of whole numbers. Questions similar in form to the second question above need not have answers. For example, what number must be added to 5 to get 4? What number added to 3 is 0?

$$5 + ? = 4$$
$$3 + ? = 0.$$

In order to answer these simple questions and similar ones we define a new set, J, which we call the *integers*.

Let us say that

> $^-3$ is the number which when added to 3 gives 0 and is the only such number.
> $^-1$ is the number which when added to 1 gives 0 and is the only such number.
> $^-15$ is the number which when added to 15 gives 0 and is the only such number.

In general, if n is any number, ^-n is the number which when added to n gives 0 and is the only such number. The new number, ^-n, is called the *additive inverse* of n. Since the number n may be *any* element of J, the *additive inverse* of n is a more appropriate name than "negative n" (see problem 6, Exercise 6.3).

DEFINITION 6.2. The *set* J of integers will consist of the set N of natural numbers, zero, and for each n in N, the number ^-n, such that $n + {^-n} = 0$.

$$J = \{\ldots, {^-n}, \ldots, {^-4}, {^-3}, {^-2}, {^-1}, 0, 1, 2, 3, 4, \ldots, n, \ldots\}.$$

We will extend the binary operations of addition and multiplication to these new numbers and require that the Closure Laws, the Commutative Laws, the Associative Laws, and the Distributive Law be satisfied. The new system, consisting of the set J of integers, the binary operations defined on J and the laws governing these operations, will be called the *system of integers*.

6.3 PROPERTIES OF THE SET OF INTEGERS

Notice that the set N of natural numbers is a subset of the set J of integers. As integers, we will refer to the natural numbers as *positive integers*. The additive inverses of the positive integers will be called *negative integers*.

The Set J		
		The Set N
$\ldots {^-4}, {^-3}, {^-2}, {^-1},$	$0,$	$1, 2, 3, 4, 5, 6, \ldots$
Negative integers,	Zero,	Positive integers

When we say m is an integer, *only one* of the following statements must be true.

1. $m = 0$, or
2. m is positive, or
3. ^-m is positive.

For example: $0 = 0$; 1 is positive; $^-1$ is such that $^-(^-1)$ is positive; etc. That is, the *set of integers* is partitioned into three mutually disjoint sets, and any integer can belong to one and only one of these three sets. This is a statement of the *Trichotomy Law.*

6.3a Properties of the Positive Integers

Recall that the natural numbers are the *positive integers* when considered as a subset of the integers. But the natural numbers are closed under the binary operations of addition and multiplication. We restate the Closure Laws (1 and 2 below), for they will be useful later in establishing properties of the order relation.

1. The sum of two positive integers is a positive integer.
2. The product of two positive integers is a positive integer.
3. If m is an integer and $m \neq 0$, then either m is positive or ^-m is positive.

Exercise 6.3

1. Is 0 a positive number? Why?
2. Is $^-0$ a negative number?
3. Is $0 = {}^-0$? Show why.
4. If a is an integer, is $^-(^-a)$ positive? What is the meaning of $^-(^-a)$? What is it equal to? What is $^-(^-3)$? What is ^-m if $m = {}^-2$?
5. Show that $^-(^-m) = m$ for any integer m.
   (We shall use this freely in what follows and refer to this fact by the symbol (I-1).)
6. Is ^-m a negative integer if m is an integer?
7. What is $^-(m + n)$?
8. What is the additive inverse of $^-3$?
9. What is the additive inverse of ^-m?
10. What is the additive inverse of 0?

6.4 THE SYSTEM OF INTEGERS

The *set* of integers can be thought of as an enlarged set of numbers which contain the natural numbers and zero as proper subsets. When we speak of the *system of integers*, we mean the *set J* defined in Section 6.2 and binary operations, addition and multiplication, satisfying certain laws. We want addition of the integers to be an extension of the binary operation of addition of the natural numbers in the sense that when we think of the natural numbers as positive integers, addition of the positive integers should be consistent with the addition of natural numbers. The same is true for multiplication.

In the system of integers, which is an enlargement of the system of whole numbers, we require the binary operations to satisfy the same laws as for the whole numbers and one new law concerning the existence and uniqueness of the additive inverse of any element.

DEFINITION 6.4. By the *system of integers* we mean the set

$$J = \{\ldots, {}^-n, \ldots, {}^-4, {}^-3, {}^-2, {}^-1, 0, 1, 2, 3, 4, \ldots, n, \ldots\},$$

the binary operations, addition $(+)$ and multiplication $(\cdot)$, and the following laws.

Closure Laws

1. For m and n in J there is a uniquely determined sum, which we write $m + n$, in J.

2. For m and n in J there is a uniquely determined product, which we write $m \cdot n$, in J.

Associative Laws. For m, n, and k in J,

3. $m + (n + k) = (m + n) + k$.
4. $m \cdot (n \cdot k) = (m \cdot n) \cdot k$.

Commutative Laws. For m and n in J,

5. $m + n = n + m$.
6. $m \cdot n = n \cdot m$.

Distributive Law. For m, n, and k in J,

7. $m \cdot (n + k) = m \cdot n + m \cdot k$.

Identities

8. There is a unique element 0 such that for any m in J, $m + 0 = 0 + m = m$.

9. There is a unique element 1 such that for any m in J, $1 \cdot m = m \cdot 1 = m$.

Additive Inverses

10. For each m in J there is a unique element ${}^-m$ in J such that $m + {}^-m = {}^-m + m = 0$, where 0 is the additive identity.

6.4a Addition of Integers

The use of the above laws enables us to extend the binary operation of addition to the set of integers, using what we already know about addition in the set of whole numbers.

The positive integers are the natural numbers renamed so that addition of the positive integers is addition of the natural numbers.

To extend the binary operation of addition to the negative integers we make use of our knowledge of the addition of positive integers. If m and n are any two integers, we assert that

$$^{-}m + {}^{-}n = {}^{-}(m + n). \qquad \text{(A-1)}$$

This assertion states that the binary operation, addition, assigns to the ordered pair $(^{-}m, {}^{-}n)$ the number we write as $(^{-}m + {}^{-}n)$, which has another name, $^{-}(m + n)$. This "other name" for the number is the one that enables us to find the sum in terms of addition of positive integers.

We shall indicate the procedure for establishing this assertion by means of an example, using positive integers for m and n. The proof, in general, will be left as an exercise for the reader.

Example 1

We wish to show that $(^{-}2 + {}^{-}3) = {}^{-}(2 + 3)$.

$$
\begin{aligned}
^{-}(2 + 3) + (2 + 3) &= 0 \text{ by the property of additive inverses.} \\
(^{-}2 + {}^{-}3) + (2 + 3) &= (^{-}2 + {}^{-}3) + (3 + 2) && \text{Why?} \\
&= {}^{-}2 + (^{-}3 + 3) + 2 && \text{Why?} \\
&= {}^{-}2 + 0 + 2 && \text{Why?} \\
&= {}^{-}2 + 2 && \text{Why?} \\
&= 0 && \text{Why?}
\end{aligned}
$$

We have

$$^{-}(2 + 3) + (2 + 3) = 0$$

and

$$(^{-}2 + {}^{-}3) + (2 + 3) = 0.$$

Since the additive inverse of any number, in this case $(2 + 3)$, must be unique (one and only one), we conclude that

$$(^{-}2 + {}^{-}3) = {}^{-}(2 + 3).$$

To extend the binary operation of addition to the addition of a negative integer and a positive integer, using properties already developed, we assert that if m and n are integers, $(^{-}m + n)$ is the number which when added to m gives n.

This assertion states that the binary operation, addition, assigns to the ordered pair $(^{-}m, n)$ the number we write as $(^{-}m + n)$. It is the solution to the equation

$$m + ? = n.$$

We shall indicate the procedure for establishing this assertion and actually finding a new name for the number $(^{-}m + n)$ by several examples. For this purpose, recall the simple equation

$$3 + x = 7, \quad x = ?$$

What number must be added to 3 to get 7?

Let us proceed to "solve" this equation. Adding the additive inverse of 3 to each side of the equation we get

$$
\begin{aligned}
{}^{-}3 + (3 + x) &= 7 + {}^{-}3 \\
({}^{-}3 + 3) + x &= (7 + {}^{-}3) && \text{Why?} \\
0 + x &= (7 + {}^{-}3) && \text{Why?} \\
x &= (7 + {}^{-}3) && \text{Why?}
\end{aligned}
$$

But from the table of elementary facts we know that $4 + 3 = 7$. Then by substitution we have

$$
\begin{aligned}
x &= (4 + 3) + {}^{-}3 \\
&= 4 + (3 + {}^{-}3) && \text{Why?} \\
&= 4 + 0 && \text{Why?} \\
&= 4 && \text{Why?}
\end{aligned}
$$

This tells us that $(7 + {}^{-}3)$ is just another name for 4, or that $(7 + {}^{-}3) = 4$.

By convention we write this as $(7 - 3)$ instead of $(7 + {}^{-}3)$.

This may seem like an unnecessarily complicated way of solving a very simple problem. We admit that it may seem so, but the object of this example is to illustrate the role of the basic laws in understanding arithmetic. The following problem is essentially the same as the last problem but one which is usually avoided at primary and intermediate levels because of the fact that the result is a negative integer.

$$9 + x = 4, \quad x = ?$$

What number added to 9 gives 4?

Again, we proceed by "solving" this equation.

$$
\begin{aligned}
9 + x &= 4 \\
{}^{-}9 + (9 + x) &= 4 + {}^{-}9 && \text{Why?} \\
({}^{-}9 + 9) + x &= 4 + {}^{-}9 && \text{Why?} \\
0 + x &= 4 + {}^{-}(4 + 5) && \text{Why?} \\
x &= 4 + ({}^{-}4 + {}^{-}5) && \text{Why?} \\
x &= (4 + {}^{-}4) + {}^{-}5 && \text{Why?} \\
x &= 0 + {}^{-}5 && \text{Why?} \\
x &= {}^{-}5 && \text{Why?}
\end{aligned}
$$

It is essential to see $(7 - 3)$, that is, $(7 + {}^{-}3)$, is the number which when added to 3 gives 7. Also, $(11 - 5)$, which is $(11 + {}^{-}5)$, is the number which when added to 5 gives 11.

These remarks lead naturally to the generalization, $(n - m)$ is that number which when added to m gives n.

$$(n - m) + m = n.$$

Furthermore, since

$$m + (^-m + n) = n,$$

then

$$(^-m + n) = (n + ^-m) = n - m. \qquad \text{(A-2)}$$

This expression may not have meaning in the system of whole numbers because $n - m$ may not be a whole number. In elementary arithmetic $n - m$ is usually interpreted as the *difference* of n and m or as m *subtracted* from n. "Subtraction" as a binary operation is neither associative nor commutative (see Sections 5.6c, 5.6d).

To summarize this section on the addition of integers, let us consider several numerical examples.

Example 2

(a) $^-5 + ^-9 = ^-(5 + 9) = ^-14$
(b) $^-5 + 9 = ^-5 + (5 + 4) = (^-5 + 5) + 4 = 0 + 4 = 4$
(c) $5 + ^-9 = 5 + ^-(5 + 4) = 5 + (^-5 + ^-4) = (5 + ^-5) + ^-4$
$= 0 + ^-4 = ^-4$

Example 3

(a) $^-6 + ^-15 = ^-(6 + 15) = ^-21$
(b) $^-6 + 15 = ^-6 + (6 + 9) = (^-6 + 6) + 9 = 0 + 9 = 9$
(c) $6 + ^-15 = 6 + ^-(6 + 9) = 6 + (^-6 + ^-9) = (6 + ^-6) + ^-9$
$= 0 + ^-9 = ^-9$

Exercise 6.4a

1. Add $9 + ^-3$, showing and justifying each step.
2. Add $^-7 + 4$, showing and justifying each step.
3. Rewrite the problems of Examples 2 and 3, justifying each step.
4. Show that $(^-m + ^-n) = ^-(m + n)$ for any integers m and n.
5. Write the additive inverses of each of the following:

(a) 12	(b) 2	(c) $^-3$	(d) $^-1$
(e) 0	(f) a	(g) ^-a	(h) $2 + a$
(i) $^-2 + a$	(j) $^-a + 2$	(k) $^-3 + 3$	(l) $^-5 + 3$
(m) $^-(a + b) + 2$	(n) $^-2 + (a + b)$	(o) $^-a + b + 3$	(p) $^-3 + ^-2$

6. Add

(a) $^-3 + ^-5$	(b) $^-2 + ^-1 + ^-6$
(c) $a + ^-3 + ^-1$	(d) $^-13 + ^-8$
(e) $^-18 + 3 + ^-7$	(f) $(18 + ^-3) + ^-7$
(g) $18 + (^-3 + ^-7)$	(h) $^-9 + ^-13$

7. Solve the following equations in detail and justify each step

(a) $3 + n = 10$	(b) $n + 5 = 1$
(c) $a + x = b$	(d) $x + a = b$

8. Show that $17 - 12$ is another name for 5.
9. Show that $372 - 176$ is another name for 196.

10. We break a yardstick into two pieces. If one piece is n in. long, how long is the other piece?
11. Where would you break the yardstick if the longer piece is 3 times the length of the shorter piece?
12. Is subtraction as an operation commutative. Use a numerical example to justify your answer?
13. Is subtraction as an operation associative? Use a numerical example to justify your answer.
14. Use the properties of the System of Integers (see Definition 6.4) to prove that $m \cdot 0 = 0 \cdot m = 0$ for any integer m.

6.4b Multiplication of Integers

The set of positive integers is the same as the set of natural numbers. Thus multiplication of the positive integers will be the same as multiplication of the natural numbers.

In order to extend the operation of multiplication to the integers, we show that, for m and n integers

$$({}^{-}m)(n) = {}^{-}(m \cdot n). \qquad \text{(M-1)}$$

Before attempting the general case, let us look at a numerical example. We shall use the fact that a number can have only one additive inverse to show that $({}^{-}4)(3) = {}^{-}12$.

Example 1

$$^{-}12 + 12 = 0 \qquad \text{Why?}$$
$$^{-}(4 \cdot 3) + (4 \cdot 3) = 0 \qquad \text{Why?}$$

Thus $^{-}(4 \cdot 3)$ is the additive inverse of $(4 \cdot 3)$.

But $$({}^{-}4)(3) + (4)(3) = ({}^{-}4 + 4)3 \qquad \text{Why?}$$
$$({}^{-}4 + 4)3 = 0 \cdot 3 = 0 \qquad \text{Why?}$$

Hence $({}^{-}4)(3)$ is also an additive inverse of $(4 \cdot 3)$. But the additive inverse of any number is unique. Hence $({}^{-}4)(3) = {}^{-}(4 \cdot 3) = {}^{-}12$.

Now let us show, in general, that $({}^{-}m)(n) = {}^{-}(m \cdot n)$.

$^{-}(m \cdot n) + (m \cdot n) = 0$ by the properties of the additive inverse.

$({}^{-}m)(n) + (m)(n) = ({}^{-}m + m)n$ by the Distributive Law.

$({}^{-}m + m)n = 0 \cdot n = 0$ by the properties of the additive inverse and zero. (See problem 14, Exercise 6.4a.)

We have shown that $^{-}(m \cdot n) + (m \cdot n) = 0$. We have also shown that $({}^{-}m)(n) + (m \cdot n) = 0$. But $(m \cdot n)$ has only one additive inverse, so $({}^{-}m)(n) = {}^{-}(m \cdot n)$.

In particular, note that we have now shown how to find the product of a positive integer and a negative integer in terms of the product of two positive integers.

Similarly, for any integers m and n,

$$(m)(^-n) = ^-(m \cdot n).$$

The proof of this will be left as an exercise for the reader.

The above statements may be summarized by saying that the binary operation of multiplication assigns to any ordered pair which consists of an integer and the additive inverse of an integer, the additive inverse of the product of the integers. The statement, "A negative number times a positive number is a negative number," is seen to be a simple consequence of the basic laws.

We now consider the product of the additive inverses of any two integers. We will show that

$$(^-m)(^-n) = m \cdot n. \qquad \text{(M-2)}$$

To do this we begin with the expression

$$(^-m)(^-n) + (^-m)(n) + (m)(n)$$

and show that it is simultaneously equal to $(^-m)(^-n)$ and $(m)(n)$, and the result follows from the transitivity of equals.

$(^-m)(^-n) + (^-m)(n) + (m)(n) =$	$(^-m)(^-n) + (^-m)(n) + (m)(n) =$
$(^-m)(^-n) + [(^-m)(n) + (m)(n)] =$	$[(^-m)(^-n) + (^-m)(n)] + (m)(n) =$
$(^-m)(^-n) + (^-m + m)(n) =$	$(^-m)(^-n + n) + (m)(n) =$
$(^-m)(^-n) + 0 \cdot n =$	$(^-m)(0) + (m)(n) =$
$(^-m)(^-n) + 0 =$	$0 + (m)(n) =$
$(^-m)(^-n)$	$(m)(n)$

Hence $(^-m)(^-n) = m \cdot n$. This implies the familiar rule, "A negative number times a negative number is a positive number." We have demonstrated this, also, to be a fact which is a consequence of the basic laws.

Exercise 6.4b

Establish the following equalities, using the properties of the system of integers, I-1, A-1, A-2, M-1, M-2, and properties of zero.

1. $^-(1 \cdot 1) = ^-1$.

e.g., $^-(1 \cdot 1) = (^-1)(1)$ by M-1

$= ^-1$ by Mult. identity

2. $(^-1)(^-1) = 1$.

3. $(^-2)(^-3) = (2)(3)$.

4. $(^-5)(0) = 0$.

5. $(^-2)(^-3)(^-4) = ^-24$.

6. $(^-2)(^-3 + ^-4) = 14$, in two ways.
7. $(^-3)(^-4 + ^-5) = 27$.
8. $8(7 - 3) = 32$, in two ways.
9. $8(3 - 7) = {}^-32$, in two ways.
10. $^-(7 - 3) = (3 - 7)$.
11. $^-(m - n) = (n - m)$.
12. $^-(^-3) = 3$.
13. $(^-2)(3) = {}^-(2 \cdot 3)$.
14. $(m)(^-n) = {}^-(m \cdot n)$.
15. $(^-n)(0) = 0$.

6.5 THE CANCELLATION LAWS

We saw earlier that $1 \cdot 0 = 0$. Using this, we showed that $2 \cdot 0 = 0$. Recall how we did this.

$$\begin{aligned} 2 \cdot 0 &= (1 + 1) \cdot 0 && \text{Why?} \\ &= 1 \cdot 0 + 1 \cdot 0 && \text{Why?} \\ &= 0 + 0 && \text{Why?} \\ &= 0 && \text{Why?} \end{aligned}$$

We have seen that $n \cdot 0 = 0$ in general. (See problem 14, Exercise 6.4a.) This is somewhat surprising to most people. In fact, most people confuse the number 0 with the meaning of the word "nothing." We repeat again that 0 is not nothing, *0 is a number*, a very important and useful number. We used the number 0 to define the additive inverses. We will use this number again when we speak about *order* in the integers. For the present we consider another seemingly obvious arithmetical statement involving 0.

The system of integers has no zero divisors. We mean by this that the product of two integers is zero if and only if one of the factors is zero, that is, $a \cdot b = 0$ if and only if either $a = 0$ or $b = 0$. (The "or" here is the inclusive or.) (See problem 7, Exercise 7.10a.) This statement would undoubtedly mean more if one were familiar with a mathematical system where the product of two nonzero elements is zero. We will consider such systems later (see Section 6.14b). For the present we consider the following examples:

$$2 \cdot 0 = 3 \cdot 0 \text{ because both } 2 \cdot 0 = 0 \text{ and } 3 \cdot 0 = 0.$$

In general,

$$x \cdot 0 = y \cdot 0.$$

Now consider the following:

$$x \cdot 2 = y \cdot 2.$$

Adding the additive inverse of $y \cdot 2$ to both sides of the equation we get

$$x \cdot 2 + {}^{-}(y \cdot 2) = y \cdot 2 + {}^{-}(y \cdot 2)$$
$$= 0.$$

Then $(x + {}^{-}y) \cdot 2 = 0$ by the Distributive Law.

Notice that we are looking at the product of two terms, one being $(x + {}^{-}y)$ and the other, 2. Using the fact that the product of two terms is 0 if and only if one of the factors is 0, we see that, since 2 is not 0, $(x + {}^{-}y)$ must be 0, that is,

$$(x + {}^{-}y) = 0.$$

Then
$$(x + {}^{-}y) + y = 0 + y$$
$$x + ({}^{-}y + y) = y \qquad \text{Why?}$$
$$x + 0 = y \qquad \text{Why?}$$
$$x = y \qquad \text{Why?}$$

The above is an example of the *Cancellation Law for Multiplication.*

If a is an integer and $a \cdot x = a \cdot y$, can we conclude that $x = y$? We have seen that if $a = 0$, we cannot. If $a \neq 0$ (a is not 0), then we can say that $x = y$.

The Cancellation Law for Multiplication. If $a \neq 0$ and $a \cdot x = a \cdot y$, then $x = y$.

We are not "dividing" by a. This is a subtle point which will be explained further when we discuss the system of rational numbers.

There is also a *Cancellation Law for Addition.* However, this law is based on the definition of the additive inverses and does not need conditions on the terms.

Cancellation Law for Addition. If $a + x = a + y$, then $x = y$.

The Cancellation Law for Addition can be proved as follows:

$$a + x = a + y \qquad \text{Hypothesis}$$
$${}^{-}a + (a + x) = {}^{-}a + (a + y) \qquad \text{Why?}$$
$$({}^{-}a + a) + x = ({}^{-}a + a) + y \qquad \text{Why?}$$
$$0 + x = 0 + y \qquad \text{Why?}$$
$$x = y \qquad \text{Why?}$$

Exercise 6.5

1. If $(x - 3)(x - 7) = 0$, what can you say about x? Why? (This type of argument is used in solving quadratic equations by factoring.)

2. If $x + 3 = y + 3$, what can you say about x? Why?

3. If $y = \dfrac{6}{x - 1}$, what must you say about x? Why?

4. Name the law that is exemplified by each of the following:

(a) $xy = yx$
(b) $(x + y) + z = x + (y + z)$

(c) $xy + xz = x(y + z)$
(d) $x + a = a + x$
(e) $(2a)b = 2(ab)$
(f) $a + 0 = a$
(g) $a = 1 \cdot a$
(h) $0 = a + {}^{-}a$
(i) $({}^{-}a)(b + {}^{-}b) = ({}^{-}a)(b) + ({}^{-}a)({}^{-}b)$

5. State the reason that justifies each of the following steps in proving that $({}^{-}a)({}^{-}b) = (a)(b)$:

$$\begin{aligned} (a)(b) + 0 &= (a)(b) \\ ({}^{-}a)(b) + ({}^{-}a)({}^{-}b) &= 0 \\ (a)(b) + [({}^{-}a)(b) + ({}^{-}a)({}^{-}b)] &= (a)(b) \\ [(a)(b) + ({}^{-}a)(b)] + ({}^{-}a)({}^{-}b) &= (a)(b) \\ (a + {}^{-}a)b + ({}^{-}a)({}^{-}b) &= (a)(b) \\ (0)(b) + ({}^{-}a)({}^{-}b) &= (a)(b) \\ 0 + ({}^{-}a)({}^{-}b) &= (a)(b) \\ ({}^{-}a)({}^{-}b) &= (a)(b) \end{aligned}$$

6. What is meant by ${}^{-}({}^{-}a)$?
7. What is ${}^{-}({}^{-}a)$? Can you prove this?
8. If m is an integer, is ${}^{-}m$ a negative number?
9. If m is an integer, is ${}^{-}(m^2)$ a negative number?
10. If m and n are integers, is $({}^{-}m)({}^{-}n)$ a positive integer?
11. Justify each step in the proof of the Cancellation Law for Addition.
12. What do we mean by zero divisors?
13. State the Cancellation Law for Multiplication of integers.

6.6 PRIME NUMBERS AND COMPOSITE NUMBERS

We introduced the divisibility concept for the natural numbers earlier. Thus 12 is divisible by 3, 72 is divisible by 12, and 72 is also divisible by 9 and 8. We extend this concept to the integers.

DEFINITION 6.6a. An integer n is divisible by an integer m, $m \neq 0$, if there is an integer k such that $n = m \cdot k$.

DEFINITION 6.6b. We say that m is a *divisor* of n if n is divisible by m.

It is obvious that 1 divides n and also n divides n, since $n = n \cdot 1$.

DEFINITION 6.6c. We say that m is a *proper divisor* of n if m is a divisor of n and $m \neq 1$, $m \neq -1$, $m \neq n$, and $m \neq -n$. In this case m is called a *proper factor* of n.

(*Note:* Here and in what follows we use the traditional $-n$ for the additive inverse of n.)

Thus 2 is a proper divisor of 18. 9 is also a proper divisor of 18, and 2 and 9 are factors of 18.

Note that we cannot say that 0 divides any number. Suppose we ask, "Does 0 divide 2?" If so, we should be able to write 2 as some multiple of 0. But 0 times any number is 0, not 2. On the other hand, every nonzero integer divides 0, since $0 = 0 \cdot n$.

Now let us consider the set of positive integers in terms of the divisibility concept.

$$\{1, 2, 3, 4, 5, 6, 7, 8, 9, 10, 11, 12, 13, 14, \ldots\}.$$

Notice that some can be factored: $4 = 2 \cdot 2$; $6 = 2 \cdot 3$; $8 = 2 \cdot 2 \cdot 2$; $9 = 3 \cdot 3$; and so forth. Others cannot be factored. Those numbers that have no proper factors are called *prime numbers*.

DEFINITION 6.6d. An integer, p, $p > 1$, is a *prime* if it has no proper divisors.

The only divisors of a prime, p, are 1, -1, p, and $-p$.

DEFINITION 6.6e. A positive integer different from 1 which is not a prime is called a *composite*.

The negative integers may be classified in a similar manner by considering the negative integer $(-n)$, $n \neq 1$, as $(-1)(n)$ and examining the positive integer n.

Exercise 6.6

1. List all the primes less than 50.
2. List *all* the positive divisors of 36. The *prime* divisors.
3. List *all* the positive divisors of 52. The *prime* divisors.
4. List *all* the positive divisors of 14. The *prime* divisors.
5. List *all* the positive divisors of 39. The *prime* divisors.
6. Find all primes less than 100 by first throwing away multiples of 2, then multiples of 3, then multiples of 5, and so on. (The Sieve of Eratosthenes, see Swain, p. 114.)
7. How can you tell whether a number is divisible by 2? by 3? by 4? by 5? by 9?
8. List the common divisors of 50 and 52, of 36 and 39, of 39 and 52.
9. Write the following numbers as products of prime factors: (a) 72, (b) 356, (c) 512, (d) 1000.
10. Is 1 divisible by 0? Why? Is 0 divisible by 1? Why?

6.7 PRIME FACTORIZATION

The set of positive integers greater than 1 is partitioned into two disjoint sets, the set consisting of the primes and the set consisting of the composites. The primes are, in a sense, the building blocks of the composites as indicated in the next statement.

The Fundamental Theorem of Arithmetic

Any integer, different from 0 and ± 1, can be written as a product of primes and ± 1 in one and only one way, except possibly for the order in which the factors occur.

Example 1

Consider the integer 72. We can think of this as $9 \cdot 8$; then factoring further as $3 \cdot 3 \cdot 8 = 3 \cdot 3 \cdot 2 \cdot 4 = 3 \cdot 3 \cdot 2 \cdot 2 \cdot 2 = 3^2 \cdot 2^3$. On the other hand, we could think as follows: $72 = 6 \cdot 12 = 2 \cdot 3 \cdot 12 = 2 \cdot 3 \cdot 3 \cdot 4 = 2 \cdot 3 \cdot 3 \cdot 2 \cdot 2 = 2 \cdot 2 \cdot 2 \cdot 3 \cdot 3 = 2^3 \cdot 3^2$. We have looked at the factorization of 72 into prime factors in two different ways but have arrived at a unique factorization except for order of the factors.

The Fundamental Theorem of Arithmetic can be proved by using some of the elementary notions of number theory and mathematical induction. For our purposes we shall accept it as a fundamental principle.

The problem of finding the prime factors of a number is, in general, tedious. For large numbers the problem has been turned over to modern high-speed computers. For small numbers there are a few divisibility facts which enable one to tell by inspection whether a given number is divisible by the first few small numbers. We present these, some with proof and some without, to assist you in prime factorization of numbers.

Divisibility by 2. A number is divisible by 2 if and only if the units digit of its numeral is even. The reason for this is that every power of 10 except 10^0 is divisible by 2. Hence the number is divisible by 2 if and only if the units digit of its numeral is divisible by 2.

Divisibility by 3. A number is divisible by 3 if and only if the sum of the digits of its numeral is divisible by 3. We make this seem reasonable by citing an example.

$$\begin{aligned} 378 &= 3 \cdot 10^2 + 7 \cdot 10 + 8 \\ &= 3 \cdot 100 + 7 \cdot 10 + 8 \\ &= 3(99 + 1) + 7(9 + 1) + 8 \\ &= 3 \cdot 99 + 3 \cdot 1 + 7 \cdot 9 + 7 \cdot 1 + 8 \\ &= (3 \cdot 99 + 7 \cdot 9) + (3 + 7 + 8) \\ &= (3 \cdot 33 + 7 \cdot 3)3 + (3 + 7 + 8) \end{aligned}$$

By inspection we see that 3 divides the first term on the right in the last equation. If it also divides the second term $(3 + 7 + 8)$, then it must divide 378. Hence, if 3 divides $(3 + 7 + 8)$, 3 divides 378. Furthermore, if 3 divides 378, it must divide $(3 + 7 + 8)$. This argument is based on the Distributive Law and the meaning of "divides."

Divisibility by 4. A number is divisible by 4 if and only if the last two digits of its numeral (tens, units) represent a number that is divisible by 4. The reason for this is that 10^2 and higher powers of ten are divisible by 4.

Divisibility by 5. A number is divisible by 5 if and only if the units digit of its numeral is 0 or 5.

Divisibility by 6. A number is divisible by 6 if and only if it is divisible by 2 *and* by 3.

Divisibility by 8. A number is divisible by 8 if and only if the last three digits of its numeral (hundreds, tens, units) represent a number that is divisible by 8. The reason for this is that 10^3 and higher powers of 10 are divisible by 8.

Divisibility by 9. A number is divisible by 9 if and only if the sum of the digits of its numeral is divisible by 9. We make this seem reasonable by citing an example.

$$\begin{aligned}
288 &= 2\cdot 10^2 + 8\cdot 10 + 8 \\
&= 2(100) + 8(10) + 8 \\
&= 2(99 + 1) + 8(9 + 1) + 8 \\
&= 2\cdot 99 + 2\cdot 1 + 8\cdot 9 + 8\cdot 1 + 8 \\
&= (2\cdot 99 + 8\cdot 9) + (2 + 8 + 8) \\
&= (2\cdot 11 + 8\cdot 1)9 + (2 + 8 + 8)
\end{aligned}$$

By inspection we see that 9 divides the first term on the right side in the last equation. If it also divides the second term on the right, $(2 + 8 + 8)$, it must divide 288. Hence if 9 divides $(2 + 8 + 8)$, 9 divides 288. Also, if 9 divides 288, it must divide $(2 + 8 + 8)$. This argument is based on the Distributive Law and the meaning of "divides".

Exercise 6.7

1. List all the positive divisors of 72.
2. List the prime numbers less than 100.
3. Express each of the following as a product of prime factors: (a) 84, (b) 198, (c) 975, (d) 144, (e) 4455.

An integer d is a common divisor of a set of integers if it is a divisor of each of them.

4. List all common divisors of 198 and 144.
5. List all common divisors of 84, 198, and 405.
6. Write 21,489 as a product of prime factors.
7. Write 4408 as a product of prime factors.
8. Write the common divisors of 4408 and 72.

9. Test the following for divisibility by 2, 3, 4, 5, 6, 7, 8, 9, 10: (a) 627,433, (b) 2,288,817, (c) 324,244, (d) 625,530.

10. To preface this exercise we remark that remembering the multiplication table for 9 seems to be difficult for some people. Consider the following:

$$9 \times 4 = ? \quad 10 - 4 = \mathbf{6},\ 9 - 6 = \mathbf{3}, \text{ hence } 9 \times 4 = 36.$$
$$9 \times 8 = ? \quad 10 - 8 = \mathbf{2},\ 9 - 2 = \mathbf{7}, \text{ hence } 9 \times 8 = 72.$$
$$9 \times 5 = ? \quad 10 - 5 = \mathbf{5},\ 9 - 5 = \mathbf{4}, \text{ hence } 9 \times 5 = 45.$$

(a) Why does this give the correct answer?
(b) Can you extend this idea to 9 times any digit?

6.8 THE DIVISION ALGORITHM

The "divides" relation holds only between certain ordered pairs of integers. Even so, we can say something about *any* given pair. For example, given the integers 16 and 7, we can express 16 as a multiple of 7 plus a remainder of 2.

$$16 = 7 \cdot 2 + 2.$$

This very obvious arithmetical statement illustrates the division algorithm.

The Division Algorithm. If m and n are any two integers, such that n is greater than 0, then there is a unique pair of integers, q and r, such that

$$m = n \cdot q + r$$

where r is less than n and greater than or equal to 0. If $r = 0$, then n divides m.

The division algorithm is a statement deducible from other basic assumptions; however, we accept it here as a fundamental principle that is intuitively plausible.

The division algorithm is a comparative statement about the pair of integers, m and n. If we think of n as some fixed positive integer (say 3), then the division algorithm says that any integer, m, can be written as a multiple of 3 with only 0, 1, or 2 as possible remainders. If we let $n = 7$, the remainders of integers when divided by 7 are 0, 1, 2, 3, 4, 5, 6. We shall refer to this again. For the present we shall see how it can be applied in finding the greatest common divisor and the least common multiple of a pair of integers.

6.9 THE GREATEST COMMON DIVISOR

In the later sections of this book we will need to "reduce" fractions. We may find it convenient to write $\frac{3}{4}$ instead of $\frac{39}{52}$. The idea of "reducing" involves the greatest common divisor.

DEFINITION 6.9a. A positive integer, d, is the *greatest common divisor* of the integers a and b if d is a common divisor of a and b and is a multiple of every other common divisor. (See problem 4, Exercise 3.12.)

The abbreviation "g.c.d." will designate greatest common divisor.

Example 1

$$\text{g.c.d. } (36, 60) = 12$$
$$\text{g.c.d. } (-10, 35) = 5$$
$$\text{g.c.d. } (6, 12) = 6$$
$$\text{g.c.d. } (5, 7) = 1$$

DEFINITION 6.9b. If g.c.d. $(a, b) = 1$, we say a and b are *relatively prime.*

6.9a The G.C.D. Using Prime Factorization

The problem of finding the g.c.d. of two integers is simple when the integers are small. This can usually be done by inspection. There are systematic procedures for determining the g.c.d. of two integers. We shall examine two methods. We illustrate the first method with numerical examples.

Example 2

We wish to find the g.c.d. (6, 15). Factoring, we have

$$6 = 2 \cdot 3,$$

and

$$15 = 3 \cdot 5.$$

We note that 3 is a divisor both of 6 and of 15 and is the only positive common divisor other than 1. Thus, g.c.d. $(6, 15) = 3$.

Example 3

We wish to find the g.c.d. (72, 90). Factoring, we have

$$72 = 2 \cdot 2 \cdot 2 \cdot 3 \cdot 3 = 2^3 \cdot 3^2,$$

and

$$90 = 2 \cdot 3 \cdot 3 \cdot 5 = 2 \cdot 3^2 \cdot 5.$$

The only power of the prime 2 which divides both 72 and 90 is 2^1. The highest power of the prime 3 which divides both 72 and 90 is 3^2. We can write these numbers as

$$72 = (2 \cdot 3^2) \cdot 2^2$$

and

$$90 = (2 \cdot 3^2) \cdot 5,$$

which shows that $(2 \cdot 3^2)$ is a common divisor of 72 and 90. It is the greatest common divisor of 72 and 90. It is the product of the highest powers of the primes *common to both* numbers.

In general, the g.c.d. of two numbers, m and n, is the product of the highest powers of the primes *common to* the factorizations of *both* m and n.

Exercise 6.9a

1. Find the g.c.d. of 84 and 198. Of 36 and 54.
2. Find the g.c.d. of 975 and 144. Of 17 and 51.
3. Find the g.c.d. of -84 and 144. Of -96 and 336.
4. Find the g.c.d. of 198 and 975.
5. Find the g.c.d. of -198 and -144.
6. Find the g.c.d. of 84, 198, and 144.
7. Find the g.c.d. of 144, 198, and 975.
8. 11 divides $(10 + 1)$, $(10^2 - 1)$, $(10^3 + 1)$, $(10^4 - 1)$, etc. Using a procedure similar to the check for divisibility by 9, determine a check for divisibility by 11.
9. If p is a prime and n is any integer, what is the g.c.d. (p, n)?

6.9b The G.C.D. Using the Division Algorithm

The second method of finding the g.c.d. of two integers involves the division algorithm. Suppose we are interested in finding the g.c.d. of 58 and 16. The division algorithm allows us to write

$$58 = 16 \cdot 3 + 10, \quad \text{where } 0 \leqq 10 < 16.$$

Notice that any number that divides 58 and 16 must also divide 10 because we can write

$$10 = 58 - 16 \cdot 3.$$

In particular, the g.c.d. of 58 and 16 must divide 10. This is a consequence of the Distributive Law and the meaning of "divides." This implies that this g.c.d.—let us call it d—is a common divisor of 16 and 10. Further, it must be the greatest common divisor of 16 and 10 because if there were another common divisor greater than d, this divisor would also have to divide 58 and d would not be the g.c.d. of 58 and 16. Furthermore, any number which divides 16 and 10 must divide 58 so

$$\text{g.c.d. } (58, 16) = \text{g.c.d. } (16, 10).$$

Now we have reduced our problem to that of finding the g.c.d. of 16 and 10. Applying the division algorithm again, we have

$$16 = 10 \cdot 1 + 6.$$

Again, any number that divides 16 and 10 must also divide 6 because we have

$$6 = 16 - 10.$$

In particular, the g.c.d. of 16 and 10 must divide 6. Also, any number which divides 10 and 6 must divide 16, so

$$\text{g.c.d. } (16, 10) = \text{g.c.d. } (10, 6).$$

By using the transitivity of equals we have reduced the problem to that of finding the g.c.d. of 10 and 6. Applying the division algorithm and reasoning as before, we have

$$10 = 6 \cdot 1 + 4,$$

and

$$6 = 4 \cdot 1 + \mathit{2},$$

and

$$4 = \mathit{2} \cdot 2.$$

The last statement identifies d for us. It says that g.c.d. $(4, 2) = 2$. Following back up the chain of equations, we have $2|2$ and $2|4$, so $2|6$; $2|4$ and $2|6$, so $2|10$; $2|6$ and $2|10$, so $2|16$; $2|10$ and $2|16$, so $2|58$; $2|16$ and $2|58$, and it has been identified as the g.c.d. at each step; hence g.c.d. $(58, 16) = 2$.

Example 1

Find the g.c.d. (84, 198):

$$\begin{aligned} 198 &= 84 \cdot 2 + 30 \qquad & \text{g.c.d. } (198, 84) &= \text{g.c.d. } (84, 30) \\ 84 &= 30 \cdot 2 + 24 & \text{g.c.d. } (84, 30) &= \text{g.c.d. } (30, 24) \\ 30 &= 24 \cdot 1 + \mathit{6} & \text{g.c.d. } (30, 24) &= \text{g.c.d. } (24, 6) \\ 24 &= \mathit{6} \cdot 4 & \text{g.c.d. } (24, 6) &= 6. \end{aligned}$$

Hence 6 is the g.c.d. (84, 198).

Example 2

Find the g.c.d. (198, 144):

$$\begin{aligned} 198 &= 144 \cdot 1 + 54 \qquad & \text{g.c.d. } (198, 144) &= \text{g.c.d. } (144, 54) \\ 144 &= 54 \cdot 2 + 36 & \text{g.c.d. } (144, 54) &= \text{g.c.d. } (54, 36) \\ 54 &= 36 \cdot 1 + \mathit{18} & \text{g.c.d. } (54, 36) &= \text{g.c.d. } (36, 18) \\ 36 &= \mathit{18} \cdot 2 & \text{g.c.d. } (36, 18) &= 18. \end{aligned}$$

Hence g.c.d. $(198, 144) = 18$.

The work for finding the g.c.d. by the division algorithm may be arranged as follows:

We want the g.c.d. (84, 198).

```
      2
84/ 198                    198 = 84·2 + 30
    168   2
    30/ 84                  84 = 30·2 + 24
        60   1
        24/ 30              30 = 24·1 + 6
            24   4
             6/ 24          24 = 6·4
g.c.d. (84, 198)—↑
```

This procedure for finding the g.c.d. is called the *Euclidean algorithm*. The greatest common divisor of three or more numbers, say a, b, and c, can be found by pairing. First find g.c.d. $(a, b) = d$; then g.c.d. $(d, c) = g$, then g.c.d. $(a, b, c) = g$ (see problem 3c, Exercise 6.9b).

Example 3

Find the g.c.d. (12, 18, 33):

$$\text{g.c.d. } (12, 18) = 6$$
$$\text{g.c.d. } (6, 33) = 3$$

Hence g.c.d. (12, 18, 33) = 3.

Exercise 6.9b

1. Find the g.c.d. of the following sets of numbers by the prime factorization method:

   (a) 84, 198 (b) 252, 144
   (c) 36, 54 (d) 12, 30, 42

2. Find the g.c.d. of the following sets of numbers by the Euclidean algorithm:

   (a) 14, 198 (b) 210, 126
   (c) 735, 858 (d) 84, 210, 126

3. We define the binary operation $\odot$ on the set J of integers as follows. For integers m and n

$$m \odot n = \text{g.c.d. } (m, n).$$

   (a) Is the set J closed with respect to this operation?
   (b) Is this operation commutative? Illustrate numerically.
   (c) Is this operation associative? Illustrate numerically.

4. In which type of arithmetic computation is the g.c.d. used? Illustrate numerically.
5. Find the g.c.d. of the following pairs: (a) 0, 9, (b) 0, -12, (c) -9, 0, (d) 0, 1.
6. What can you say about g.c.d. $(0, n)$ for any integer n?
7. What is g.c.d. (p, q) if p and q are both prime numbers?

6.9c Special Properties of the G.C.D. (optional)

An interesting and useful property of the g.c.d. of a pair of numbers, a and b, which is also a consequence of the division algorithm, is that the g.c.d. (a, b) can be written as the sum of some multiples of a and b.

Example 1

g.c.d. (7, 17) = 1
Multiples of 7: 7, 14, 21, 28, **35**, 42, . . .
Multiples of 17: 17, **34**, 51, 68, . . .

$$1 = (5)(7) + (-2)(17)$$

Example 2

g.c.d. (6, 15) = 3
Multiples of 6: 6, **12**, 18, 24, 30, . . .

Multiples of 15: 15, 30, 45, 60, 75, . . .

$$3 = (1)(15) + (-2)(6)$$

THEOREM I. In general, if g.c.d. $(a, b) = d$, then there are multiples $s \cdot a$ and $t \cdot b$ of a and b such that

$$d = s \cdot a + t \cdot b.$$

The proof of this theorem is not difficult but considered unnecessary for our purposes (see Hamilton and Landin, pp. 152–3).

We now prove some simple theorems concerning prime numbers that serve as a review of a few of the definitions and concepts we have introduced.

THEOREM II. If p is a prime and p divides the product $a \cdot b$, then either p divides a or p divides b.

Proof. If a is a multiple of p, then p divides a. If a is not a multiple of p, since p is a prime whose only divisors are $\pm p$ and ± 1, g.c.d. $(a, p) = 1$ (see problem 9, Exercise 6.9a).

Hence $\quad 1 = s \cdot a + t \cdot p. \quad$ Theorem I

Multiplying by b we have

$$b = s(ab) + t(pb).$$

We assumed that p divides ab, so p divides $s(ab)$. Also, p divides $t(pb)$, since this is a multiple of p. The Distributive Law implies that p divides $s(ab) + t(pb)$. Hence p divides b.

THEOREM III. If m and n are relatively prime and m divides $n \cdot a$, then m must divide a.

Proof. $1 = s \cdot m + t \cdot n$ — Why?
$a = s \cdot m \cdot a + t \cdot n \cdot a$ — Why?
Then m divides a. — Why?

THEOREM IV. If a and b are relatively prime and a divides m and b divides m, then ab divides m.

Proof. $m = a \cdot k$. — Why?
b divides ak. — Why?
Hence b divides k. — Theorem III
Hence $k = b \cdot e$, for some e. — Why?

Substituting $b \cdot e$ for k in the first equation we get

$m = a \cdot b \cdot e$.
Hence $a \cdot b$ divides m.

6.10 THE LEAST COMMON MULTIPLE

The *least common multiple*, l.c.m., of a pair of positive integers, m and n, is the smallest positive integer that is divisible by both m and n. The l.c.m. of 6 and 5 is 30; the l.c.m. of 12 and 18 is 36.

DEFINITION 6.10. The positive integer d is the l.c.m. of positive integers m and n (1) if m divides d and n divides d and (2) if k is any other multiple of m and n, then d divides k.

The l.c.m. of three or more positive integers can be found by finding the l.c.m. of pairs in the same way that the g.c.d. of three or more numbers was found, that is, to find the l.c.m. (a, b, c), first find l.c.m. $(a, b) = k$, then l.c.m. $(k, c) = m$. Then l.c.m. $(a, b, c) = m$ (see problem 5c, Exercise 6.10).

6.10a The L.C.M. by Prime Factorization

The problem of finding the l.c.m. of a set of positive integers is an essential step in handling rational numbers (fractions). Here again we have more than one way of determining the l.c.m. First let us examine the method involving prime factorization.

Example 1

Find the l.c.m. of 12 and 18:

$$12 = 2^2 \cdot 3$$
$$18 = 2 \cdot 3^2$$

The l.c.m. evidently must contain factors of 2 and 3. More than this, the 2 must be of the second power. The same is true for the 3. Then l.c.m. $(12, 18) = 2^2 \cdot 3^2 = 36$.

In general, the l.c.m. of two positive integers, m and n, is the product of the highest powers of all the *different* factors that occur in the prime factorization of either integer.

Example 2

We wish to find the l.c.m. of 60 and 36. Factoring we have

$$60 = 2^2 \cdot 3 \cdot 5$$

and

$$36 = 2^2 \cdot 3^2.$$

We see that the *different* prime factors that occur in either factorization are 2, 3, and 5. The highest power of 2 that occurs is 2^2, the highest of 3 that occurs is 3^2, and the highest of 5 that occurs is 5^1.

Thus the l.c.m. $(60, 36) = 2^2 \cdot 3^2 \cdot 5 = 180$.

6.10b Finding the L.C.M. from the G.C.D.

Another method of finding the l.c.m. of a *pair* of positive integers, m and n, is to divide their product by their g.c.d. This is intuitively evident. If d is the g.c.d. of m and n, then $m = d \cdot a$; $n = d \cdot b$; and g.c.d. $(a, b) = 1$. $m \cdot n = d \cdot a \cdot d \cdot b$. But $a \cdot d \cdot b$ is a multiple of both m and n, since $a \cdot m = adb = m \cdot b$, and it is the l.c.m. (m, n). That is,

$$\text{l.c.m. } (m, n) = adb = \frac{dadb}{d} = \frac{m \cdot n}{\text{g.c.d. } (m, n)}.$$

When the numbers are large, this is the most practical way of finding the l.c.m.

Example 1

Find the l.c.m. (285, 76):

$$\begin{aligned} 285 &= 76 \cdot 3 + 57 \\ 76 &= 57 \cdot 1 + 19 \\ 57 &= 19 \cdot 3 \end{aligned}$$

Hence, g.c.d. $(285, 76) = 19$.

Then l.c.m. $(285, 76) = \dfrac{(285)(76)}{19} = (285)(4) = 1140.$

Exercise 6.10

1. Find the l.c.m. of each of the following, using the prime factorization method:
   (a) 32, 40 (b) 8, 18, 27
   (c) 36, 56 (d) 17, 7
2. Find the l.c.m. of each of the following using the g.c.d.:
   (a) 18, 84 (b) 36, 27
   (c) 96, 84 (d) 252, 33
3. Find the g.c.d. of each of the following sets of numbers:
   (a) (9, 16) (b) (22, 46)
   (c) (30, 42) (d) (35, 66)
   (e) (42, 90) (f) (74, 111)
   (g) (260, 611) (h) (264, 1512)
   (i) (806, 1116) (j) (1936, 3630)
   (k) (1728, 5400) (l) (6912, 20160)
4. Find the l.c.m. of each of the sets of problem 3.
5. We define the binary operation * on the set J of integers as follows: For integers m and n

$$m * n = \text{l.c.m. } (m, n).$$

   (a) Is the set J closed with respect to this operation?
   (b) Is this operation commutative? Illustrate numerically.
   (c) Is this operation associative? Illustrate numerically.

6. In which type of arithmetic computation is the l.c.m. used? Illustrate numerically.

6.11 ORDER RELATIONS FOR THE INTEGERS

We defined a "less than" relation and a "less than or equal to" relation for the natural numbers in terms of one-to-one correspondence between sets. This is not very meaningful for negative integers. Hence we define these relations for *integers* in terms of the positive integers.

DEFINITION 6.11a. If m and n are any two *integers*, we say m "is less than" n if $(n - m)$ is a positive integer.

We denote this $m < n$. Expressions involving the relation $<$ are called *inequalities*. This is different from "not equal."

DEFINITION 6.11b. If m and n are any two integers, we say m is "less than or equal to" n if either $(n - m)$ is a positive integer or $(n - m)$ is 0.

We denote this $m \leqq n$. The relation, $\leqq$, is also called an *inequality*, or a *weak inequality*.

Example 1

$5 < 7$, since $7 - 5 = 2$, a positive integer.
$0 < m$ for any positive integer m, since $m - 0 = m$, a positive integer.
$-7 < -5$, since $-5 - (-7) = 2$, a positive integer.

We indicate hereafter that a number, m, is positive by the symbol $m > 0$.

The order relation $<$ for the integers does not have the reflexive property because $n - n = 0$ and 0 is not a positive integer. On the other hand, $\leqq$ is reflexive.

Neither the $<$ nor the $\leqq$ relation is symmetric.

Both relations are transitive; that is, if $m < n$ and $n < k$, then $m < k$. Let us establish this for the "less than" relation. We observe that

$$m < n \text{ means } n - m > 0,$$

and

$$n < k \text{ means } k - n > 0.$$

We need to show that these two statements imply $m < k$, that is, that $k - m > 0$. Then

$$\begin{aligned}(k - n) + (n - m) &= [k + (-n)] + [n + (-m)] \\ &= k + [(-n) + n] + (-m) \\ &= k + (-m) \\ &= k - m.\end{aligned}$$

Since the sum of two positive integers is a positive integer, $k - m$ is a positive integer. Then, by definition, $m < k$.

The proof for $\leqq$ can be made by replacing $<$ by $\leqq$ throughout.

Defining order for the integers in terms of the positive elements of the system has certain algebraic advantages, for example, the Trichotomy Law can be stated as follows.

The Trichotomy Law for Integers

$$\text{If } m \neq 0, \text{ then either } m > 0 \text{ or } -m > 0.$$

This means that we can compare any two *integers*. If m and n are any two integers, then

1. $m = n$, or
2. $m < n$, or
3. $n < m$

and *only one* of the relations must hold.

The order relations have some additional properties that are both interesting and useful.

Properties of the Inequalities < and ≦

For a, b, and c integers

1. If $a < b$, then $a + c < b + c$.
2. If $a < b$ and $c > 0$, then $ac < bc$.
3. If $a < b$ and $c < 0$, then $ac > bc$.

Statements (1), (2), and (3) can also be written with $\leqq$ in place of $<$. The last statement, (3), says that multiplying both members of an inequality by the same negative number reverses the sense of the inequality.

Exercise 6.11

1. Describe the following sets:

(a) $A = \{n|n \text{ is an integer and } -3 < n \leqq 5\}$.
(b) $B = \{n|n \text{ is an integer and } 0 \leqq n \leqq 7\}$.
(c) $C = \{n|n \text{ is an integer and } n < 0\}$.
(d) $N = \{n|n \text{ is an integer and } 0 < n\}$.
(e) $O = \{n|n \text{ is an integer and } n = -n\}$.
(f) $J = \{n|n \text{ is an integer}\}$.

2. For the sets of problem 1 describe the following, using the relation $\leqq$:

(a) $A \cap B$, (b) $B \cap C$, (c) $A \cap C$, (d) $B \cap N$.

3. List the elements of $B \times B$ and draw a geometric representation of $B \times B$ (set B of problem 1).

4. List the elements of $A \times A$ and draw a geometric representation of $A \times A$ (set A of problem 1).
5. Describe $N \times N$ (set N of problem 1).
6. Describe $J \times J$ (set J of problem 1).
7. Is there a smallest integer? Is there a smallest positive integer? If so, what is it?
8. Is there a smallest non-negative integer? What is it?
9. Is there a largest negative integer? What is it?
10. How many integers satisfy the inequalities $-5 < n < 5$? List them and indicate them on the number line. (See next section.)
11. Show that if $a < b$, then $a + c < b + c$.
12. Show that if $a < b$ and $c > 0$, then $ac < bc$.
13. Show that if $a < b$ and $c < 0$, then $ac > bc$.
14. How many solutions does the inequality $3 + n < 10$ have in the set of natural numbers? In the integers?
15. What is the sum of the first 5 positive integers?
16. What is the sum of the first 10 positive integers? Here is an easy way to add the first 5 positive integers:

$$\begin{array}{c} 1 + 2 + 3 + 4 + 5 \\ \underline{5 + 4 + 3 + 2 + 1} \\ 6 + 6 + 6 + 6 + 6 \end{array}$$

Five 6's is 30, but we added each of the numbers twice, so we must divide our answer by 2. Hence the sum of the first 5 positive integers is $\frac{5(6)}{2}$.

17. Write out the sum of the first 10 positive integers in the same way and find the sum.
18. Find the sum of the first 20 positive integers by the method suggested in problem 16.
19. Find the sum of the first 50 positive integers.
20. Write an expression for the sum of the first n positive integers in the form suggested by problem 16.
21. What is the sum of the first 3 positive odd integers?
22. What is the sum of the first 4 positive odd integers?
23. What is the sum of the first 5 positive odd integers?
24. Write an expression for the kth positive odd integer.
25. How are the answers to problems 21, 22, and 23 related?
26. What is the sum of the first 10 positive odd integers?
27. What is the sum of the first 11 positive odd integers?
28. Write an expression for the sum of the first n positive odd integers in the form suggested by problems 21 through 27.

6.12 THE NUMBER LINE FOR THE INTEGERS

Although the concept of the number line is a familiar notion, we review it briefly for convenience in presenting subsequent material.

On a line, which we denote by L, we choose an arbitrary point and label this point 0. We then choose any other point on the line L to the right of the point labeled 0 and label this point 1.

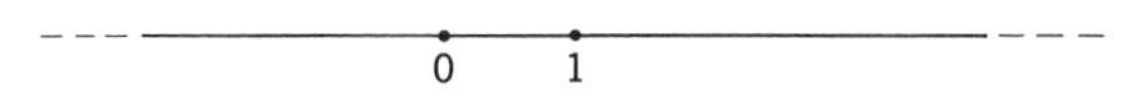

We use the line segment from the point labeled 0 to the point labeled 1 to mark off consecutive points to the right and label these points with the natural numbers. Each natural number corresponds to just one such point, and each such point corresponds to just one such number. Disregard the point labeled 0 for the moment and consider the rest. We have a one-to-one correspondence between the natural numbers and the points obtained in this manner.

Hereafter we shall not distinguish between these points and their corresponding labels. This allows us to speak of the numbers between 5 and 17, for example, with the concept of "between-ness" as related to the number line.

If we use the line segment from 0 to 1 to mark off points in the opposite direction from 0, we use the negative integers to label these new points. We now have a one-to-one correspondence between the designated points on the line and the set of integers.

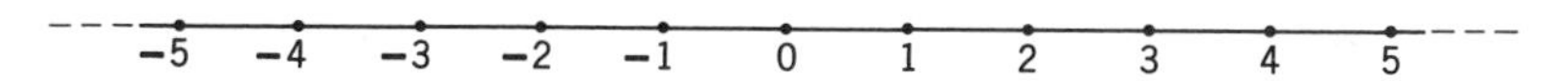

Notice that if a number is "less than" another number, the point on the number line corresponding to the first number is to the left of the point labeled by the second.

6.12a Distances on the Number Line

If we wish to know the number of intervals between pairs of points, it is simple enough to count them. This, however, is not necessary if we use the names we have attached to the points.

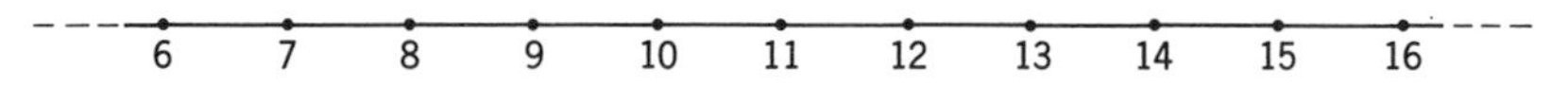

For example, we might ask how many units it is from the point labeled 7 to the point labeled 13. The result can be obtained if we notice that the 7 label actually can be interpreted to mean that there are 7 intervals between that point and the point labeled 0. Also, the 13 label indicates that there are 13 intervals between 0 and 13. We see immediately that there are $13 - 7 = 6$ intervals from the point labeled 7 to the point labeled 13.

We might be tempted to say, in general, that the number of intervals from the point labeled m to the point labeled n is $n - m$. However, if we ask how many intervals there are between the point labeled 13 and the point labeled 7, our generalization would yield -6, which is meaningless as an answer to the question, "How many?"

The *number* of intervals between points on a line is called the *distance* between points on the line. In order to properly define the distance between points in terms of the labels attached to the points we introduce the concept of *absolute value* of a number.

DEFINITION 6.12a. If m is a number, the *absolute value* of m—denoted by $|m|$—is defined as follows:

$$\begin{aligned} &\text{If } m > 0, \text{ then } |m| = m. \\ &\text{If } m = 0, \text{ then } |m| = 0. \\ &\text{If } m < 0, \text{ then } |m| = -m. \end{aligned}$$

Example 1

$$\begin{aligned} |3| &= 3, \text{ since } 3 > 0. \\ |-7| &= 7, \text{ since } -7 < 0 \text{ and } -(-7) = 7. \\ |0| &= 0 \end{aligned}$$

6.12b Properties of Absolute Value

1. The absolute value of the product of two numbers is the product of the absolute values of the numbers.

$$|m \cdot n| = |m| \cdot |n|.$$

2. The absolute value of the sum of two numbers is not always the same as the sum of the absolute values. It may be less but never greater. We indicate this as follows:

$$|m + n| \leqq |m| + |n|.$$

DEFINITION 6.12b. The distance between points labeled m and n on the number line is $|m - n|$.

6.12c Properties of Distance

1. The distance between two points is a non-negative number. It may be 0. This happens when the two points are the same.
2. The distance from point A to point B is the same as the distance from point B to point A.
3. The distance from A to B plus the distance from B to C is greater

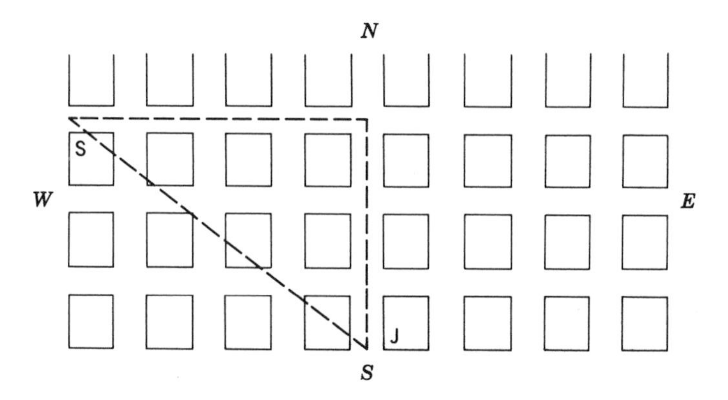

Figure 1

than or equal to the distance from A to C. This property is referred to as the *triangular inequality*. Why?

Heretofore we have been speaking of distances along a line. We can also speak of distances in a plane. Here there are two kinds of distances familiar to most people, the "street" distance and the distance "as the crow flies." Consider a portion of a city map as shown in Figure 1.

How far is it from the Smith's house (S) to the Jones' house (J)? If one is to drive, the answer is 4 blocks east and 3 blocks south, or a total of 7 blocks. We might also say 3 blocks south and 4 blocks east. This is one meaning of "distance" in the plane. We could also be concerned with how far it was between houses "as the crow flies." Here we mean the straight-line distance from house to house. You may recall that we compute this as shown in Figure 2.

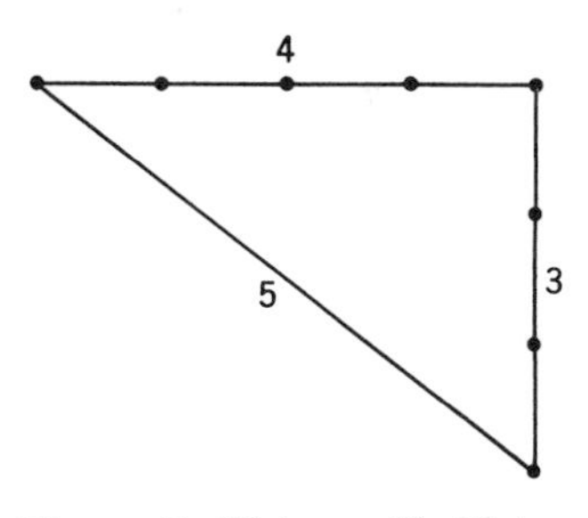

Figure 2. Distance (Smith to Jones): $\sqrt{4^2 + 3^2} = \sqrt{25} = 5$.

We have two distances from Smith's to Jones', by following the streets (7 blocks) and as the crow flies (5 blocks). We assert that both "distances" satisfy the properties of distances listed at the beginning of this section.

Exercise 6.12

1. List the integers that satisfy the following inequalities:

(a) $|m| < 5$. (b) $|m| < 4$.
(c) $m < 5$ and $m > -2$. (d) $|m - 5| < 2$.

2. Interpret the questions in problem 1 geometrically.

3. List the integers satisfying the following inequalities:

(a) $|n| \leqq 3$. (b) $|n - 8| \leqq 2$. (c) $|n| \leqq 1$.
(d) $|n + 5| \leqq 3$. (e) $|n - 6| = 2$.

4. Interpret the questions in problem 3 geometrically.

5. (a) Write an expression for the distance from the point 3 to the point 9 on the number line.
(b) Write an expression for the distance from the point 11 to the point 8.

6. (a) Write an expression for the distance from the point 4 to the point n.
(b) Write an expression for the distance from the point n to the point 18.

7. On the number line for the integers, which integers correspond to points whose distance from 7 is 3?

8. Which integers correspond to points whose distance from 7 is less than or equal to 3?

9. If m and n are integers, is $(-m)(n)$ a negative integer?

6.13 CLOCK ARITHMETIC (optional)

The numbers on the face of a clock are used to tell us the time of day. When used to speak of past events or to plan future events, one subtracts or adds a fixed number of hours to the present time. Suppose it is 9 o'clock. We had breakfast two hours ago. We plan to have a meeting in four hours (see Figure 3).

Two hours before 9 o'clock is 7 o'clock. Four hours after 9 o'clock is 1 o'clock. If we think of adding and subtracting hours, we have

$$9 - 2 = 7.$$
$$9 + 4 = 1.$$

If we didn't know we were speaking about "time," this would be a strange arithmetic indeed. What time is 17 hours after 6 o'clock?

$$6 + 17 = 11.$$

Because one needs to know whether the time is morning or evening, the time is sometimes expressed in terms of a 24-hour clock. Thus 2200 hours is 10 o'clock P.M. 0300 hours is 3 o'clock A.M. 1200 hours is noon. Note that in

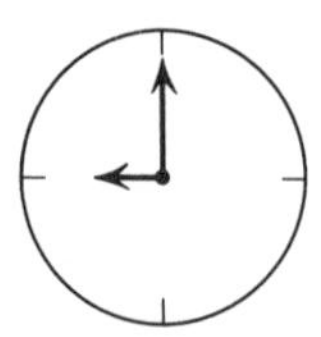 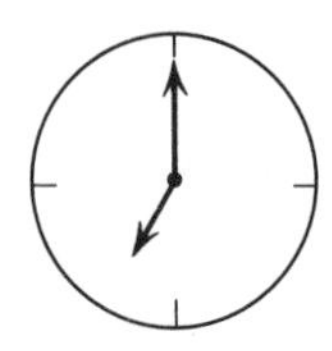 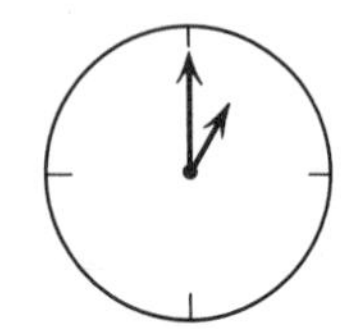

Figure 3

these four-digit numerals related to time, the first pair range from 00 to and including 24 and the second pair range from 00 to and including 59.

In working time problems on the 12-hour clock it does not take long to realize that the correct time is obtained by adding the clock hours to the given hours, dividing by 12, and taking the remainder as the result.

Example 1

$$9 + 4 = 13 = 12\cdot 1 + 1 \equiv 1$$
$$9 + 17 = 26 = 12\cdot 2 + 2 \equiv 2$$
$$8 + 8 = 16 = 12\cdot 1 + 4 \equiv 4$$

Whenever we add or subtract h hours to a given time t, we obtain the "sum," using the division algorithm as follows:

$$t + h = 12\cdot g + r, \text{ and } r \text{ is the clock time.}$$

Example 2

Add 26 hours to 9 o'clock.

$$9 + 26 = 35 = 12\cdot 2 + 11$$

Hence the clock time is 11 o'clock.

Exercise 6.13

1. What is the clock time in each of the following:

(a) 75 hours after 3:00 A.M.? Will it be A.M. or P.M.?
(b) You plan to serve a roast which takes 15 hours to cook. Dinner is to be at 7:00 P.M. What time do you put the roast in the oven?
(c) It takes 7 hours to climb Harding Peak. You want to reach the summit at 3:00 P.M. What time should you start the climb?

2. Add the following in "clock arithmetic": (a) $9 + 5$, (b) $11 + 6$, (c) $8 + 15$, (d) $4 + 22$.

3. What is the clock time of the following:

(a) 112 hours after 3:00 P.M.?
(b) 64 hours after 7:00 A.M.?
(c) 42 hours after 5:00 P.M.?

6.14 THE CONGRUENCE RELATION

The congruence relation is a familiar relation although we have not called it by this name before, in fact, we didn't give it a special name (see problem 5, Exercise 3.12 and problem 4, Exercise 5.4). In these problems we defined the relation, denoted by $\equiv$, as follows: For integers m and n, $m \equiv n$ if $m - n$ is a multiple of 4 (or 5), or, alternately, $m \equiv n$ if they each give the same remainder when divided by 4 (or 5). Let us define this relation more specifically.

DEFINITION 6.14a. If a, b, and m are integers and $m \neq 0$, *a is congruent to b*, modulo m, if $(a - b)$ is a multiple of m.

Symbolically,

$$a \equiv b \pmod{m} \text{ if } a - b = k \cdot m, \text{ for some integer } k.$$

The definition given here is equivalent to the definitions a is congruent to b, modulo m, if they each give the same remainder when divided by m, and a is congruent to b, modulo m, if $a - b$ is divisible by m. The student will be asked to verify this in Exercise 6.14a.

Example 1

$39 \equiv 3 \pmod{12}$ because $39 - 3 = 36$, a multiple of 12.
$65 \equiv 113 \pmod{12}$ because $65 - 113 = -48$, a multiple of 12.
Or we could say
$39 \equiv 3 \pmod{12}$ because $39 = 3 \cdot 12 + 3$, $3 = 0 \cdot 12 + 3$; they both give the same remainder when divided by 12.
Similarly, 65 and 113 both give a remainder of 5 when divided by 12.

Recall the definition of an equivalence relation. (See Section 3.12.) Let us show that the congruence relation possesses the necessary properties of an equivalence relation.

The Reflexive Property.

$$a \equiv a \pmod{m} \text{ because } a - a = 0 = 0 \cdot m.$$

The Symmetric Property. If $a \equiv b \pmod{m}$, then $b \equiv a \pmod{m}$. To prove this we note that $a \equiv b \pmod{m}$ means $a - b = k \cdot m$, for some k. Then $b - a = (-k)m$, but this is also a multiple of m. Hence, if $a \equiv b \pmod{m}$, then $b \equiv a \pmod{m}$.

The Transitive Property. If $a \equiv b \pmod{m}$ and $b \equiv c \pmod{m}$, then $a \equiv c \pmod{m}$. To prove this we note that $a \equiv b \pmod{m}$ means $a - b = k \cdot m$, and $b \equiv c \pmod{m}$ means $b - c = j \cdot m$, for integers k and j.

Adding

$$\begin{aligned} (a - b) + (b - c) &= k \cdot m + j \cdot m \\ a - b + b - c &= (k + j)m \\ a - c &= (k + j)m. \end{aligned}$$

But $(k + j)$ is an integer, so $a - c$ is a multiple of m. This means that if $a \equiv b \pmod{m}$ and $b \equiv c \pmod{m}$, then $a \equiv c \pmod{m}$.

Since the congruence relation as defined above has the reflexive, symmetric, and transitive properties, it is an equivalence relation. Recall again the effect of an equivalence relation defined on a set (see Section 3.12). The relation partitions the set into disjoint subsets called equivalence classes.

Let us see what the congruence relation, modulo 12, does to the set J, the integers.

We first ask, "What numbers are congruent to 0, mod 12?" Obviously they are multiples of 12. We call this the 0-class.

We next ask, "What numbers are congruent to 1, mod 12?" These are 1, 13, 25, etc., and in general, any number in the 0-class + 1. How do we get the numbers congruent to 2, mod 12? How many classes will we have? We answer the last question by asking, "How many remainders are possible when integers are divided by 12?"

We have twelve classes as follows:

...	−24	−12	0	12	24	36	...
...	−23	−11	1	13	25	37	...
...	−22	−10	2	14	26	38	...
...	−21	−9	3	15	27	39	...
...	−20	−8	4	16	28	40	...
...	−19	−7	5	17	29	41	...
...	−18	−6	6	18	30	42	...
...	−17	−5	7	19	31	43	...
...	−16	−4	8	20	32	44	...
...	−15	−3	9	21	33	45	...
...	−14	−2	10	22	34	46	...
...	−13	−1	11	23	35	47	...

Notice that any number in any row has the same remainder as any other number in the same row when divided by 12. These rows, where the dots indicate that these are unending sequences of integers, are the *equivalence classes*, modulo 12, of the set of integers. Notice that each integer occurs in one and only one class. The classes are disjoint subsets of the set of integers.

Let us name the classes the 0-class, 1-class, 2-class, and so on and use the following symbols:

$$[0], [1], [2], [3], [4], [5], [6], [7], [8], [9], [10], [11].$$

We will call the set of equivalence classes, modulo 12, J_{12}.

6.14a Addition in $\mathbf{J_{12}}$

Now we observe an interesting phenomenon. Consider the numbers, 27 and 38. Their sum is 65. Notice that 27 is in the class labeled [3] and 38 is in the class labeled [2], and their sum, 65, is in the class labeled [5]. Now try any number in [2] and any number in [3]. Find their sum and you will find that it will always be in [5]. We indicate this by writing

$$[2] + [3] = [5].$$

We interpret this to mean that any number in the 2-class added to any number in the 3-class is a number in the 5-class.

Let us try some more "class" addition.

$$[5] + [9] = ?$$

5 is in [5]; and 9 is in [9]; 5 + 9 = 14; 14 is in [2].

Hence $$[5] + [9] = [2].$$

If this seems like a strange kind of arithmetic, recall that in our "clock" arithmetic, 9 hours added to 5 o'clock was 2 o'clock.

We now consider the new set, which we have labeled J_{12}, and whose elements are [0], [1], [2], [3], [4], [5], [6], [7], [8], [9], [10], [11]. We define a binary operation in J_{12} as we have carried it out by example above, and we call this operation "addition." If we let $[a]$ and $[b]$ be any elements in J_{12}, then

$$[a] + [b] = [a + b],$$

where $[a + b]$ is the class of $a + b$ reduced modulo 12. In order to show that this "operation" is "well defined," we must show that the "operation" is independent of the representatives of the classes, that is, regardless of which representative of the classes $[a]$ and $[b]$ are chosen, the "sum" will be in the class labeled $[a + b]$. This can be made plausible by looking at some numerical examples. The formal proof is not difficult and is left as a challenge to the student.

Table 1 shows "addition" for this system.

TABLE 1

ADDITION IN J_{12}

+	[0]	[1]	[2]	[3]	[4]	[5]	[6]	[7]	[8]	[9]	[10]	[11]
[0]	0	1	2	3	4	5	6	7	8	9	10	11
[1]	1	2	3	4	5	6	7	8	9	10	11	0
[2]	2	3	4	5	6	7	8	9	10	11	0	1
[3]	3	4	5	6	7	8	9	10	11	0	1	2
[4]	4	5	6	7	8	9	10	11	0	1	2	3
[5]	5	6	7	8	9	10	11	0	1	2	3	4
[6]	6	7	8	9	10	11	0	1	2	3	4	5
[7]	7	8	9	10	11	0	1	2	3	4	5	6
[8]	8	9	10	11	0	1	2	3	4	5	6	7
[9]	9	10	11	0	1	2	3	4	5	6	7	8
[10]	10	11	0	1	2	3	4	5	6	7	8	9
[11]	11	0	1	2	3	4	5	6	7	8	9	10

Looking at the addition table, we observe the following interesting properties of "addition" as it is defined in the set J_{12}. (Note that in the body of the table we have omitted the square brackets.)

The commutative property of "addition" results in the symmetry about the upper-left to lower-right diagonal, that is, $[a] + [b] = [b] + [a]$.

The first row and the first column in the body of the table indicate that [0] is the *additive identity.*

The element [0] occurs once and only once in each row or column. This means that the pair of elements whose sum is [0] are *additive inverses* of each other, for example, $[5] + [7] = [0]$. Hence [7] is the additive inverse of [5] and [5] is the additive inverse of [7]. The element [6] is its own additive inverse.

Not immediately evident but still something that can be shown is the fact that "addition" in this system is associative.

Exercise 6.14a

1. Use numerical examples to illustrate the fact that "addition" in J_{12} is associative.
2. Solve the following equations in J_{12}:

   (a) $[3] + [x] = [7]$ (b) $[4] + [5] = [x]$
   (c) $[8] + [x] = [0]$ (d) $[8] + [8] = [x]$
   (e) $[x] + [x] = [0]$ (f) $[x] + [x] = [6]$

3. Show that the alternate methods of defining the congruence relation are equivalent (see Section 6.14).
4. How would you interpret $-[3]$?
5. Explain the following:

   (a) $-[3] = [-3]$ (b) $-[3] = [9]$
   (c) $-[6] = [6]$ (d) $[-2] = [10]$

6.14b Multiplication in J_{12}

We now define another binary operation, which we call "multiplication," in much the same way that we defined "addition."

If we let $[a]$ and $[b]$ be any elements in J_{12}, then

$$[a] \cdot [b] = [a \cdot b],$$

where $[a \cdot b]$ is the class of $a \cdot b$ reduced, modulo 12. This "operation" is also well defined. The proof is again left as a challenge to the reader.

Table 2 shows "multiplication" for this system.

Examining the table closely, we observe that "Multiplication" is commutative. Notice the symmetry about the main diagonal.

TABLE 2

MULTIPLICATION IN J_{12}

·	[1]	[2]	[3]	[4]	[5]	[6]	[7]	[8]	[9]	[10]	[11]
[1]	1	2	3	4	5	6	7	8	9	10	11
[2]	2	4	6	8	10	0	2	4	6	8	10
[3]	3	6	9	0	3	6	9	0	3	6	9
[4]	4	8	0	4	8	0	4	8	0	4	8
[5]	5	10	3	8	1	6	11	4	9	2	7
[6]	6	0	6	0	6	0	6	0	6	0	6
[7]	7	2	9	4	11	6	1	8	3	10	5
[8]	8	4	0	8	4	0	8	4	0	8	4
[9]	9	6	3	0	9	6	3	0	9	6	3
[10]	10	8	6	4	2	0	10	8	6	4	2
[11]	11	10	9	8	7	6	5	4	3	2	1

The first row and the first column in the body of the table indicate that [1] is the *multiplicative identity.*

The system has many "zero divisors," that is, $[3] \neq [0]$ and $[4] \neq [0]$ but $[3] \cdot [4] = [0]$. By our definition of "divides," [3] and [4] are both nonzero divisors of zero.

We remark that J_{12} is a mathematical system. It is closed under two binary operations, which are commutative and associative, and the Distributive Law, multiplication with respect to addition, holds. The system possesses an additive identity and a multiplicative identity, and there are inverses under addition. This system contains zero divisors and the cancellation law for multiplication does not hold.

6.14c Congruence Modulo 2

For integers a and b, $a \equiv b(\text{mod } 2)$ if $b - a$ is a multiple of 2. This is equivalent to saying a and b have the same remainders when divided by 2. The division algorithm tells us that the only possible remainders when dividing integers by 2 are 0 and 1. The congruence relation divides the set of integers into two disjoint subsets, those that have remainder 0 (the *even* integers) and those that have remainder 1 (the *odd* integers).

Equivalence Classes, Mod 2

$\ldots -14, -12, -10, -8, -6, -4, -2, 0, 2, 4, 6, 8, 10, 12, 14, \ldots$

$\ldots -13, -11, -9, -7, -5, -3, -1, 1, 3, 5, 7, 9, 11, 13, 15, \ldots$

Addition Table Mod 2

+	[0]	[1]
[0]	0	1
[1]	1	0

Multiplication Table Mod 2

·	[1]
[1]	1

Exercise 6.14c

1. Interpret the addition table mod 2 in terms of addition of even and odd integers.
2. Use numerical examples to illustrate the fact that multiplication is associative in J_{12}.
3. Can you always find a solution for the equation

$$[a]\cdot[x] = [b]? \quad \text{(modulo 12)}$$

4. Solve the equations: (modulo 12)

   (a) $[x]\cdot[x] = [0]$ (b) $[x]\cdot[x] = [x]$
   (c) $[3]\cdot[x] = [3]$ (d) $[3]\cdot[x] = [5]$

5. Does the Cancellation Law for Multiplication hold in J_{12}? Illustrate with a numerical example.
6. If $[x+3]\cdot[x+4] = [0]$ in J_{12}, what can you say about x? List some solutions of this equation.
7. Let J_3 denote the equivalence classes, modulo 3. Use [0], [1], and [2] to denote the elements. Construct the addition and multiplication tables for this system.
8. Does J_3 have zero divisors?
9. What is the additive inverse of [2] in J_3?
10. What is the multiplicative inverse of [2] in J_3?
11. What is the g.c.d. (7980, 2310)? The l.c.m. (7980, 2310)?
12. What is the g.c.d. of 300, 210, and 230? The l.c.m.?
13. What is the fallacy in the following argument? Let $a = b$. Then

$$\begin{aligned} a^2 &= ab \\ a^2 - b^2 &= ab - b^2 \\ (a-b)(a+b) &= b(a-b) \\ a+b &= b \\ 2a &= a \\ 2 &= 1 \end{aligned}$$

REFERENCES

Banks, J. Houston, *Elements of Mathematics*, Allyn and Bacon, Boston, 1956, sections 3.16–17; 5.8–5.12.

Hafstrom, John E., *Basic Concepts in Modern Mathematics*, Addison-Wesley Publishing Co., Reading, Mass., 1961, ch. 7.

Hamilton, Norman T. and Joseph Landin, *Set Theory, the Structure of Arithmetic*, Allyn and Bacon, Boston, 1961, sections 3.1, 3.2, and 3.3.

Mueller, Francis J., *Arithmetic, Its Structure and Concepts*, Prentice-Hall, Englewood Cliffs, N.J., 1956, unit 17.

Swain, Robert L., *Understanding Arithmetic*, Rinehart and Co., New York, 1952, ch. III, sections 7–9; chs. IV, V, and VII.

*
*
*

CHAPTER SEVEN

The System of Rational Numbers

7.1 INTRODUCTION

In the same way that an individual may be a teacher, a baseball player, a father, and a homeowner, the symbols which we call numerals have more than one interpretation. The natural numbers can be thought of as *elements* of the *System of Whole Numbers.* When considered as a subsystem of the *System of Integers,* they are called the *positive integers.* We are making ordinal use of the natural numbers in answering the question, "Which one?" We are making cardinal use of the natural numbers in answering the question, "How many?"

7.2 INTERPRETATIONS OF NUMBER PAIRS

We now consider those numbers commonly referred to as *fractions* and written in the form $\frac{2}{5}$, $\frac{7}{11}$, $\frac{16}{3}$, and so forth. Again we have several seemingly unrelated *interpretations* of the symbols for these number pairs. We distinguish four principal meanings or interpretations of these number pair symbols. These interpretations are familiar to the reader but may not have been distinguished and fully appreciated.

The interpretations are

1. The "element of a mathematical system" interpretation.
2. The "division" interpretation.
3. The "fraction" or "partition" interpretation.
4. The "ratio" or "rate pair" interpretation.

Each of these interpretations is much used, important, and in no danger of being made obsolete in any modern approach to arithmetic.

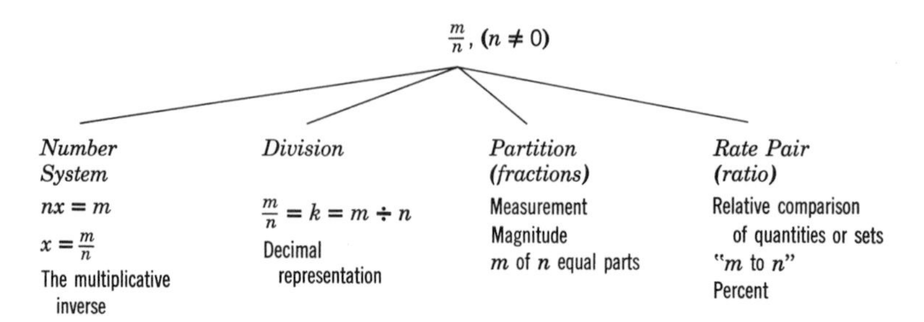

Figure 1

Any restriction to a single interpretation can be as misleading and narrow as the interpretation of one of the six blind men who examined the elephant. Each interpretation is associated with a reasonably well-defined problem situation. The schematic diagram of Figure 1 presents some of the ideas associated with the various interpretations.

We shall consider the number pairs first as elements of that mathematical system called the *System of Rational Numbers*. The other interpretations will be treated when and where it seems appropriate.

Exercise 7.2

1. Indicate the ordinal or cardinal use of the numbers in the following:

(a) The numbers used to indicate the ranking of the baseball teams in the American League.
(b) The score in the championship basketball game.
(c) The left-hand number at the top of this page.

2. Discuss the cardinal use of 1 and 0.
3. Discuss the numbers 1 and 0 as elements of the system of integers.
4. Give a precise definition of the additive identity; the multiplicative identity.
5. Numbers are often used for the sole purpose of naming objects, events, or even people. In this sense the only property of the numbers used is the property that there is an endless source of new, distinct names. Social Security No. 517-16-1722 identifies one and only one person. Give other examples of the use of numbers as names.

7.3 THE SET OF RATIONAL NUMBERS

The number systems discussed so far can be thought of in terms of the type of mathematical questions that can be answered in a particular system. The system of whole numbers is adequate for the following questions:

$$m + n = ?$$
$$m \cdot n = ?$$

In these questions m and n represent any elements in the system of whole numbers. The arithmetic operations are used to find names for these numbers.

The following questions may or may not have answers in the system of whole numbers:

$$m + ? = n$$
$$n \cdot ? = m$$

For example,

$$9 + ? = 4$$
$$3 \cdot ? = 2$$

Since there is no *whole number* that when added to 9 gives 4, we define new numbers $-1, -2, -3, \ldots, -n, \ldots$ in such a way that $-1 + 1 = 0$, $-2 + 2 = 0, \ldots, -n + n = 0, \ldots$. These numbers, together with the whole numbers and with addition and multiplication defined appropriately, constitute the system of integers. The system of integers can be thought of as an enlargement of the system of whole numbers in which the question

$$m + ? = n$$

can be answered for any integers m and n.

This enlarged system is still inadequate for answering the question

$$n \cdot ? = m.$$

(Note that if n is zero, so is m, since $0 \cdot a = 0$ for all a. We therefore rule out zero as a candidate for n.)

We are now interested in a mathematical system in which not only $m + ? = n$ is solvable, but also in which

$$a \cdot ? = b$$

has solutions in the system for any a and b, $a \neq 0$. The question has *integer* solutions for some pairs. For example,

$$3 \cdot ? = 15$$

has the solution 5. (Recall that we say that 3 "divides" 15.) For other pairs there is no integer solution. For example,

$$3 \cdot ? = 2.$$

We are looking for a number that when multiplied by 3 is the number 2. The fact that this number is intimately related to the numbers 2 and 3 is recognized and incorporated into the symbol representing that number. We must turn to "ordered pairs" of integers to answer our question.

DEFINITION 7.3. A *rational number* is a class of ordered pairs of integers. The ordered pairs are written in the form m/n, with the restriction that n is never 0.

The fact that rational numbers are defined as *classes* will be made clear in what follows. Initially we will treat them as ordered pairs of integers, and the reader should be cautioned that in so doing we are assuming the identification of a particular ordered pair with a *class*.

The fact that we require $n \neq 0$ is an acknowledgment of the "division" interpretation. In the ordered pair m/n, m is called the *numerator* and n is called the *denominator*. This terminology has its roots in the "fraction" interpretation.

Up to this point we have discussed natural numbers, whole numbers, positive integers, negative integers, and now we are introducing rational numbers. We emphasize that the terms are used as *names* of *sets*. Later we will speak of irrational numbers, real numbers, imaginary numbers, and complex numbers. Again, the terms are used strictly in the sense that they are *names* of various *sets of numbers*. The choice of names is very unfortunate because the literal meanings, which the terms carry, prejudice the student and tend to obstruct the learning of mathematics. The terms reflect the attitudes and suspicions which the number concepts have had to survive. There is no reason why this distrust and nonacceptance should be promulgated and the teaching of arithmetic made to suffer as a consequence. Hence, we repeat, the term negative integers does not mean nonintegers but is the name of a definite set of numbers. The term rational numbers is the name of a definite set of numbers. The term irrational numbers is the name of a definite set of numbers.

There is a mathematical distinction between integers and rational numbers. Eventually we want to interpret the integers as rational numbers.

When we consider the set of all possible ordered pairs of integers, m/n, $n \neq 0$, there are many ordered pairs that appear different but that we are accustomed to regard as the same.

Example 1

$$\tfrac{1}{2}, \tfrac{2}{4}, \tfrac{3}{6}, \tfrac{4}{8}, \tfrac{5}{10}, \tfrac{6}{12}, \ldots$$
$$\tfrac{2}{3}, \tfrac{4}{6}, \tfrac{6}{9}, \tfrac{8}{12}, \tfrac{10}{15}, \tfrac{12}{18}, \ldots$$
$$\tfrac{2}{1}, \tfrac{4}{2}, \tfrac{6}{3}, \tfrac{8}{4}, \tfrac{10}{5}, \tfrac{12}{6}, \ldots$$

For simple ordered pairs it is easy to recognize this relationship. It is not so obvious for the numerals

$$\frac{27946}{845692} \quad \text{and} \quad \frac{307406}{9302612}.$$

These numerals may be names for the same number, but how do you determine whether they are or not? To answer this question we define a relation in the set of ordered pairs of integers, m/n, $n \neq 0$.

7.4 EQUIVALENCE RELATION FOR ORDERED PAIRS OF INTEGERS

DEFINITION 7.4. We say two ordered pairs of integers, m/n and p/q are equivalent and write

$$\frac{m}{n} \doteq \frac{p}{q} \quad \text{if and only if} \quad mq = np.$$

We use the symbol $\doteq$ instead of $=$ to emphasize that this is a *new* relation defined on the set of ordered pairs of integers in terms of the relation, "equals," on the set of integers. This relation will eventually be written as "=" with the "names of the same number" meaning except when the ordered pairs are interpreted as ratios or rate pairs. The connection between $\doteq$ and $=$ is clarified in Section 7.7.

Exercise 7.4

1. Write five numerals equivalent to each of the following:

(a) $\frac{2}{3}$ (b) $\frac{-17}{19}$ (c) $\frac{10}{10}$

(d) $\frac{0}{5}$ (e) $\frac{17}{-19}$ (f) $\frac{4}{1}$

(g) $\frac{9}{1}$ (h) $\frac{0}{10}$ (i) $\frac{3}{4}$

(j) $\frac{-2}{3}$ (k) $\frac{4}{-6}$ (l) $\frac{-1}{-1}$

2. Which of the following are equivalent?

$$\frac{27946}{854692}, \frac{11}{45}, \frac{3157898}{96580196}, \frac{3333}{13329}, \frac{63327}{253251}.$$

3. Which of the following are equivalent?

$$\frac{33}{29}, \frac{33-2}{29-2}, \frac{2\cdot 33}{2\cdot 29}, \frac{2+33}{2+29}.$$

4. Show that each of the following pairs are equivalent.

(a) $\frac{-2}{3}$ and $\frac{2}{-3}$ (b) $\frac{-4}{-1}$ and $\frac{8}{2}$

(c) $\frac{-5}{3}$ and $\frac{10}{-6}$ (d) $\frac{-m}{-m}$ and $\frac{m}{m}$

(e) $\frac{0}{7}$ and $\frac{0}{6}$ (f) $\frac{1}{1}$ and $\frac{3}{3}$

(g) $\frac{0}{-1}$ and $\frac{0}{1}$ (h) $\frac{-m}{n}$ and $\frac{m}{-n}$

5. Find the rational number equivalent to each of the following for which the g.c.d. of the numerator and denominator is 1.

(a) $\frac{3964}{87258}$ (b) $\frac{57}{76}$ (c) $\frac{144}{504}$

6. There are some problems of the type $ax + b = c$ that are understandable to elementary level students if they are stated in a reasonable manner. "I am thinking of a number. By doubling it and adding 1, I get 9. What is the number?" Try this on fourth or fifth graders and get their response.

   State the following problems in words.

(a) $3x + 1 = 7$ (b) $2x + 3 = 13$ (c) $3x + 1 = 10$

7. Make a partial list, including both positive and negative integers, of each of the equivalence classes of the integers modulo 13.

7.4a Properties of the Equivalence Relation $\doteq$

The relation $\doteq$ *is transitive.* The proof of this assertion proceeds as follows. We must show that if $a/b \doteq c/d$ and if $c/d \doteq e/f$, then $a/b \doteq e/f$, for a/b, c/d, and e/f ordered pairs of integers.

1. $\frac{a}{b} \doteq \frac{c}{d}$ means $ad = bc$

2. $\frac{c}{d} \doteq \frac{e}{f}$ means $cf = de$

If we show that $af = be$, then $a/b \doteq e/f$.

Multiplying (1) by f and (2) by b we get

$$adf = bcf \quad \text{and} \quad bcf = bde$$

By the transitivity of "equals" we have $adf = bde$.

Using the Cancellation Law of Multiplication for the integers, we have

$$af = be \quad \text{or} \quad a/b \doteq e/f$$

The relation $\doteq$ *is symmetric.* We need to show that if $a/b \doteq c/d$, then $c/d \doteq a/b$. We leave this as an exercise.

The relation $\doteq$ *is reflexive.* This is also left as an exercise.

If a/b is an ordered pair of integers and x is an integer, $x \neq 0$, then $a/b \doteq ax/bx$.

Proof. $(ab)x = (ab)x$ by the reflexive property of equals in the system of integers.

$(ab)x = (ba)x$ by the commutative property of multiplication in the system of integers.

$a(bx) = b(ax)$ by the associative property of multiplication in the system of integers.

$\frac{a}{b} \doteq \frac{ax}{bx}$ by the definition of $\doteq$ in the set of ordered pairs.

7.5 EQUIVALENCE CLASSES OF ORDERED PAIRS OF INTEGERS

We have shown that the relation $\doteq$ is reflexive, symmetric, and transitive. This relation is an equivalence relation. An equivalence relation partitions the set in which it is defined into disjoint subsets.

Recall how the congruence relation modulo m, defined in the set of integers, partitioned the set into equivalence classes. The relation $\doteq$ has a similar effect on the set of ordered pairs of integers. We shall tabulate a few of the classes.

The class to which $\frac{1}{2}$ belongs is as follows:

$$\ldots, \frac{-5}{-10}, \frac{-4}{-8}, \frac{-3}{-6}, \frac{-2}{-4}, \frac{-1}{-2}, \frac{1}{2}, \frac{2}{4}, \frac{3}{6}, \frac{4}{8}, \frac{5}{10}, \frac{6}{12}, \frac{7}{14}, \ldots$$

We denote this class by $\left[\frac{1}{2}\right]$, although any other pair of the class could be used. The bracket notation denotes the class to which the object enclosed by the brackets belongs; $\left[\frac{10}{20}\right]$ denotes the same equivalence class as $\left[\frac{1}{2}\right]$; $\frac{1}{2}$ is simply a representative of the class $\left[\frac{1}{2}\right]$.

The class to which $\frac{-2}{3}$ belongs is as follows:

$$\ldots, \frac{8}{-12}, \frac{6}{-9}, \frac{4}{-6}, \frac{2}{-3}, \frac{-2}{3}, \frac{-4}{6}, \frac{-6}{9}, \frac{-8}{12}, \frac{-10}{15}, \frac{-12}{18}, \frac{-14}{21}, \ldots$$

We denote this class by $\left[\frac{-2}{3}\right]$. It is the same as $\left[\frac{-6}{9}\right]$ or $\left[\frac{4}{-6}\right]$.

The class to which $\frac{1}{1}$ belongs is as follows:

$$\ldots, \frac{-6}{-6}, \frac{-5}{-5}, \frac{-4}{-4}, \frac{-3}{-3}, \frac{-2}{-2}, \frac{-1}{-1}, \frac{1}{1}, \frac{2}{2}, \frac{3}{3}, \frac{4}{4}, \frac{5}{5}, \frac{6}{6}, \ldots$$

It is denoted by $\left[\frac{1}{1}\right]$ and will play a special role in operations with rational numbers.

Similarly, the class to which $\frac{0}{1}$ belongs plays a special role. The class is denoted by $\left[\frac{0}{1}\right]$ and is as follows:

$$\ldots, \frac{0}{-6}, \frac{0}{-5}, \frac{0}{-4}, \frac{0}{-3}, \frac{0}{-2}, \frac{0}{-1}, \frac{0}{1}, \frac{0}{2}, \frac{0}{3}, \frac{0}{4}, \frac{0}{5}, \frac{0}{6}, \ldots$$

Exercise 7.5

1. Show that $\doteq$ has the symmetric property.
2. Show that $\doteq$ has the reflexive property.
3. Indicate as above the class to which each of the following numerals belong.

(a) $\frac{54}{81}$ (b) $\frac{16}{16}$ (c) $\frac{19}{2}$

(d) $\frac{0}{100}$ (e) $\frac{0}{-3}$ (f) $\frac{7}{36}$

4. Indicate as above the class to which the following numerals belong.

(a) $\frac{-1}{2}$ (b) $\frac{2}{-1}$ (c) $\frac{-2}{3}$

(d) $\frac{-7}{6}$ (e) $\frac{0}{-3}$ (f) $\frac{-22}{2}$

(g) $\frac{2}{-3}$ (h) $\frac{4}{5}$ (i) $\frac{-4}{-5}$

(j) $\frac{1}{-2}$ (k) $\frac{12}{-3}$ (l) $\frac{12}{3}$

5. (a) Show that $\frac{2}{3}$ and $\frac{2 \cdot 2}{2 \cdot 3}$ belong to the same class.

(b) Show that $\frac{2}{3}$ and $\frac{2 \cdot n}{3 \cdot n}$ are related by $\doteq$ for any integer $n \neq 0$.

(c) Show that $\frac{m}{n}$ and $\frac{2m}{2n}$ are equivalent.

(d) Show that $\frac{a}{b}$ and $\frac{na}{nb}$ are equivalent. $n \neq 0$.

6. Use the ordered pairs $\frac{3}{5}, \frac{9}{15}$, and $\frac{-3}{-5}$ and illustrate that the $\doteq$ relation is transitive.

7. What can you say about $\left[\frac{-2}{3}\right]$ and $\left[\frac{2}{-3}\right]$?

8. What do we mean when we write

$$\left[\frac{0}{11}\right] = \left[\frac{0}{4}\right]?$$

9. What do we mean when we write

$$\left[\frac{6}{6}\right] = \left[\frac{-3}{-3}\right]?$$

7.6 RATIONAL NUMBERS AS EQUIVALENCE CLASSES

In the last section we constructed several equivalence classes. We saw how any member of a class might act as a representative of the class to which it belongs. This is the reason for identifying particular ordered pairs with a *class*. The ability to think of a rational number as an equivalence class of ordered pairs of integers will be helpful in understanding fractions in arithmetic. This idea is not new. It is in fact a familiar concept. What comes to mind when you see $\frac{2}{2}$? What comes to mind when you see $\frac{8}{8}$? What comes to mind when you see $\frac{12}{6}$ or $\frac{6}{3}$? When one adds $\frac{2}{3}$ and $\frac{5}{6}$, the usual procedure is to add $\frac{4}{6}$ and $\frac{5}{6}$. That is, $\frac{4}{6}$ is the same, in some sense, as $\frac{2}{3}$.

The objects in the system of rational numbers will be these equivalence classes. We will define the binary operations on these *classes.*

The binary operations will be defined in terms of *representatives of the classes.* Addition and multiplication as we define them may not yield directly the most convenient methods of finding the sum and product of two rational numbers, but the usual (convenient) way of performing these operations can be made reasonable in terms of our definitions.

7.7 ADDITION OF RATIONAL NUMBERS

Let $\frac{3}{4}$ and $\frac{1}{6}$ be representatives of the equivalence classes $[\frac{3}{4}]$ and $[\frac{1}{6}]$, respectively. The usual procedure for handling rational numbers does not make the distinction between the representative of a class and the class itself. For clarity of presentation and ease in understanding computations involving "fractions," we wish to keep this distinction for the present.

To the ordered pair $(\frac{3}{4}, \frac{1}{6})$ the binary operation "addition" assigns the numeral which we write as $(\frac{3}{4} + \frac{1}{6})$. We want this to be an ordered pair of integers in order that the *Closure Law* be satisfied. Furthermore, we want this to be consistent with the addition of integers when we interpret the integers as a subset of the rational numbers.

There are several ways of determining which ordered pair of integers this should be. We will discuss the usual procedure involving the "least common denominator" later. For the present, we find the ordered pair represented by $\frac{3}{4} + \frac{1}{6}$ in the following way:

Example 1

$$\frac{3}{4} + \frac{1}{6} = \frac{3 \cdot 6 + 4 \cdot 1}{4 \cdot 6} = \frac{18 + 4}{24} = \frac{22}{24}$$

Notice that we are using the "names for the same number" interpretation of $=$. Since the relation $\doteq$ as defined for the ordered pairs has the same properties as $=$, when we wish to use the "names for the same number" interpretation, we shall drop the new symbol and revert to the symbol $=$.

In general, we define addition of a/b and c/d as follows:

DEFINITION 7.7. For a/b and c/d representatives of rational numbers,

$$\frac{a}{b} + \frac{c}{d} = \frac{a \cdot d + b \cdot c}{b \cdot d}$$

The expression $\dfrac{ad + bc}{bd}$ represents an ordered pair of integers because the set of integers is closed with respect to addition and multiplication. This procedure is not the usual way of adding numbers of the form $\frac{3}{4}$ and $\frac{1}{6}$. However, it is consistent with the procedure for addition of integers when the ordered pairs are interpreted as integers (see problem 9, Exercise 7.7).

The usual procedure uses the least common denominator with considerable economy of manipulation as follows:

Example 2

$$\frac{3}{4} + \frac{1}{6} = \frac{9}{12} + \frac{2}{12} = \frac{9 + 2}{12} = \frac{11}{12}$$

The two methods involve essentially the same amount of work when the denominators are relatively prime.

Example 3

$$\frac{3}{4} + \frac{1}{5} = \frac{3 \cdot 5 + 4 \cdot 1}{4 \cdot 5} = \frac{15 + 4}{20} = \frac{19}{20}$$

$$\frac{3}{4} + \frac{1}{5} = \frac{15}{20} + \frac{4}{20} = \frac{15 + 4}{20} = \frac{19}{20}$$

In either case, the important thing to note is that the sums may not look the same but they will be related by "equals" in the sense of "names for the same number." From Examples 1 and 2 above, $\frac{22}{24} = \frac{11}{12}$ because these numerals are simply different names for the same number. Thinking of the rational numbers as equivalence classes, we see that $\frac{22}{24}$ and $\frac{11}{12}$ are different representatives of the class $[\frac{11}{12}]$.

Let us recapitulate. We wanted to define addition of "rational numbers." We wanted addition to satisfy the Closure Law. We also wanted the sum to be uniquely determined, that is, we wanted the binary operation to assign to any particular pair of numbers one and only one number. This is the reason we define the operation on the *classes*. Thus a representative of the class $[\frac{3}{4}]$ added to a representative of the class $[\frac{1}{6}]$ is a representative of the class $[\frac{3}{4}+\frac{1}{6}]$.

We have seen that this class can be determined in two ways. One way identified this class as $[\frac{22}{24}]$, another way as $[\frac{11}{12}]$. But $\frac{22}{24} \doteq \frac{11}{12}$, so $[\frac{22}{24}] = [\frac{11}{12}]$.

$$\frac{3}{4} \text{ is in } \left\{\ldots, \frac{-6}{-8}, \frac{-3}{-4}, \frac{3}{4}, \frac{6}{8}, \frac{9}{12}, \frac{12}{16}, \frac{15}{20}, \ldots\right\}$$

$$\frac{1}{6} \text{ is in } \left\{\ldots, \frac{-2}{-12}, \frac{-1}{-6}, \frac{1}{6}, \frac{2}{12}, \frac{3}{18}, \frac{4}{24}, \frac{5}{30}, \ldots\right\}$$

$$\frac{3}{4}+\frac{1}{6} \text{ is in } \left\{\ldots, \frac{-22}{-24}, \frac{-11}{-12}, \frac{11}{12}, \frac{22}{24}, \frac{33}{36}, \ldots\right\}$$

The circled numbers indicate addition as defined. The numbers in squares indicate addition in the usual way.

We state, but do not prove, the fact that *addition as defined on the classes is independent of the representatives of the classes.* Any representative of $[\frac{3}{4}]$ added to any representative of $[\frac{1}{6}]$ is in the class $[\frac{3}{4}+\frac{1}{6}]$. In other words, the *class* of the sum is uniquely determined. This is essentially the reason why the procedure as defined produces the "same" result as the method of least common denominators. The latter method merely uses a more convenient set of representatives of the classes. This usually results in less work in determining the class of the sum.

Exercise 7.7

1. Verify that $\frac{ad+bc}{bd}$ is an ordered pair of integers with nonzero denominator if b and d are nonzero integers.
2. Add $\frac{12}{16}$ and $\frac{4}{24}$ and show that your result is equivalent to $\frac{33}{36}$.
3. Add $\frac{-3}{-4}$ and $\frac{1}{6}$ and show that your result is equivalent to $\frac{11}{12}$.
4. Explain the following: $\left[\frac{3}{4}\right]+\left[\frac{1}{6}\right]=\left[\frac{3}{4}+\frac{1}{6}\right]$.
5. Explain the following: $\left[\frac{3}{4}+\frac{1}{6}\right]=\left[\frac{3\cdot 6+4\cdot 1}{4\cdot 6}\right]$.
6. Add the following:

(a) $\frac{2}{3}+\frac{0}{1}$ (b) $\frac{0}{3}+\frac{4}{3}$

(c) $\frac{2}{3}+\frac{-4}{6}$ (d) $\frac{1}{2}+\frac{1}{2}$

7. Add the following:

(a) $\frac{39}{27} + \frac{54}{144}$ (b) $\frac{369}{288} + \frac{39}{306}$

8. Show that addition as defined on the classes is independent of the representatives chosen.

9. Let the integer m correspond to the rational number $\left[\frac{m}{1}\right]$, and the integer n correspond to the rational number $\left[\frac{n}{1}\right]$. Then show that addition as defined for rational numbers produces a sum that corresponds to $(m + n)$.

7.8 MULTIPLICATION OF RATIONAL NUMBERS

Let $\frac{1}{2}$ and $\frac{3}{5}$ be representatives of the equivalence classes to which they belong. The binary operation, multiplication, assigns to the pair $(\frac{1}{2}, \frac{3}{5})$ the numeral $(\frac{1}{2} \cdot \frac{3}{5})$. Again, we want this product to be an ordered pair of integers so that multiplication will satisfy the Closure Law. This ordered pair is determined as follows:

$$\frac{1}{2} \cdot \frac{3}{5} = \frac{1 \cdot 3}{2 \cdot 5} = \frac{3}{10}$$

Bear in mind that the numerals $\frac{1}{2}$, $\frac{3}{5}$, and $\frac{3}{10}$ are representatives of the classes $[\frac{1}{2}]$, $[\frac{3}{5}]$, and $[\frac{3}{10}]$.

In general, we define multiplication of rational numbers as follows:

DEFINITION 7.8. For representatives of rational numbers m/n and r/s

$$\frac{m}{n} \cdot \frac{r}{s} = \frac{m \cdot r}{n \cdot s}.$$

The product represents an ordered pair of integers.

The binary operations "addition" and "multiplication" for rational numbers could more properly be written as follows:

$$\left[\frac{a}{b}\right] + \left[\frac{c}{d}\right] = \left[\frac{ad + bc}{bd}\right]$$

$$\left[\frac{a}{b}\right] \cdot \left[\frac{c}{d}\right] = \left[\frac{a \cdot c}{b \cdot d}\right].$$

The brackets denote the equivalence class to which the numeral between the brackets belongs. We repeat, it is only in terms of the equivalence classes that the binary operations are *well defined.*

Exercise 7.8

1. Multiply: $\left(\frac{7}{3}\right)\left(\frac{2}{9}\right)$. **2.** Multiply: $\left(\frac{4}{6}\right)\left(\frac{6}{4}\right)$.

3. Multiply: $\left(\frac{8}{12}\right)\left(\frac{6}{4}\right)$.

4. Multiply: $\left(\frac{3}{3}\right)\left(\frac{1}{2}\right)$.

5. Write each of the following as a product, e.g., $\frac{14}{10} = \frac{2\cdot 7}{2\cdot 5} = \left(\frac{2}{2}\right)\left(\frac{7}{5}\right)$.

(a) $\frac{35}{49}$ (b) $\frac{33}{39}$

6. Show that multiplication is well defined, that is, the product is independent of the representative chosen.

7. Let the integer m correspond to $\left[\frac{m}{1}\right]$ and the integer n correspond to $\left[\frac{n}{1}\right]$. Show that multiplication as defined for rational numbers gives a product that corresponds to $m\cdot n$.

8. Carry out the indicated binary operation as defined.

(a) $\frac{5}{7}+\frac{5}{9}$ (b) $\frac{2}{3}+\frac{4}{3}$ (c) $\frac{4}{3}+\frac{0}{2}$

(d) $\frac{0}{5}+\frac{2}{5}$ (e) $\frac{16}{4}+\frac{12}{4}$ (f) $\frac{0}{1}+\frac{2}{1}$

(g) $\frac{-3}{2}+\frac{3}{2}$ (h) $\frac{3}{2}+\frac{3}{-2}$ (i) $\frac{4}{9}+\frac{0}{6}$

(j) $\frac{4}{9}+\frac{4}{-9}$ (k) $\frac{2994}{876658}+\frac{779922}{9197245}$

9. Carry out the indicated binary operation as defined.

(a) $\frac{2}{3}\cdot\frac{6}{5}$ (b) $\frac{9}{3}\cdot\frac{10}{7}$ (c) $\frac{13}{1}\cdot\frac{1}{13}$

(d) $\frac{19}{4}\cdot\frac{3}{3}$ (e) $\frac{7}{6}\cdot\frac{1}{1}$ (f) $\frac{4}{7}\cdot\frac{0}{2}$

(g) $\frac{6}{3}\cdot\frac{8}{2}$ (h) $\frac{5}{4}\cdot\frac{4}{4}$ (i) $\frac{7}{1}\cdot\frac{1}{1}$

(j) $\frac{2}{1}\cdot\frac{1}{2}$ (k) $\frac{2994}{876658}\cdot\frac{779922}{9187245}$

10. Explain the meaning of each of the following:

(a) $\left[\frac{6}{8}\right]+\left[\frac{4}{8}\right]=\left[\frac{5}{4}\right]$ (b) $\left[\frac{4}{7}\right]+\left[\frac{0}{6}\right]=\left[\frac{4}{7}\right]$

(c) $\left[\frac{7}{12}\right]+\left[\frac{-7}{12}\right]=\left[\frac{0}{1}\right]$ (d) $\left[\frac{6}{9}\right]+\left[\frac{2}{-3}\right]=\left[\frac{0}{-1}\right]$

(e) $\left[\frac{0}{100}\right]+\left[\frac{1}{1}\right]=\left[\frac{7}{7}\right]$

11. Explain the meaning of each of the following:

(a) $\left[\frac{9}{18}\right] \cdot \left[\frac{6}{3}\right] = \left[\frac{1}{1}\right]$ (b) $\left[\frac{4}{4}\right] \cdot \left[\frac{5}{7}\right] = \left[\frac{5}{7}\right]$

(c) $\left[\frac{0}{7}\right] \cdot \left[\frac{1}{1}\right] = \left[\frac{0}{1}\right]$ (d) $\left[\frac{18}{18}\right] \cdot \left[\frac{27}{36}\right] = \left[\frac{3}{4}\right]$

(e) $\left[\frac{-2}{3}\right] \cdot \left[\frac{4}{5}\right] = \left[\frac{-8}{15}\right]$

12. (a) Give a numerical example illustrating the fact that addition of rational numbers is commutative.
(b) Give a numerical example illustrating the fact that addition of rational numbers is associative.

13. (a) Give a numerical example illustrating the fact that multiplication of rational numbers is commutative.
(b) Give a numerical example illustrating the fact that multiplication of rational numbers is associative.

14. (a) $\left[\frac{5}{3} \cdot \frac{4}{7}\right] + \left[\frac{5}{3} \cdot \frac{9}{4}\right] = ?$ (b) $\left[\frac{4}{7} + \frac{9}{4}\right] \cdot \left[\frac{5}{3}\right] = ?$

15. (a) $\left[\frac{5}{5} \cdot \frac{16}{9}\right] + \left[\frac{7}{5} \cdot \frac{16}{9}\right] = ?$ (b) $\left[\frac{5}{5} + \frac{7}{5}\right] \cdot \left[\frac{16}{9}\right] = ?$

16. (a) $\left[\frac{0}{1} + \frac{5}{5}\right] \cdot \left[\frac{7}{7}\right] = ?$ (b) $\left[\frac{6}{3} + \frac{2}{-1}\right] \cdot \left[\frac{17}{19}\right] = ?$

17. (a) $\frac{784327}{2994463} + \frac{9548012}{1988544} = ?$ (b) $\frac{784327}{2994463} \cdot \frac{9548012}{1988544} = ?$

7.9 NAMING THE CLASSES (REDUCING FRACTIONS)

Any of the number pairs in an equivalence class can be used to name the class. However, among all the number pairs in an equivalence class, there is always one that is in some sense the simplest or most convenient, for example, $\frac{8}{12}$ is in the following class:

$$\ldots, \frac{-14}{-21}, \frac{-12}{-18}, \frac{-10}{-15}, \frac{-8}{-12}, \frac{-6}{-9}, \frac{-4}{-6}, \frac{-2}{-3}, \frac{2}{3}, \frac{4}{6}, \frac{6}{9}, \frac{8}{12}, \frac{10}{15}, \frac{12}{18}, \ldots$$

When one encounters $\frac{8}{12}$ one naturally thinks of $\frac{2}{3}$, so we tend to identify $\frac{8}{12}$ with $\frac{2}{3}$. We do not mean to imply that the two numerals are identical. We mean simply that $\frac{8}{12}$ and $\frac{2}{3}$ are in the same class, namely the class $[\frac{2}{3}]$ which we call $\frac{2}{3}$. We call this class $\frac{2}{3}$ because $\frac{2}{3}$ is the representative that is in *simplified* or *reduced* form.

DEFINITION 7.9. A rational number, $\left[\frac{m}{n}\right]$, is in *reduced* form if the greatest common divisor of the integers m and n is 1, n positive.

Notice that $\frac{2}{3}$ is in reduced form; $\frac{7}{12}$ is in reduced form; $\frac{14}{24}$ is not in reduced form. If the equivalence class is written out as above, the reduced form is easy to pick out. It is that element whose denominator is the least positive integer in the set of denominators.

Without writing out the equivalence class, there are essentially two approaches to "reducing" fractions. One approach uses the fundamental theorem of arithmetic. The other is based on finding the g.c.d. of the two integers. We discuss both approaches because both are used.

Let us simplify $\frac{6}{8}$ and $\frac{1,439,900}{3,496,900}$. When we simplify, or reduce, $\frac{6}{8}$, it is easily recognized as $\frac{3}{4}$. To a beginner, however, the process appears as $\frac{6}{8} = \frac{3 \cdot 2}{4 \cdot 2}$. We saw in Section 7.5 that $\frac{3 \cdot 2}{4 \cdot 2}$ is equivalent to $\frac{3}{4}$, that is, we factor the two integers and use the definition of our relation. This same technique will work for reducing $\frac{1,439,900}{3,496,900}$ but involves a great deal of computation. An alternate method for reducing $\frac{1,439,900}{3,496,900}$ is by finding the greatest common divisor of the number pair using the Euclidean algorithm. The reduced form is easily recognized as soon as it is put in the form $\frac{md}{nd}$, where d is the g.c.d. of the two integers. The problem of finding the reduced form of this particular number is left as an exercise. One gains a healthy respect for the Euclidean algorithm in such applications.

Exercise 7.9

Find the name of the class to which each of the following belong. That is, *simplify* each of the following:

1. $\frac{72}{144}$

2. $\frac{727}{1441}$

3. $\frac{163264}{2754108}$

4. $\frac{1,439,900}{3,496,900}$

5. $\frac{39 \cdot 27}{52 \cdot 26}$

6. $\frac{228 \cdot 19}{204 \cdot 19}$

7. $\frac{39}{52} \cdot \frac{26}{27}$

8. $\frac{72}{38} + \frac{16}{19}$

9. $\frac{-54}{81}$

10. $\frac{108}{-162}$

11. $\frac{0}{5}$

12. $\frac{27}{27}$

7.10 THE SYSTEM OF RATIONAL NUMBERS

We review briefly the development of the system of rational numbers as far as we have progressed. We considered all possible ordered pairs of integers of the form m/n, where $n \neq 0$. We defined a criterion for determining when these ordered pairs are "related." This relation, $\doteq$, was shown to be an equivalence relation. This brought a certain amount of orderliness to the collection of the ordered pairs of integers, that is, the set of ordered pairs of integers was partitioned into disjoint classes of related elements. We denoted these classes by $\left[\frac{m}{n}\right]$. The binary operations were defined on these classes in terms of representatives of the classes.

Example 1

$$\left[\frac{2}{3}\right] + \left[\frac{5}{6}\right] = \left[\frac{2}{3} + \frac{5}{6}\right] = \left[\frac{2\cdot 6 + 3\cdot 5}{3\cdot 6}\right]$$

$$\left[\frac{2}{3}\right] \cdot \left[\frac{5}{6}\right] = \left[\frac{2}{3} \cdot \frac{5}{6}\right] = \left[\frac{2\cdot 5}{3\cdot 6}\right]$$

Recall again the meaning of these symbols. They are to be interpreted to mean that any representative in the class $\left[\frac{2}{3}\right]$ added to any representative in the class $\left[\frac{5}{6}\right]$ is an element of the class of the ordered pairs obtained by carrying out the indicated operations in the last brackets.

Simplifying fractions then amounted to finding the usual name of the class of the resultant, that is, the name of the class $\left[\frac{2\cdot 6 + 3\cdot 5}{3\cdot 6}\right]$ is found by reducing $\frac{12 + 15}{18} = \frac{27}{18}$ to $\frac{3}{2}$. We write this $\left[\frac{2}{3}\right] + \left[\frac{5}{6}\right] = \left[\frac{3}{2}\right]$. For convenience and economy of symbols, this can be shortened to $\frac{2}{3} + \frac{5}{6} = \frac{3}{2}$ without loss of meaning.

Similar remarks apply to multiplication.

7.10a Identities and Inverses

The *additive identity* for the system of rational numbers is that element which when added to any other element leaves it unchanged.

Example 1

$$\frac{0}{1} + \frac{3}{7} = \frac{0\cdot 7 + 1\cdot 3}{1\cdot 7} = \frac{0 + 3}{7} = \frac{3}{7}$$

$$\frac{a}{b} + \frac{0}{1} = \frac{a\cdot 1 + b\cdot 0}{b\cdot 1} = \frac{a + 0}{b} = \frac{a}{b}$$

It appears that $\frac{0}{1}$ is the *additive identity.* But $\frac{0}{1}$ is just one representative of the class $[\frac{0}{1}]$. Another element of this class is $\frac{0}{5}$.

Example 2

$$\frac{3}{7}+\frac{0}{5}=\frac{3\cdot 5+7\cdot 0}{7\cdot 5}=\frac{3\cdot 5+0}{7\cdot 5}=\frac{3\cdot 5}{7\cdot 5}$$

But

$$\frac{3\cdot 5}{7\cdot 5}\doteq\frac{3}{7}$$

It is more appropriate to write

$$\left[\frac{3}{7}\right]+\left[\frac{0}{1}\right]=\left[\frac{3}{7}\right]$$

If we interpret this statement correctly, any member of $\left[\frac{0}{1}\right]$ can act as an additive identity, that is,

$$\frac{a}{b}+\frac{0}{n}\doteq\frac{a}{b},\quad n\neq 0$$

The *multiplicative identity* is defined in much the same way with respect to multiplication. The *multiplicative identity* for the system of rational numbers is that element which when multiplied into any rational number gives a product which is identically equal to that number.

Example 3

$$\frac{4}{5}\cdot\frac{1}{1}=\frac{4\cdot 1}{5\cdot 1}=\frac{4}{5}.$$

Remembering that $\frac{4}{5}$ and $\frac{1}{1}$ are representatives of the classes to which they belong, we should write

$$\left[\frac{4}{5}\right]\cdot\left[\frac{1}{1}\right]=\left[\frac{4}{5}\right].$$

We are saying that any member of the class $[\frac{1}{1}]$ can act as the multiplicative identity, that is,

$$\frac{a}{b}\cdot\frac{n}{n}\doteq\frac{a}{b}\qquad\text{for any integer } n\neq 0.$$

By the *additive inverse* of the element m/n in the system of rational numbers we mean that element which when added to m/n is the additive identity of the system of rational numbers. Just as the additive inverse of n in the system of integers is denoted by $-n$, we denote the additive inverse of m/n by $-m/n$. Thus

$$\frac{m}{n}+\left(-\frac{m}{n}\right)=\frac{0}{1}.$$

Note, however, that

$$\frac{m}{n}+\frac{-m}{n}=\frac{mn+(-mn)}{nn}=\frac{0}{n^2}\doteq\frac{0}{1},$$

and
$$\frac{m}{n} + \frac{m}{-n} = \frac{-mn + mn}{-nn} = \frac{0}{-n^2} \doteq \frac{0}{1}.$$

That is, $\frac{-m}{n}$ and $\frac{m}{-n}$ behave the same as $\left(-\frac{m}{n}\right)$. We found earlier that $\left[\frac{-m}{n}\right] = \left[\frac{m}{-n}\right]$. (See problem 4h, Exercise 7.4.) We are now saying that

$$\left[-\frac{m}{n}\right] = \left[\frac{-m}{n}\right] \quad \text{and} \quad \left[-\frac{m}{n}\right] = \left[\frac{m}{-n}\right].$$

In general, $-\frac{m}{n} = \frac{-m}{n} = \frac{m}{-n}$, where we are using the "names of the same number" meaning of the "equals" relation. We adopt the convention here, as we did with the integers, and write $\frac{7}{5} - \frac{2}{3}$ instead of $\frac{7}{5} + \left(-\frac{2}{3}\right)$.

Recall that we introduced the negative integers so that we would have a mathematical system rich enough to provide a solution to the equation

$$m + x = n,$$

for any pair of whole numbers m and n. This system was called the system of integers.

We constructed the rational numbers in order to have a number system rich enough to provide a solution to the equation

$$n \cdot x = m,$$

for any pair of integers m and n, except when $n = 0$. More generally, we constructed a number system rich enough to provide a solution to the equation

$$a \cdot x = b,$$

for any pair of numbers a and b in our system, where a is not in the zero class. Since the elements of our system of rational numbers can be written in the form $\left[\frac{m}{n}\right]$, we are saying that our number system is complete enough to provide solutions to the equation

$$\left[\frac{m}{n}\right] \cdot x = \left[\frac{r}{s}\right],$$

where $\left[\frac{m}{n}\right]$ and $\left[\frac{r}{s}\right]$ are any rational numbers and $\left[\frac{m}{n}\right] \neq \left[\frac{0}{1}\right]$.

Example 4

Find x so that $$\frac{3}{1} \cdot x = \frac{1}{1}.$$

We have $$x = \frac{1}{3},$$

since $$\frac{3}{1} \cdot \frac{1}{3} = \frac{3 \cdot 1}{1 \cdot 3} = \frac{3}{3} \doteq \frac{1}{1}.$$

The *multiplicative inverse* of any rational number $\left[\frac{m}{n}\right]$, which is not a member of $\left[\frac{0}{1}\right]$, is that element which when multiplied by $\left[\frac{m}{n}\right]$ gives the multiplicative identity.

The multiplicative inverse of $\left[\frac{m}{n}\right]$ will be denoted by $\left[\frac{m}{n}\right]^{-1}$.

If we use the letter a to represent a rational number, we will write the multiplicative inverse of a as a^{-1}. The multiplicative inverse is also called the *reciprocal*.

We defined $\left[\frac{m}{n}\right]^{-1}$ as that element which when multiplied by $\left[\frac{m}{n}\right]$ is $\left[\frac{1}{1}\right]$.

$$\left[\frac{m}{n}\right] \cdot \left[\frac{m}{n}\right]^{-1} = \left[\frac{1}{1}\right]$$

Example 5

$$\frac{3}{11} \cdot \left(\frac{3}{11}\right)^{-1} = \frac{1}{1}.$$

Notice, however, that

$$\frac{3}{11} \cdot \frac{11}{3} = \frac{33}{33} = \frac{1}{1}.$$

The numbers $\left(\frac{3}{11}\right)^{-1}$ and $\frac{11}{3}$ both give the multiplicative identity when multiplied by $\frac{3}{11}$. So we write $\left(\frac{3}{11}\right)^{-1} = \frac{11}{3}$, in the sense that these are both names of the same number.

In general,

$$\left[\frac{m}{n}\right]^{-1} = \left[\frac{n}{m}\right]$$

That is, $$\left[\frac{m}{n}\right] \cdot \left[\frac{n}{m}\right] = \left[\frac{1}{1}\right]$$

In the special case when $n = 1$, $m/n = m/1$, and we have

$$\left[\frac{m}{1}\right]^{-1} = \left[\frac{1}{m}\right]$$

Exercise 7.10

1. Write the additive inverse of each of the following and carry out the addition to verify the correctness of your choice.

(a) $\frac{5}{1}$ (b) $\frac{137}{329}$ (c) $\frac{-19}{3}$ (d) $\frac{2}{-10}$

(e) $\frac{6}{-7}$ (f) $\frac{5}{8}$ (g) $\frac{0}{-1}$ (h) $\frac{-3}{-4}$

(i) $\frac{0}{10}$ (j) $\frac{239}{316}$ (k) $\frac{m}{n}$ (l) $-\frac{m}{n}$

2. Write the multiplicative inverse of each of the following rational numbers in two ways and carry out the computation to verify the correctness of your choice.

(a) $\frac{2}{5}$ (b) $\frac{9}{14}$ (c) $\frac{17}{6}$ (d) $\frac{100}{19}$

(e) $\frac{-2}{11}$ (f) $\frac{8}{-3}$ (g) $\frac{-5}{-4}$ (h) $\frac{6}{1}$

(i) $\frac{9}{1}$ (j) $\frac{1}{23}$ (k) $\frac{33}{3}$ (l) $\frac{-13}{26}$

(m) $\frac{0}{1}$ (n) $\frac{2}{2}$ (o) $\frac{4}{1}$ (p) $\frac{1976}{1967}$

3. Carry out the indicated operations and simplify.

(a) $\frac{2}{5}+\frac{5}{2}$ (b) $\left(\frac{7}{3}+\frac{7}{3}\right)+\frac{7}{3}$

(c) $\frac{5}{3}\cdot\left(\frac{3}{17}+\frac{9}{4}\right)$ (d) $\frac{1}{3}+\left(\frac{1}{5}\right)^{-1}$

(e) $\left(\frac{1}{3}\right)^{-1}+\left(\frac{1}{5}\right)^{-1}$

4. What is the additive inverse of each of the numbers in problem 2?

5. What is the multiplicative inverse of each of the numbers in problem 1?

6. Carry out the indicated operations:

(a) $\frac{2}{9}-\left(\frac{9}{2}\right)^{-1}$ (b) $\frac{5}{7}-\left(\frac{7}{5}\right)^{-1}$

(c) $\frac{11}{5}-\frac{4}{2}$ (d) $\frac{3}{4}-\frac{0}{2}$

The reader was asked in Exercise 7.8 to illustrate the commutative, associative, and distributive properties of addition and multiplication of rational numbers through the use of numerical examples. We will state these as laws which govern the behavior of operations with rational numbers, even though they can be proved to be satisfied by using the properties of the integers and the definitions of equality, addition, and multiplication of rational numbers.

DEFINITION 7.10a. By the *system of rational numbers* we mean the set

$$R = \left\{x | x = \left[\frac{a}{b}\right], \ a \text{ and } b \text{ integers}, \ b \neq 0\right\},$$

the binary operations, addition (+) and multiplication (·), the relation $\left[\frac{a}{b}\right] = \left[\frac{c}{d}\right]$ if and only if $ad = bc$, and the following laws:

(*Hereafter, for simplicity, we will omit the use of the square brackets.*)

Closure Laws

1. For $\frac{a}{b}$ and $\frac{c}{d}$ in R there is a uniquely determined sum, which we write $\frac{a}{b} + \frac{c}{d} = \frac{ad + bc}{bd}$ in R.

2. For $\frac{a}{b}$ and $\frac{c}{d}$ in R there is a uniquely determined product, which we write $\frac{a}{b} \cdot \frac{c}{d} = \frac{a \cdot c}{b \cdot d}$ in R.

Associative Laws. For $\frac{a}{b}$, $\frac{c}{d}$, and $\frac{e}{f}$ in R

3. $\frac{a}{b} + \left(\frac{c}{d} + \frac{e}{f}\right) = \left(\frac{a}{b} + \frac{c}{d}\right) + \frac{e}{f}$.

4. $\frac{a}{b} \cdot \left(\frac{c}{d} \cdot \frac{e}{f}\right) = \left(\frac{a}{b} \cdot \frac{c}{d}\right) \cdot \frac{e}{f}$.

Commutative Laws. For $\frac{a}{b}$ and $\frac{c}{d}$ in R

5. $\frac{a}{b} + \frac{c}{d} = \frac{c}{d} + \frac{a}{b}$.

6. $\frac{a}{b} \cdot \frac{c}{d} = \frac{c}{d} \cdot \frac{a}{b}$.

Distributive Law. For $\frac{a}{b}$, $\frac{c}{d}$, and $\frac{e}{f}$ in R

7. $\frac{a}{b} \cdot \left(\frac{c}{d} + \frac{e}{f}\right) = \frac{a}{b} \cdot \frac{c}{d} + \frac{a}{b} \cdot \frac{e}{f}$.

Identities

8. There is a unique element, $\frac{0}{1}$, such that for any $\frac{a}{b}$ in R, $\frac{a}{b} + \frac{0}{1} = \frac{0}{1} + \frac{a}{b} = \frac{a}{b}$.

9. There is a unique element, $\frac{1}{1}$, such that for any $\frac{a}{b}$ in R, $\frac{a}{b} \cdot \frac{1}{1} = \frac{1}{1} \cdot \frac{a}{b} = \frac{a}{b}$.

Additive Inverses

10. For each $\frac{a}{b}$ in R there is a unique element, $-\frac{a}{b} = \frac{-a}{b}$, in R such that $\frac{a}{b} + \left(-\frac{a}{b}\right) = \left(-\frac{a}{b}\right) + \frac{a}{b} = \frac{0}{1}$, where $\frac{0}{1}$ is the additive identity.

Multiplicative Inverses

11. For each $\frac{a}{b}$ in R, $\frac{a}{b} \neq \frac{0}{1}$, there is a unique element, $\left(\frac{a}{b}\right)^{-1} = \frac{b}{a}$, in R such that $\frac{a}{b} \cdot \left(\frac{a}{b}\right)^{-1} = \left(\frac{a}{b}\right)^{-1} \cdot \frac{a}{b} = \frac{1}{1}$, where $\frac{1}{1}$ is the multiplicative identity.

Exercise 7.10a

1. Use numerical examples to illustrate each of the laws in the preceding section.
2. State in words the meaning of each of the laws in the preceding section.
3. Is the set of rational numbers closed with respect to subtraction?
4. Use the properties of the system of integers and the definition of addition and multiplication for rational numbers to show that

   (a) $\frac{a}{b} + \frac{c}{d} = \frac{c}{d} + \frac{a}{b}$

   (b) $\frac{a}{b} \cdot \frac{c}{d} = \frac{c}{d} \cdot \frac{a}{b}$

   (c) $\frac{a}{b} \cdot \left(\frac{c}{d} + \frac{e}{f}\right) = \frac{a}{b} \cdot \frac{c}{d} + \frac{a}{b} \cdot \frac{e}{f}$

5. Write a cancellation law for the addition of rational numbers and prove it.
6. Write a cancellation law for the multiplication of rational numbers and prove it.
7. If $a \cdot b = 0$, then $a = 0$ or $b = 0$.

   Proof. If $a = 0$, then the statement is true.
   If $a \neq 0$, then $1/a$ is the multiplicative inverse of a.

   (a) Use this fact to show that if $a \neq 0$, $b = 0$.
   (b) Use the statement to show that if $(x - 3)(x - 7) = 0$, then $x = 3$ or $x = 7$.

7.10b The Integers as a Subsystem of the Rational Numbers

We have studied the system of integers as a number system apart from the system of rational numbers. The realization that each is a number system with its own interesting properties is of considerable importance. It represents the point of view of the algebraists and number theorists who are interested in the structure of mathematics. This concept is fundamental in the understanding of the solvability of equations. As we have repeatedly emphasized in our development, *the solvability of equations depends on the number system in which the equation is to be solved.*

It is desirable to interpret the system of integers as a subsystem of the system of rational numbers. Eventually we will consider the system of rational numbers as a subsystem of the system of real numbers.

We have identified $\left[\frac{m}{1}\right]$ with m and $\left[\frac{n}{1}\right]$ with n, where m and n are integers, and examined their behavior under the binary operations (see problem 9, Exercise 7.7 and problem 7, Exercise 7.8). Addition and multiplication of those rational numbers identified with the integers were consistent with addition and multiplication of the integers.

We now see that this same identification of integers with rational numbers, that is, m corresponding to $m/1$, gives us

$$m^{-1} = \frac{1}{m}. \qquad \text{(see Section 7.10)}$$

This is also consistent with the definition of exponents (see Section 4.1).

Example 1

$$\frac{7}{1} + \frac{5}{1} = \frac{7\cdot 1 + 1\cdot 5}{1\cdot 1} = \frac{7+5}{1} = \frac{12}{1} \qquad \text{Rational numbers}$$

$$7 + 5 = 12 \qquad \text{Integers}$$

$$12 = \frac{12}{1} \qquad \text{Names for the same number}$$

$$\frac{7}{1} \cdot \frac{5}{1} = \frac{7\cdot 5}{1\cdot 1} = \frac{35}{1} \qquad \text{Rational numbers}$$

$$7\cdot 5 = 35 \qquad \text{Integers}$$

$$35 = \frac{35}{1} \qquad \text{Names for the same number}$$

Thus the system of rational numbers actually contains a subsystem which acts just like the integers. They are not exactly the same as the integers because they are classes of ordered pairs of integers. We will take the naive point of view that because they act exactly like the integers they can be interpreted as integers. Hereafter we will use m and $m/1$ interchangeably as names for the same number.

7.11 INTERPRETATIONS OF RATIONAL NUMBERS

As indicated in Section 7.2, we now turn to the other interpretations of rational numbers.

7.11a The "Division" Interpretation

We have identified the integers with particular rational numbers, that is,

$$\frac{2}{1} = 2 \quad \text{or} \quad 2 = \frac{2}{1},$$

$$\frac{3}{1} = 3 \quad \text{or} \quad 3 = \frac{3}{1},$$

$$\frac{n}{1} = n \quad \text{or} \quad n = \frac{n}{1},$$

and so forth. But $\frac{2}{1}$ is just one of the representatives of the class $[\frac{2}{1}]$. We could use $\frac{4}{2}$, $\frac{6}{3}$, $\frac{8}{4}$, and so forth, as representatives of this class:

$$\tfrac{4}{2} = \tfrac{6}{3} = \tfrac{8}{4} = 2.$$

To establish a connection between m/n and division, let us return to our definition of "divides" on the set of integers. Recall that $a|b$ if there is an integer k such that $b = a \cdot k$. This can also be stated, b "divided by" a is k or, with the usual symbol, $b \div a = k$.

Since $8 = 4 \cdot 2$, $4|8$. Using the "divided by" language, we have $8 \div 4 = 2$. But from the statement above we see that $\frac{8}{4} = 2$. Then $\frac{8}{4}$ can be interpreted as $8 \div 4$. This is the "division" interpretation of the rational number $\frac{8}{4}$.

Generalizing, we say that m/n can be interpreted as $m \div n$.

The "division" interpretation serves many purposes. We will see in a later section how it is used to obtain a very useful representation of numbers.

7.11b Division of Fractions

The usual rule associated with the division of fractions is "invert the denominator and multiply."

Example 1

$$\frac{\frac{3}{7}}{\frac{2}{11}} = \frac{3}{7} \cdot \frac{11}{2} = \frac{33}{14}$$

The explanation of this procedure is based on the fact that a/a can be used as a representative of the class $[\frac{1}{1}]$, the multiplicative identity for the rational numbers. The choice of a is that number which, when multiplied by the denominator, gives $\frac{1}{1} = 1$. In the above example we would choose a to be the multiplicative inverse of $\frac{2}{11}$.

Example 2

$$\left(\frac{2}{11}\right)^{-1} = \frac{11}{2}$$

$$\frac{\frac{3}{7}}{\frac{2}{11}} = \frac{\frac{3}{7}}{\frac{2}{11}} \cdot \frac{\frac{11}{2}}{\frac{11}{2}} = \frac{\frac{3}{7} \cdot \frac{11}{2}}{\frac{2}{11} \cdot \frac{11}{2}} = \frac{\frac{33}{14}}{\frac{1}{1}} = \frac{\frac{33}{14}}{1} = \frac{33}{14}.$$

Notice that we are using the fact that

$$\frac{\frac{3}{7}}{\frac{2}{11}} \cdot \frac{\frac{11}{2}}{\frac{11}{2}} = \frac{\frac{3}{7}}{\frac{2}{11}}.$$

That is, that $\frac{\frac{11}{2}}{\frac{11}{2}}$ is a form of the multiplicative identity.

Example 2 illustrates the procedure that is being presented in many of the newer arithmetic textbooks.

An alternate approach to the division of fractions would be to consider the type of problem that requires a numeral of the form $\frac{\frac{3}{7}}{\frac{2}{11}}$ as an answer. This can be interpreted as a special case of b/a where b/a is that number which when multiplied by a gives b, where a and b are rational numbers, that is, b/a is the solution of the problem

$$a \cdot x = b.$$

The numeral $\frac{\frac{3}{7}}{\frac{2}{11}}$ can be interpreted as the solution of the equation:

$$\tfrac{2}{11} \cdot x = \tfrac{3}{7}.$$

We can solve for x by multiplying both sides of the equation by the multiplicative inverse of $\frac{2}{11}$ and making use of the Commutative and Associative Laws.

$$\begin{aligned} \tfrac{2}{11} \cdot x &= \tfrac{3}{7} \\ (\tfrac{2}{11})^{-1} \cdot \tfrac{2}{11} \cdot x &= \tfrac{3}{7} \cdot (\tfrac{2}{11})^{-1} \\ 1 \cdot x &= \tfrac{3}{7} \cdot (\tfrac{2}{11})^{-1} \\ x &= \tfrac{3}{7} \cdot \tfrac{11}{2}. \end{aligned}$$

It follows that

$$\frac{\frac{3}{7}}{\frac{2}{11}} = \tfrac{3}{7} \cdot \tfrac{11}{2}.$$

Exercise 7.11b

1. Carry out the indicated operations:

(a) $\frac{\frac{2}{3}}{\frac{3}{4}}$ (b) $\frac{\frac{5}{6}}{\frac{3}{6}}$ (c) $\frac{\frac{5}{2}}{\frac{3}{4}}$

2. Solve each of the following equations:

(a) $\frac{3}{4} \cdot x = \frac{5}{6}$ (b) $\frac{11}{3} \cdot x = \frac{2}{3}$ (c) $\frac{4}{7} \cdot x = \frac{7}{4}$

3. What is the multiplicative inverse of each of the following:

(a) $\frac{2}{3}$ (b) 1 (c) $\frac{1}{5}$

(d) $(\frac{3}{4})^{-1}$ (e) 31 (f) $(\frac{6}{1})^{-1}$

4. What is the additive inverse of each of the following:

(a) $\frac{4}{5}$ (b) $\frac{3}{4} + \frac{2}{3}$ (c) $\frac{3}{4} - \frac{2}{3}$

5. Explain in detail why the numerator is multiplied by the reciprocal of the denominator to get the quotient of two rational numbers.

6. Carry out the indicated operations:

(a) $\dfrac{\frac{1}{7}}{\frac{7}{2}}$ (b) $\dfrac{\frac{1}{2} + \frac{1}{3}}{\frac{2}{6}}$ (c) $\dfrac{\frac{1}{2} + \frac{2}{3}}{\frac{3}{2} - \frac{1}{3}}$

(d) $\dfrac{\frac{1}{2}}{\frac{1}{3} + \frac{1}{2}}$ (e) $\frac{2}{5} \cdot (\frac{3}{4} - \frac{1}{2})$ (f) $\dfrac{\frac{1}{15} + \frac{1}{5}}{\frac{1}{5}}$

7. Solve each of the following equations:

(a) $\frac{3}{4} \cdot x - \frac{2}{3} = \frac{1}{2}$ (b) $\frac{4}{5} \cdot x = \frac{2}{3} - \frac{3}{7}$ (c) $\frac{5}{2} \cdot x + \frac{0}{1} = \frac{3}{3}$

8. Give an example of a problem situation in which it would be useful to write $1 \cdot 3$ instead of 3. (*Hint:* factor $3x + 3$.)

9. Give an example of a problem situation in which it would be useful to write $\frac{15}{3}$ instead of 5. (*Hint:* add $\frac{2}{3}$ to 5.)

10. Give an example of a problem situation in which it would be useful to write 1 as $\frac{2}{2}$.

7.11c "Fraction" Interpretation

In the early development of fractions in an arithmetic textbook you will encounter an illustration similar to the following.

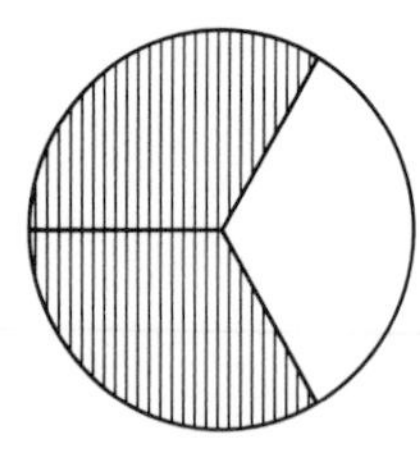

Figure 2

Example 1

Look at Figure 2. The disc is marked off in 3 equal parts. The numerals 2 and 3 can be used to tell how much of the disc is shaded.

This tells the number of equal parts.	$\frac{2}{3}$	Two of the parts are shaded.

Many other examples could be cited. This is the "fraction" interpretation or, as some authors term it, the "partition" interpretation of the rational number. This is probably the most familiar interpretation of rational numbers, so it needs but little mention here.

In the rational number, m/n, used in the "fraction" sense, the n is called the *denominator* and the m is called the *numerator*. Denominator is derived from the Latin word denominatus, "to call by name." It designates by name (number name) the parts into which the whole is divided. Numerator is derived from the Latin numeratus, "to count," and "counts" the parts under consideration. The symbol, m/n, under the "fraction" interpretation designates m of n equal parts.

$$\frac{m}{n} = m \cdot \frac{1}{n}.$$

Example 2

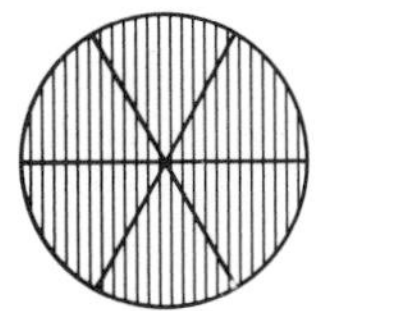
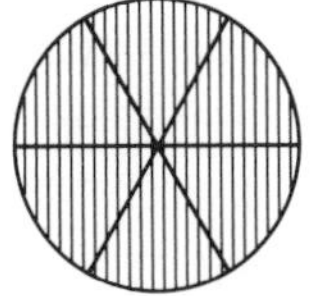
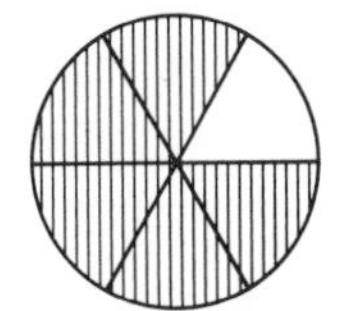

Figure 3

How do we express the shaded portion of the circles?

$$2\tfrac{5}{6} \quad \text{or} \quad \tfrac{17}{6}?$$

The symbol $2\frac{5}{6}$ is recognized and accepted as the name of a number. It is read, "two and five sixths." It means $2 + \frac{5}{6}$. As written, it is the sum of an integer and a rational number. We know how to add integers to integers and rational numbers to rational numbers, but we have not defined addition of integers to rational numbers.

To give the numeral $(2 + \frac{5}{6})$ meaning, we must turn to the system of rational numbers. We must interpret the integer 2 as a rational number as we agreed earlier that we could. The obvious choice for a rational number to represent 2 would be $\frac{2}{1}$. By $\frac{2}{1}$ we mean $[\frac{2}{1}]$. We have considerable freedom in choosing a representative of $[\frac{2}{1}]$.

The term "five sixths" suggests the "fraction" or "partition" interpretation of the rational number, $\frac{5}{6}$. The "5 of 6 equal parts" approach is conventional but technically to be cautioned about. To introduce the fraction $\frac{5}{6}$ as

$$\tfrac{5}{6} = \tfrac{1}{6} + \tfrac{1}{6} + \tfrac{1}{6} + \tfrac{1}{6} + \tfrac{1}{6}$$

assumes the learner knows how to add rational numbers or to multiply an integer times a rational number.

$$\tfrac{1}{6} + \tfrac{1}{6} + \tfrac{1}{6} + \tfrac{1}{6} + \tfrac{1}{6} = 5 \cdot \tfrac{1}{6} = \tfrac{5}{6}.$$

In order to avoid this assumption we introduced the system of rational numbers before we discussed the various interpretations. From our previous discussions we can proceed as follows:

$$\tfrac{5}{6} = \tfrac{5}{1}\cdot\tfrac{1}{6}.$$

But $\frac{5}{1} = 5$, so we can write

$$\tfrac{5}{6} = \tfrac{5}{1}\cdot\tfrac{1}{6} = 5\cdot\tfrac{1}{6}.$$

In the interpretation of $(2 + \frac{5}{6})$ we can choose $\frac{12}{6}$ as the representative of $[\frac{2}{1}]$ and write this as $12\cdot\frac{1}{6}$. We then have

$$2 + \tfrac{5}{6} = \tfrac{12}{1}\cdot\tfrac{1}{6} + \tfrac{5}{1}\cdot\tfrac{1}{6}.$$

Using the Distributive Law, we have

$$\begin{aligned} \tfrac{12}{1}\cdot\tfrac{1}{6} + \tfrac{5}{1}\cdot\tfrac{1}{6} &= (\tfrac{12}{1} + \tfrac{5}{1})\cdot\tfrac{1}{6} \\ &= (12 + 5)\cdot\tfrac{1}{6} \\ &= 17\cdot\tfrac{1}{6} \\ &= \tfrac{17}{6}. \end{aligned}$$

This is a tedious way to show that $2\frac{5}{6} = \frac{17}{6}$, but it is based on the fundamental properties of the number systems we have discussed. The usual procedure is to write

$$2\frac{5}{6} = 2 + \frac{5}{6} = \frac{12}{6} + \frac{5}{6} = \frac{12 + 5}{6} = \frac{17}{6}.$$

The question arises as to which is the more useful name, $2\frac{5}{6}$ or $\frac{17}{6}$? The form $2\frac{5}{6}$ reflects its origin in measuring and suggests magnitude or size. The expression, "$\frac{17}{6}$ yd of material," is not a familiar way to order yard goods. On the other hand, there are times when $\frac{17}{6}$ is a more convenient form than $2\frac{5}{6}$. For example, if $2\frac{5}{6}$ yd of material is to be divided among six people, how much does each receive?

$$\begin{aligned} &2\tfrac{5}{6} \div 6 = ? \\ &\tfrac{17}{6} \div 6 = \tfrac{17}{6}\cdot\tfrac{1}{6} = \tfrac{17}{36} \end{aligned}$$

Each person would receive $\frac{17}{36}$ yd or 17 in.

To conclude this section we illustrate the use of $2\frac{5}{6}$ and $\frac{17}{6}$ as names for the same number in computation.

Example 3

$$\begin{aligned} (2\tfrac{5}{6})(1\tfrac{1}{2}) &= (2 + \tfrac{5}{6})(1 + \tfrac{1}{2}) \\ &= (2 + \tfrac{5}{6})(1) + (2 + \tfrac{5}{6})(\tfrac{1}{2}) \\ &= 2\cdot 1 + \tfrac{5}{6}\cdot 1 + 2\cdot\tfrac{1}{2} + \tfrac{5}{6}\cdot\tfrac{1}{2} \\ &= 2 + \tfrac{5}{6} + 1 + \tfrac{5}{12} \\ &= (2 + 1) + (\tfrac{5}{6} + \tfrac{5}{12}) \\ &= (2 + 1) + (\tfrac{10}{12} + \tfrac{5}{12}) \\ &= 3 + \tfrac{15}{12} \end{aligned}$$

$$\begin{aligned} (2\tfrac{5}{6})(1\tfrac{1}{2}) &= (\tfrac{17}{6})(\tfrac{3}{2}) \\ &= \frac{17\cdot 3}{6\cdot 2} \\ &= \frac{17}{2\cdot 2} \\ &= \tfrac{17}{4} \end{aligned}$$

$$
\begin{aligned}
&= 3 + \frac{12 + 3}{12} \\
&= 3 + \tfrac{12}{12} + \tfrac{3}{12} \\
&= (3 + 1) + \tfrac{1}{4} \\
&= 4 + \tfrac{1}{4} \\
&= 4\tfrac{1}{4}
\end{aligned}
\qquad
\begin{aligned}
&= \frac{16 + 1}{4} \\
&= \tfrac{16}{4} + \tfrac{1}{4} \\
&= 4 + \tfrac{1}{4} \\
&= 4\tfrac{1}{4}
\end{aligned}
$$

$$
\begin{aligned}
2\tfrac{5}{6} + 1\tfrac{1}{2} &= 2 + \tfrac{5}{6} + 1 + \tfrac{1}{2} \\
&= (2 + 1) + (\tfrac{5}{6} + \tfrac{1}{2}) \\
&= 3 + (\tfrac{5}{6} + \tfrac{3}{6}) \\
&= 3 + \tfrac{8}{6} \\
&= 3 + \frac{6 + 2}{6} \\
&= 3 + \tfrac{6}{6} + \tfrac{2}{6} \\
&= (3 + 1) + \tfrac{1}{3} \\
&= 4\tfrac{1}{3}
\end{aligned}
\qquad
\begin{aligned}
2\tfrac{5}{6} + 1\tfrac{1}{2} &= \tfrac{17}{6} + \tfrac{3}{2} \\
&= \tfrac{17}{6} + \tfrac{9}{6} \\
&= \frac{17 + 9}{6} \\
&= \tfrac{26}{6} \\
&= \frac{24 + 2}{6} \\
&= \tfrac{24}{6} + \tfrac{2}{6} \\
&= 4 + \tfrac{1}{3} \\
&= 4\tfrac{1}{3}
\end{aligned}
$$

Exercise 7.11c

1. (a) Add $2\frac{1}{6}$ to $3\frac{2}{3}$ as you were taught in arithmetic.
(b) Add the same numbers as in Example 3, Section 7.11c, and justify each step.

2. Carry out the indicated operations and write your answer as a rational number and as an integer plus a rational number.

(a) $\dfrac{2 + \frac{5}{6}}{2}$ (b) $\dfrac{3\frac{4}{7}}{2\frac{1}{3}}$

(c) $\dfrac{(5 + \frac{1}{4}) + 2}{3 + \frac{1}{3}}$ (d) $(2\frac{1}{3})(3\frac{1}{2})$

3. Give an example of a situation in which each of the following numerals is in a convenient form.

(a) $4\frac{1}{6}$ (b) $\frac{33}{11}$ (c) $\frac{9}{6}$
(d) $\frac{5}{5}$ (e) $9\frac{2}{6}$ (f) $4 + \frac{1}{7}$

4. The following diagram represents the product $(2\frac{1}{3})(3\frac{1}{2})$. Label each part properly.

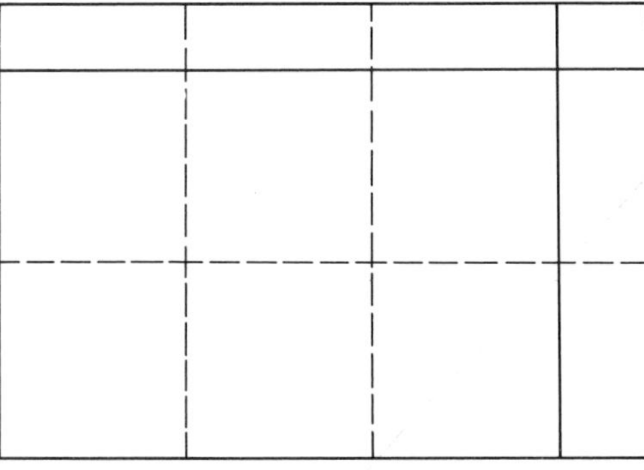

5. Carry out the computation and explain each step in the following:

$$\frac{17\frac{2}{5}}{3\frac{5}{9}}$$

6. Carry out the indicated operations.

(a) $2\frac{3}{7} \div 4\frac{3}{5}$ (b) $1 \div \frac{1}{10}$

(c) $\left(5 + \frac{2}{3}\right) \div \left(6 + \frac{1}{2}\right)$ (d) $\frac{4\frac{1}{3}}{2}$

(e) $2 \div 5\frac{3}{4}$ (f) $\frac{5 + \frac{5}{7}}{7}$

7. Solve for x: $(3\frac{1}{2})x = 4\frac{2}{9}$

8. Multiply each of the following by direct application of the Distributive Law.

(a) $(5 + \frac{4}{5})(6 + \frac{3}{10})$ (b) $(6 + \frac{1}{9})(9 + \frac{1}{6})$

(c) Represent each product as area and label each part.

(d) Change the numerals of (a) and (b) to rational form and carry out the multiplication.

9. Carry out the indicated operations and simplify.

(a) $\frac{3 + \frac{1}{3}}{2}$ (b) $\frac{3^{-1} + 3}{3}$

(c) $\frac{5 - \frac{1}{3}}{\frac{1}{3} + 1}$ (d) $2(\frac{2}{3} - \frac{1}{6})$

(e) $\frac{1}{2} \cdot (3 + \frac{5}{8})$ (f) $5\frac{2}{3} - 4\frac{7}{8}$

7.11d "Rate Pair" Interpretation (Ratio)

We have had occasion to consider whole numbers in situations in which the only properties used were their distinctiveness and their inexhaustible supply. In these situations the numbers are used as names of objects or places, for example, telephone numbers, positions on a baseball team, and so on. Addition and multiplication in these situations have no meaning. The numbers are used as names and not as numbers.

Similarly, there are many situations that call for the use of ordered pairs of whole numbers, for example, "Mary bought 3 pencils for 10 cents." The pair of whole numbers, (3, 10), is an ordered pair. "Mary bought 10 pencils for 3 cents," describes a completely different situation. (One looks like a bargain.) Another way of describing this situation is to say that Mary bought pencils which cost "3 for 10 cents." The sign in the window of the store probably had an item which read, "Pencils, 3/10¢."

The ordered pair of whole numbers is being used here to describe a *many-to-many correspondence.* In this case, a 3 to 10 correspondence. The statement "The odds are 8 to 5 on the Yankees to win" describes an 8 to 5 correspondence. As we stated before, these situations involve the ordered pairs of natural numbers but not as numbers in a number system. What would it mean to add or multiply the ordered pairs in these situations? The number pairs are used as *rate pairs.* As such, they are often written in the same way as ordinary rational numbers. As *rate pairs* they should be read "3 for 10," or "3 to 10," or "8 to 5," and not as three-tenths or eight-fifths.

In many situations involving these ordered pairs, different pairs describe the same situation. Thus 3 pencils for 10¢ describes the same situation as 6 pencils for 20¢ or 12 pencils for 40¢. Similarly, 20 miles to 1 gal is equivalent to 40 miles to 2 gal, or 100 miles to 5 gal. The criterion for determining when two rate pairs describe the same many-to-many correspondence is the same as determining when two rational numbers are *equivalent.* Thus the rate pair, m/n, will be *equivalent* to the rate pair, r/s, if and only if $m \cdot s = n \cdot r$ as integers. Let us use the symbol $=$ to indicate that two rate pairs describe the same many-to-many correspondence.

Example 1

$$\tfrac{3}{10} = \tfrac{6}{20} \text{ because } 3 \cdot 20 = 10 \cdot 6.$$
$$\tfrac{3}{10} = \tfrac{9}{30} \text{ because } 3 \cdot 30 = 10 \cdot 9.$$
$$\tfrac{8}{5} = \tfrac{16}{10} \text{ because } 8 \cdot 10 = 5 \cdot 16.$$

This relation between rate pairs is an equivalence relation and partitions all rate pairs into equivalence classes. The essential difference between working with the ordered pairs as *rate pairs* as opposed to working with ordered pairs as *rational numbers* is that as rational numbers they are added, multiplied, subtracted, and divided. These operations associate with ordered pairs of two classes, an ordered pair of a third class. On the other hand, rate pairs involve essentially working with one class at a time.

The usual problem situation involving the rate pairs is built around the following simple idea. *Three* of the four components of two equivalent rate pairs will be known. The problem is to find the *fourth.*

Example 2

If 6 apples cost 25¢, how much do 30 apples cost?

The equivalence class to which the rate pair $\tfrac{6}{25}$ belongs is

$$\tfrac{6}{25}, \tfrac{12}{50}, \tfrac{18}{75}, \tfrac{24}{100}, \tfrac{30}{125}, \tfrac{36}{150}, \ldots.$$

Now the answer to the question is quite obvious. The rate pair with 30 as its first component is $\tfrac{30}{125}$, which is to be interpreted as 30 apples for $1.25. This is usually shortened as follows:

Let N be the cost of the 30 apples; then

$$\frac{6}{25} = \frac{30}{N} \text{ if and only if } 6 \cdot N = 25 \cdot 30.$$

Then
$$N = \frac{25 \cdot 30}{6},$$

and
$$N = 125.$$

Exercise 7.11d

1. Give five examples of the use of numbers as names only.
2. What is the meaning of the expression in baseball, "Out, 6 to 3"?
3. What is the meaning of the numbers on the doors in a building?
4. A certain canned food sells at 3 cans for 38¢. How many cans can you get for $1.90?
5. A bank charges $3 for every $500 worth of certified checks it issues. If the charge on a certain check was $12, what was the value of the check?
6. On a map 1 in. represents 16 miles. What distance is represented by $5\frac{1}{2}$ in.?
7. A tree 60 ft high casts a shadow 45 ft long. What is the height of a tree that casts a shadow 30 ft long at the same time of day?
8. A man in an automobile made a trip of 125 miles in $2\frac{1}{2}$ hours. At the same rate how long would it take him to make a trip of 500 miles?
9. The scale in an architect's drawing is 1 ft to $\frac{1}{4}$ in. A distance of 10 in. on the drawing represents how many feet in the structure?
10. Every 3 gal of radiator fluid contain 2 qt of pure antifreeze. How many quarts of antifreeze are there in 45 gal of this mixture?

Special Problem (from the Scientific American)

You face the problem of crossing a desert that is 800 miles across. You have a vehicle that is capable of hauling enough gasoline to travel 500 miles, including regular supply and cargo. What is the least number of trips required to cross the desert?

7.11e "Rate Pair" Interpretation (Percent)

The rate pair is also used in making relative comparisons. Thus a person invests $3000 in a particular stock and sells it for $3450. He earns $450 profit. Another person invests $450 in some other stock which he sells for $900. He also shows a profit of $450. The total amount earned was the same, but the rate of return on the original investment is markedly different. The rate pairs, $\frac{450}{3000}$ and $\frac{450}{450}$, describe quite different aspects of this investment situation. It is possible to make a comparison of these two rate pairs; however, rate pairs with the same denominator are more conveniently compared. The usual practice is to use 100 as the common denominator. Rate pairs whose common denominator is 100 are called *percents*. Percents are rate pairs in which the second place number is 100, and when this is understood, they are usually written with the symbol % or the word "percent" in place of the 100 in the denominator.

From these examples we have

$$\tfrac{450}{3000} = \tfrac{15}{100} = 15\%$$
$$\tfrac{450}{450} = \tfrac{100}{100} = 100\%$$

Thus 15% really means 15 per 100. In terms of percent, the investment situation can be compared by inspection.

The problem of changing from percent to decimal form and vice versa simply involves remembering what percent means:

$$15\% = \frac{15}{100} = 0.15$$

$$0.02 = \frac{2}{100} = 2\%$$

Most rational numbers can be expressed only approximately in decimal form. The same is true of rate pairs and percents. That is, the rate pair $\frac{1}{3}$ can only be approximated by a percent:

$$\tfrac{1}{3} \cong \tfrac{33}{100} = 33\%$$

Convention has given meaning to the following rate pairs:

$$33\tfrac{1}{3}\% \qquad 66\tfrac{2}{3}\%$$

The meaning here is clear. Strangely enough, we seldom see such rate pairs as

$$14\tfrac{2}{7}\% \qquad 81\tfrac{9}{11}\% \qquad 74\tfrac{74}{99}\%$$

These are usually expressed as "about 14%," "about 82%," and "about 75%." We simply mention this as a convention and do not attempt to clarify it as a mathematical idea.

The traditional approach has been to present percent problems, or problems involving percent, as three different types or cases. With the use of rate pairs the percent problems are of one type—the finding of the fourth component of two equivalent rate pairs when the other three components are known.

Let us symbolize the percent by the symbol P. Then, for example, 32% would give us $P = 32$ and would be expressed as the rate pair $\frac{32}{100}$. When using P to represent the percent, $P/100$ is the rate pair. For the other equivalent rate pair in the percent problem we shall use A/B, where A shall be called the "amount" and B the "base." Now the "three" types of percent problems can be expressed in terms of these two rate pairs.

Find 32% of 400. $\dfrac{32}{100} = \dfrac{A}{400}$, $A = 128$.

What percent of 400 is 128? $\frac{P}{100} = \frac{128}{400}$, $P = 32$.

128 is 32% of what number? $\frac{32}{100} = \frac{128}{B}$, $B = 400$.

Exercise 7.11e

1. Express the following rate pairs as percents:

(a) $\frac{32}{100}$ (b) $\frac{2}{100}$ (c) $\frac{3}{4}$ (d) $\frac{13}{20}$
(e) $\frac{4}{25}$ (f) $\frac{18}{50}$ (g) $\frac{18}{75}$ (h) $\frac{96}{400}$

2. Express the following percents as rate pairs:

(a) 25% (b) 34% (c) 40% (d) 85%
(e) 125% (f) 250% (g) 400% (h) 12.5%

3. Use the rate pair idea to solve the following:
(a) What is 15% of 80?
(b) What is 45% of 2300?
(c) What percent of 248 is 31?
(d) What percent of $2000 is $160?
(e) 65% of a number is 260. What is the number?
(f) 34% of a number is 170. What is the number?

7.12 ORDER IN THE RATIONAL NUMBERS

We introduce *order* in the rational numbers in much the same way that order was introduced in the integers. First we define the *positive rational numbers* and then define the order relation in terms of them.

DEFINITION 7.12a. The rational number m/n is *positive* if the integer $n \cdot m$ is a positive integer.

We use the notation

$$\frac{m}{n} > 0$$

to indicate that m/n is positive. The numeral m/n is a representative of the class $\left[\frac{m}{n}\right]$. If m/n is positive, so also is every member of the class $\left[\frac{m}{n}\right]$, that is, the definition of positiveness is independent of the representative. We assert that such is the case, and the interested reader will find this easy to verify.

7.12a The Trichotomy Law and Order for Rational Numbers

If we let the single letter r represent a rational number, one and only one of the following possibilities holds:

1. r is positive,
2. $r = 0$, or
3. $-r$ is positive.

If r is positive, $-r$ is called a *negative* rational number.

The set of rational numbers is separated into three sets, the positive rational numbers, the negative rational numbers, and 0. (Hereafter we treat the integers as a subset of the rational numbers.)

The *positive rational numbers* are characterized in the same way as the *positive integers.*

1. The sum of two positive rational numbers is positive.
2. The product of two positive rational numbers is positive.

We are now ready to define order in the rational numbers.

DEFINITION 7.12b. If r and s denote rational numbers, then r "is less than" s if $s - r$ is positive.

We use the same notation used earlier,

$$r < s \text{ if and only if } s - r > 0.$$

We also write $r \leqq s$ if and only if $s - r \geqq 0$, and this is true if either $r < s$ or $r = s$.

We use the notation $r < x < s$ to mean that both $r < x$ and $x < s$ hold simultaneously.

We list some of the properties of order. For rational numbers p, r, and s,

1. if $r < s$, then $r + p < s + p$.
2. if $r < s$, and $p > 0$, then $rp < sp$.
3. if $0 < r < s$, then $\dfrac{1}{r} > \dfrac{1}{s}$.
4. if $r < s$, and $p < 0$, then $rp > sp$.

Exercise 7.12a

1. Verify that each of the following inequalities holds:

(a) $\dfrac{3}{5} < \dfrac{32}{51}$ (b) $\dfrac{1}{4} < \dfrac{1}{3}$ (c) $\dfrac{1}{10} < \dfrac{1}{7}$

(d) $\dfrac{1}{100} < \dfrac{2}{100}$ (e) $\dfrac{1}{1001} < \dfrac{1}{1000}$ (f) $\dfrac{2}{3} < \dfrac{2463}{3463}$

2. Verify that each of the following inequalities holds:

(a) $\dfrac{-2}{3} < \dfrac{2}{3}$ (b) $\dfrac{-1}{4} < \dfrac{1}{-5}$ (c) $\dfrac{1}{-7} < \dfrac{1}{-8}$

(d) $\dfrac{-1}{9} < \dfrac{1}{2}$ (e) $-3 < 2$ (f) $\dfrac{1}{5} < \dfrac{1}{3}$

3. If $a > 0$ and $b > 0$ and if $a < b$, how is $1/a$ related to $1/b$?
4. (a) Prove your assertion in problem 3.
   (b) Given the inequality $2 < 3$, what is the effect of multiplying both sides of the inequality by 2? By -3? By -1? By $-\frac{1}{2}$?
5. (a) List the integers which satisfy
$$-3 < x \leqq 5.$$
   (b) List the positive integers which satisfy
$$-3 < x \leqq 5.$$
   (c) Use this notation to specify the set consisting of
$$\{-3, -2, -1, 0, 1, 2, 3\}.$$
6. (a) Show that if $n^2pq > q^2mn$, then $m/n < p/q$. (*Hint:* $n^2pq > q^2mn$ if $n^2pq - q^2mn > 0$. Divide by qn.)
   (b) Show that if $m/n < p/q$, then $n^2pq - q^2mn > 0$. (*Hint:* $m/n < p/q$ if and only if $p/q - m/n > 0$. Use Definition 7.12.)
7. (a) If m, n, and k are positive integers, show that $m/k < n/k$ if and only if $m < n$.
   (b) Use (a) above to show that if m, n, p, q are positive integers, $m/n < p/q$ if and only if $mq < np$.
8. List some rational numbers which satisfy
   (a) $\frac{1}{3} < x < \frac{1}{2}$ (b) $-\frac{1}{3} < x < \frac{1}{3}$
9. Illustrate each of the properties, (1), (2), (3), and (4), of order.
10. Locate each of the following numbers on the number line:
   (a) $0, \frac{5}{7}, \frac{11}{3}, \frac{6}{8}, \frac{9}{11}$ (b) $-1, \frac{-4}{3}, \frac{-3}{5}, \frac{5}{2}, \frac{19}{7}$

7.12b Absolute Value

We repeat an earlier definition in terms of the rational numbers.

DEFINITION 7.12c. For each rational number r we define

$$|r| = \begin{cases} r \text{ if } r > 0 \\ -r \text{ if } r < 0 \\ 0 \text{ if } r = 0 \end{cases}$$

The number $|r|$ is called the *absolute value* of r.

Example 1

$$\left|\frac{-2}{3}\right| = \frac{2}{3} \qquad |-6| = 6 \qquad \left|\frac{4}{5}\right| = \frac{4}{5}$$

We list some useful properties of absolute value. For rational numbers a and b,

1. if $a \neq 0$, then $|a| > 0$, and $|a| = 0$ if and only if $a = 0$.
2. $|a - b| = |b - a|$

3. $|a + b| \leqq |a| + |b|$
4. $|a \cdot b| = |a| \cdot |b|$
5. $\big||a| - |b|\big| \leqq |a - b|$

Exercise 7.12b

1. Find the integer solutions

(a) $|x| \leqq 3$
(b) $|x - 13| \leqq 2$
(c) $|x + 5| \leqq 3$
(d) $|x - 6| < 1$
(e) $|x + 3| = 2$

2. Find the integer solutions

(a) $|3x + 2| = 5$
(b) $|2x - 3| = 7$

3. Use numerical examples to illustrate the properties of absolute value, (1) through (5), in Section 7.12b.

4. Give a numerical example of (3) and (5) in which the strict inequality holds.

7.12c The Property of Denseness

By associating to each rational number, the point on the *number line* whose *distance* from some fixed point (see Sections 6.12b and 6.12c) is the rational number, we define a one-to-one correspondence between the rational numbers and a subset of the points on the line. We shall see in Section 7.13 that there are points on the number line which do not correspond to rational numbers.

If we let a and b be any two rational numbers (assume $a < b$), then it is always possible to find another rational number c such that c is "between" a and b, that is, given a and b with $a < b$ we can find another rational number c such that

$$a < c < b.$$

One way to do this is to take half of the sum of a and b, that is, let

$$c = \frac{a + b}{2}.$$

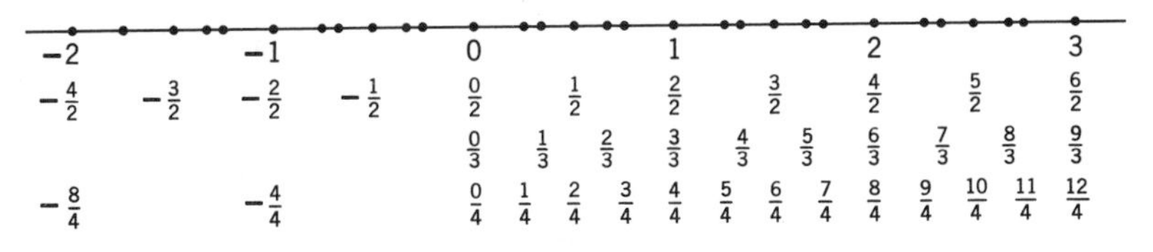

Figure 4. The rational number line.

Using the properties of order we can see this easily:

	$a < b$; hence $\frac{a}{2} < \frac{b}{2}$,	by property 2, Section 7.12
and	$a = \frac{a}{2} + \frac{a}{2} < \frac{a}{2} + \frac{b}{2}$,	by property 1, Section 7.12
Also	$\frac{a}{2} + \frac{b}{2} < \frac{b}{2} + \frac{b}{2}$,	by the same property
Thus	$a < \frac{a+b}{2} < b.$	

Speaking geometrically, we note that the point $c = (a + b)/2$ is the midpoint of the line segment from a to b.

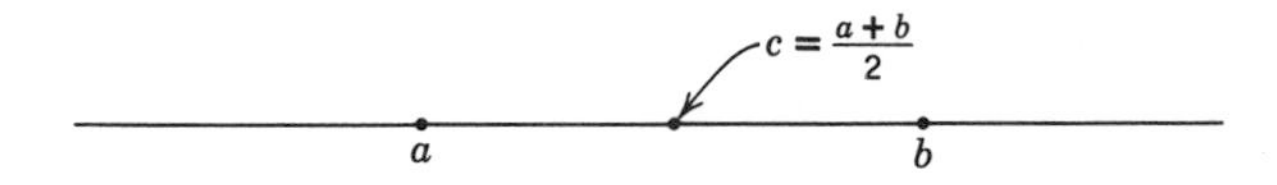

Example 1

Find the midpoint of the line segment from $\frac{1}{2}$ to $\frac{9}{11}$ and verify that it is between $\frac{1}{2}$ and $\frac{9}{11}$.

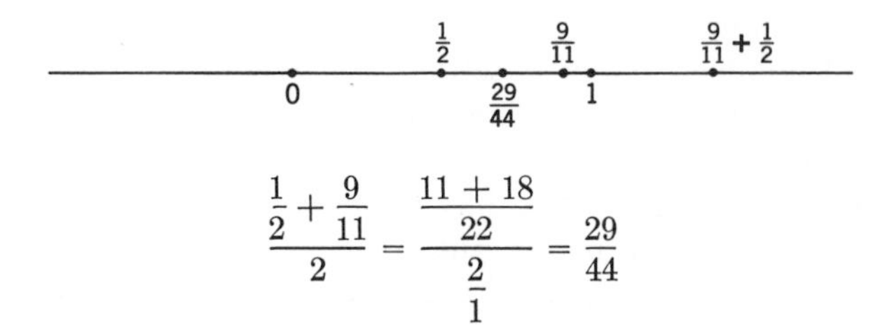

$$\frac{\frac{1}{2} + \frac{9}{11}}{2} = \frac{\frac{11 + 18}{22}}{\frac{2}{1}} = \frac{29}{44}$$

To show that $\frac{1}{2} < \frac{29}{44} < \frac{9}{11}$, we first show that $\frac{1}{2} < \frac{29}{44}$ and then show that $\frac{29}{44} < \frac{9}{11}$. $\frac{29}{44} - \frac{1}{2} = \frac{58 - 44}{88} = \frac{14}{88} > 0$ since $14 \cdot 88 > 0$. Hence $\frac{1}{2} < \frac{29}{44}$. $\frac{9}{11} - \frac{29}{44} = \frac{396 - 319}{484} = \frac{77}{484} > 0$ since $77 \cdot 484 > 0$. Hence $\frac{29}{44} < \frac{9}{11}$.

The fact that we can always find another rational number between any two distinct rational numbers implies that there are infinitely many rational numbers between any two distinct rational numbers. Why? No matter how "close together" two rational numbers may be, another rational number can be found which lies between them. This interesting property of the rational numbers is called *denseness*.

DEFINITION 7.12d. To say that the rational numbers are *dense-in-themselves* (or dense) means that between any two distinct rational numbers one can always find another rational number.

This is merely a way of saying that the rational numbers are densely distributed along the number line, that is, there is no part of the number line that contains two rational numbers without containing infinitely many rational numbers. The idea of denseness is closely related to the idea of approximations. This concept is extremely important in any situation involving measurements and indeed in much of mathematics itself. We examine it in the next chapter.

Exercise 7.12c

1. Find a rational number between 0 and 1.
2. Find 5 rational numbers between 0 and $\frac{1}{2}$.
3. Find 5 more rational numbers different from those in problem 2 which lie between 0 and $\frac{1}{2}$.
4. Is there a smallest rational number bigger than 1? Why?
5. Is there a largest rational number less than 3? Why?
6. Is there a smallest positive integer? What is it?
7. Is there a smallest positive rational number? What is it?
8. What number lies half way between 0 and $1/2^n$ for n a positive integer?
9. Is there a smallest rational number greater than $\frac{1}{3}$?
10. Is there a largest rational number smaller than $\frac{1}{3}$?
11. What is the smallest integer greater than -9?
12. What is the largest integer less than -5?
13. What is the smallest rational number x such that $x \geqq \frac{3}{4}$?
14. What is the smallest rational number x such that $x \geqq \frac{7}{1}$?
15. What do we mean when we say two rational numbers are close together?
16. Extend Definitions 5.12c, d, and f to the set of integers. To the set of rational numbers.
17. What is the least upper bound of the set A in each of the following (x rational)? (see Definition 5.12e)

    (a) $A = \{x \mid |x| \leqq 10\}$ (b) $A = \{x \mid |x| < 1\}$

    (c) $A = \{x \mid -3 < x \leqq 0\}$ (d) $A = \{x \mid -5 < x < -2\}$

7.13 INTRODUCTION TO IRRATIONAL NUMBERS

Some numbers are rational numbers, some are not, for example, $\frac{3}{4}$ is a rational number, $\frac{5}{1}$ is a rational number. Because we also interpret m/n as divides, we may consider 5 as a rational number; 0 is also a rational number; 1, -1, $\frac{17}{4}$, $\frac{2}{3}$, $-\frac{77}{13}$ are rational numbers.

Numbers that are not rational numbers are called *irrational numbers*. Examples of irrational numbers are $\sqrt{2}$, $\sqrt[3]{5}$, $\sqrt[5]{11}$, $\sqrt{13}$, π, e, ... It is not uncommon to find people who see $\sqrt{2}$ or $\sqrt{87}$ as some complicated arithmetic operation. (We remind the reader again that the addition algorithm, the multiplication algorithm, and now the square root algorithm are merely arithmetic procedures for determining another name of a number.) We repeat: $2 + 5$ is the name of a number and we recognize it as the number 7. So also is $3{,}746{,}297 + 894{,}299$. One feels he has to know *how* to add before he can say that it is *a number*. Still it is a perfectly good number as it is written. In this spirit, $\sqrt{2}$ is a number. It is that positive number which when multiplied by itself gives the number 2.

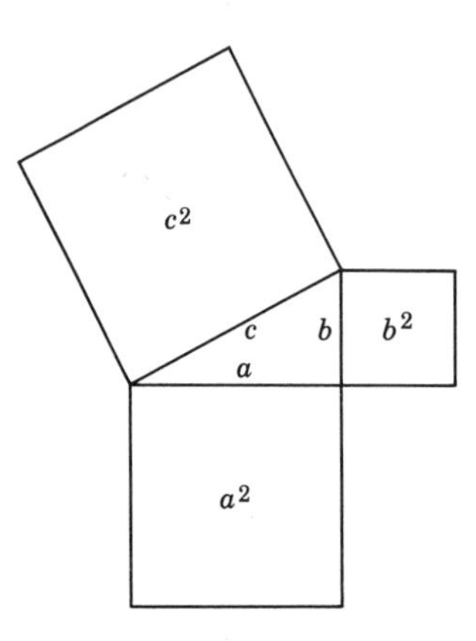

Figure 5. $a^2 + b^2 = c^2$.

$$\sqrt{2}\cdot\sqrt{2} = 2.$$

This number is not a rational number. It is called an irrational number and occurs quite naturally. There is a well-known theorem in geometry which was known to the Babylonians almost 2000 years B.C. but which is credited to the Greeks. It is called the Pythagorean Theorem. The theorem states that the sum of the squares on the legs of a right triangle is equal to the square on the hypotenuse (see Chapter 9). If we label the legs of the triangle a and b and the hypotenuse as c, then the theorem states that $a^2 + b^2 = c^2$ (see Figure 5).

Let us consider the triangle formed by the diagonal and two sides of a square whose sides are of unit length. Then we have

$$1^2 + 1^2 = 2.$$

This means the hypotenuse c must have a length such that $c^2 = 2$. At the time of the Babylonians such numbers were unknown. The Greeks referred to the hypotenuse of such a triangle as incommensurable. Thus the set of rational numbers developed for the purpose of measuring was found to be inadequate for the simplest kind of measurement.

Example 1

The side of a square whose area is 2 is $\sqrt{2}$.
The side of a square whose area is 3 is $\sqrt{3}$.
The side of a cube whose volume is 2 is $\sqrt[3]{2}$.
The radius of a circle whose area is 1 is $\sqrt{\pi}/\pi$.

These simple examples suggest that there are many numbers which are irrational numbers (not rational). There are, in fact, many more irrational numbers than rational numbers. They may not be as familiar as the rational numbers, but such numbers exist. For example, π is an irrational number, but it was a long time before it was shown to be irrational. The number whose symbol is e is familiar to the student of calculus. It is useful as a base for a system of logarithms.

At this point we demonstrate that $\sqrt{2}$ is not a rational number to strengthen the assertion that irrational numbers do, in fact, exist.

7.13a The Irrationality of $\sqrt{2}$

The argument to show that there is no rational number x such that $x^2 = 2$ is an example of the method of indirect proof. The procedure will be as follows. We *suppose* that there is a rational number p/q whose square is 2. By using correct mathematical operations we will arrive at a contradictory situation. Since we arrive at this contradiction by mathematically correct steps, the only conclusion left will be that our original assumption is false.

STATEMENT TO BE PROVED. There is no rational number p/q such that $\left(\frac{p}{q}\right)^2 = 2.$

Assumption. Suppose the statement is false, that is, suppose there does exist a rational number p/q such that $p^2/q^2 = 2$.

1. We assume that p/q is in reduced form, that is, p and q have no common factor except $+1$ or -1. We may do this without loss of generality. For if $p^2/q^2 = 2$ where p/q is not a rational number in simplest form, then

$$\frac{p}{q} = \frac{dp'}{dq'} = \frac{p'}{q'} \text{ where g.c.d. } (p', q') = 1,$$

That is, p'/q' is in reduced form.

2. $p^2/q^2 = 2$, so $p^2 = 2q^2$.

3. $p^2 = 2q^2$ implies p^2 is even. But if p^2 is even, so also is p. For if p is odd, p^2 is odd. Hence p is even.

4. p is even so we can write p in the form $p = 2m$, where m is an integer.

5. Hence $p^2 = 2m \cdot 2m = 4m^2$, that is, $p^2 = 4m^2 = 2q^2$.

6. $4m^2 = 2q^2$, so $2m^2 = q^2$.

7. Hence q^2 is even. But this means q is even. So p and q must have the common factor of 2. This cannot happen if their only common factor is $+1$ or -1.

8. Hence our assumption must be false.
9. Therefore $\sqrt{2}$ is irrational.

REVIEW EXERCISES

1. Let N denote the set of all natural numbers. Define the binary operation $\odot$ as follows:

$$m \odot n = \text{g.c.d. } (m, n).$$

(a) What is $6 \odot 9$?
(b) What is $16 \odot 12$?
(c) Is the set N closed under this operation? Explain.
(d) Is the operation commutative? Illustrate with a numerical example.
(e) Is the operation associative? Illustrate with a numerical example.

2. The even numbers are numbers of the form $2k$, where k is in N. The odd numbers are numbers of the form $(2k - 1)$ or $(2k + 1)$, where k is in N.

(a) Show that the product of two even numbers is even and justify each step.
(b) Show that the sum of two even numbers is even and justify each step.
(c) Show that the product of two odd numbers is odd and justify each step.

Give precise definitions of each of the following:

3. A proper subset of a set.
4. The intersection of two sets.
5. The universal set.
6. The "inclusion" relation for sets.
7. An equivalence relation.
8. Domain of a relation.
9. The "divides" relation for natural numbers.
10. A one-to-one correspondence.
11. A system of numeration.
12. The order relation, $\leqq$, for the integers.
13. Denseness of the rational numbers.
14. Absolute value of n, for n an integer.

List the properties of each of the following relations (a and b are integers):

15. a Ⓡ b if and only if $|a - b| = k > 0$.
16. a Ⓡ b if and only if $|a - b| = 0$.
17. a Ⓡ b if and only if $(a - b) \geqq 0$.
18. a Ⓡ b if and only if $(a - b) > 0$.

Give a formal definition of each of the following:

19. The system of integers.
20. The system of rational numbers.
21. What does it mean to say that a set is finite?
22. What does it mean to say that a set is infinite?

REFERENCE

Birkhoff, Garret, and MacLane, Saunders, *A Brief Survey of Modern Algebra*, The Macmillan Co., New York, 1953, ch. II.

*
*
*

CHAPTER EIGHT

The System of Real Numbers

8.1 INTRODUCTION

We remarked earlier that the formation of sets is a human process. It is man's way of arranging his universe. In this process numbers help him to quantify and to learn more about his environment. The assigning of numbers to objects, where the word "object" is used in its broadest sense, is called either measuring or indexing. Indexing is part of the "keeping track of" process, whereas measuring adds to man's knowledge of the object. The numbers assigned to an "object" in the measuring process are called *measurements.* The aspect or property of the object which is being measured is called the *measure* of the object. We use the broad inclusive term *measure* in general, but it might be weight, length, area, velocity, cost, time, volume, change, mass, viscosity, intelligence, or any of the multitude of *measurable quantities.* Some of these measures admit *standard units* of comparison, whereas others may not. The increased activity in scientific inquiry and the extension of the scientific method into social and economic disciplines are introducing many applications of the use of numbers in measurement, many with new units. The *barn* and the *shed* have only recently been adopted as new units of size in physics. (The barn is 10^{-24} centimeters squared and the shed is 10^{-44} centimeters squared.) The Hooper rating is a number which gives some measure of the popularity of T.V. programs. A few years ago there was a flurry of excitement caused by a public figure categorizing atomic bombs in terms of the number of cities that a particular bomb could wipe out. Today the generally accepted unit of measurement for atomic bombs seems to be the *megaton.*

We live today in a remarkable world, a world in which it is no longer true that "everything that goes up must come down." Even so, numbers continue to serve an important function. The old adage "measure it, then you know something about it" is still as valid today as at any time in the past.

One might wonder whether we have a number system adequate to meet the demands required by our rapidly changing world. Certainly the early civilizations were seriously handicapped by deficiencies in the number systems available to them. They were left with incommensurable quantities, such as the diagonal of the unit square and the circumference of a circle of unit diameter, which "stumped" even their most able intellectuals. Remnants of their frustrations can be found in such terms as negative numbers (non-numbers), irrational numbers (unreasonable numbers) and others.

The situation is not so desperate today. Fortunately the number system available to us is rich enough to meet our present need and admits of a very convenient representation, namely the decimal representation. We shall investigate the concept of *completeness* and its connection to the number line before we consider decimal fractions.

8.2 THE NUMBER LINE

In Section 7.12c we discussed the distribution of the rational numbers on the number line. We noted then that the rational numbers were *dense*. Intuitively this means that no matter which point we choose on the number line, there are infinitely many *rational numbers* arbitrarily close to it. The "point on the number line" of the last sentence may *not* be a rational number. In Chapter 7 we indicated that there are numbers such as $\sqrt{2}$ and π which are not rational. We now show informally that there are points on the number line which correspond to these irrational numbers and that there are rational numbers arbitrarily close to them.

Let a square with sides of length 1 have the line segment from 0 to 1 as a base (see Figure 1). Consider the diagonal with one end at 0. The length of this diagonal is $\sqrt{2}$. If we rotate the diagonal clockwise about the point 0 until it lies on the line, the free end of the diagonal marks the point whose distance from 0 is $\sqrt{2}$. We label this point $\sqrt{2}$. If we rotate the diagonal counterclockwise until it lies on the number line, the free end marks the point which we label $-\sqrt{2}$.

The irrational number $\sqrt{2}$ lies between 1 and 2. In fact, $\sqrt{2}$ lies between 1 and $\frac{3}{2}$, since $1^2 = 1$ and $(\frac{3}{2})^2 = \frac{9}{4} = 2\frac{1}{4}$. Any rational number between 1 and $\frac{3}{2}$ will be reasonably close to $\sqrt{2}$, for example, the

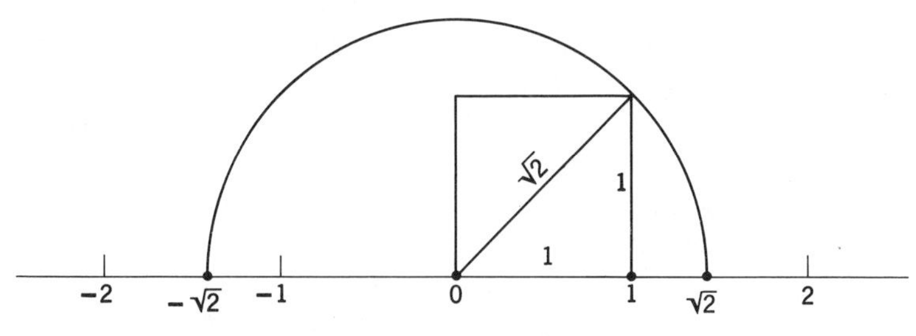

Figure 1

midpoint of the line segment from 1 to $\frac{3}{2}$. (This midpoint is also called the *arithmetic mean* or *average* of the numbers 1 and $\frac{3}{2}$.)

$$\frac{1+\frac{3}{2}}{2} = \frac{5}{4} \quad \text{(first approximation)}$$

$$\left(\frac{5}{4}\right)^2 = \frac{25}{16} < \frac{32}{16} = 2$$

We see that $\frac{3}{2}$ is greater than $\sqrt{2}$ and $\frac{5}{4}$ is less than $\sqrt{2}$. (These rational numbers which are close to $\sqrt{2}$ will be called *estimates* or *approximations* of $\sqrt{2}$.)

In order to obtain a closer approximation to $\sqrt{2}$, we divide 2 by the first estimate, $\frac{5}{4}$, and take the *average* of this quotient and $\frac{5}{4}$.

$$\frac{2}{\frac{5}{4}} = \frac{8}{5} \quad \text{(quotient)}$$

$$\frac{\frac{5}{4}+\frac{8}{5}}{2} = \frac{57}{40} \quad \text{(second approximation)}$$

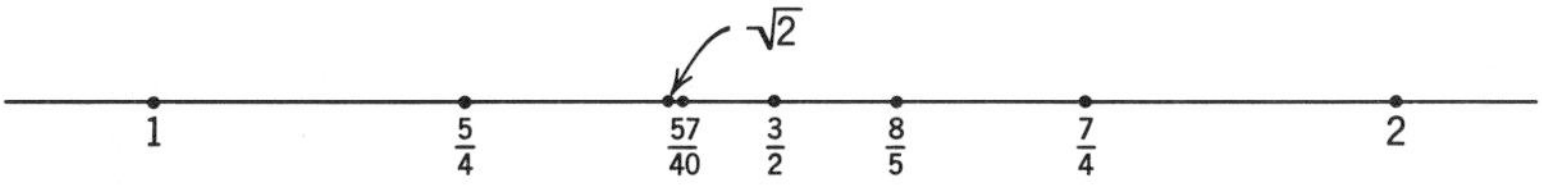

$\sqrt{2}$

1 $\quad \frac{5}{4} \quad \frac{57}{40} \quad \frac{3}{2} \quad \frac{8}{5} \quad \frac{7}{4} \quad 2$

One might wonder why we went through this unexpected procedure to get our second approximation. Actually it is a very reasonable procedure. The symbol $\sqrt{2}$ is the name of the number which when multiplied by itself gives 2.

$$\sqrt{2}\cdot\sqrt{2} = 2.$$

We are looking for a number, call it x, such that

$$x \cdot x = 2.$$

In our first attempt, we try $\frac{5}{4}$. We have the following relation to consider:

$$\tfrac{5}{4}\cdot x = 2.$$

If we solve this relation for x, we get $x = \frac{8}{5}$. Since we are using $\frac{5}{4}$ as an estimate of $\sqrt{2}$, it is reasonable to expect $\frac{8}{5}$ also to be an approximation of $\sqrt{2}$. Furthermore, if one of these estimates is too small, the other will be too large. This is the reason we take the *average* of these two "estimates" to obtain $\frac{57}{40}$ as a better approximation. This process of dividing the number by the last approximation and taking the average can be continued indefinitely. In this way we get a sequence of rational numbers approaching $\sqrt{2}$.

Any of the rational numbers $\frac{5}{4}, \frac{57}{40}, \ldots,$ can be used as *rational* approximations to $\sqrt{2}$. We saw earlier that there is no rational number whose square is 2, but the fact that the rational numbers are *dense* means that there are rational numbers whose squares differ from 2 by less than any preassigned amount.

Exercise 8.2

1. Divide $\frac{57}{40}$ into 2 and take the average of this quotient and $\frac{57}{40}$ as a new approximation to $\sqrt{2}$. Compare this approximation to the last approximation by looking at the difference of 2 and the squares of the approximation.

$$\left|2 - \left(\frac{57}{40}\right)^2\right| = ?$$

$$\left|2 - \left(\begin{matrix}\text{third}\\ \text{estimate}\end{matrix}\right)^2\right| = ?$$

2. Find the fourth approximation to $\sqrt{30}$, using 5 as your first approximation. Check your result by squaring.

$$\frac{30}{5} = 6$$

$$\frac{5+6}{2} = \frac{11}{2} \quad \text{(second approximation)}$$

3. Find the third approximation to $\sqrt{300}$, using 17 as your first estimate.
4. If a circle of diameter 1 which touches the number line at 0 is rolled along the number line, the point on the circle which was touching 0 will touch the line again at the point corresponding to the irrational number π.

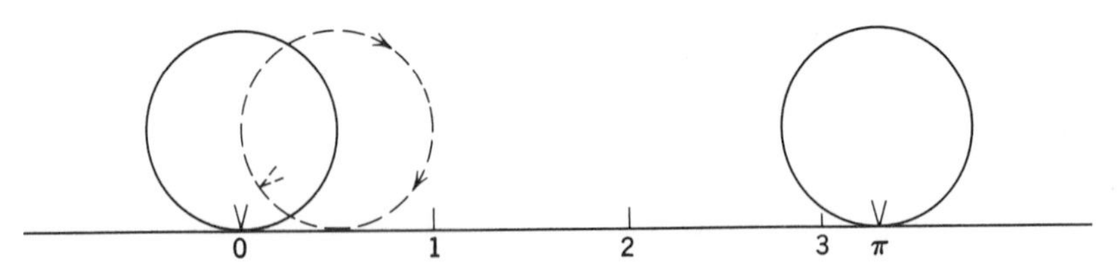

What are some rational numbers close to π?

5. Find the third approximation to $\sqrt{2}$, using $\frac{7}{5}$ as your first estimate. Compare this with the third approximation obtained in problem 1.

6. Find the second approximation to $\sqrt{30}$, using $\frac{27}{5}$ as the first approximation and compare this with the third approximation obtained in problem 2.

8.2a More Irrational Numbers on the Number Line

We plotted the irrational numbers $-\sqrt{2}$ and $\sqrt{2}$ on the number line by placing the lower left-hand corner of the unit square on the point 0. If we place this corner of the square at the point $\frac{1}{2}$ and again rotate the diagonal, the free end of the diagonal will plot new numbers. This translation of the unit square corresponds to the operation of adding $\frac{1}{2}$ to each of the numbers $-\sqrt{2}$ and $\sqrt{2}$.

The binary operation addition assigns to the pair of numbers $\frac{1}{2}$ and $\sqrt{2}$ a number which we write as $\frac{1}{2} + \sqrt{2}$. Similarly for the pair $(\frac{1}{2}, -\sqrt{2})$ we write $\frac{1}{2} + (-\sqrt{2})$ or $\frac{1}{2} - \sqrt{2}$. When we add $\frac{1}{2}$ and $\frac{1}{4}$ we write this $\frac{1}{2} + \frac{1}{4}$, but then we find a new name for this number $\frac{3}{4}$. In the case of $\frac{1}{2}$ and $\sqrt{2}$, the numeral $\frac{1}{2} + \sqrt{2}$ *is* a name of the number. It is not the only name; another is $\dfrac{1 + 2\sqrt{2}}{2}$.

These new numbers $\frac{1}{2} - \sqrt{2}$ and $\frac{1}{2} + \sqrt{2}$ are again irrational numbers (see Figure 2). The following argument can be used to prove this. Suppose $\frac{1}{2} + \sqrt{2} = p/q$, where p/q is a rational number; then $-\frac{1}{2} + \frac{1}{2} + \sqrt{2} = -\frac{1}{2} + p/q$, that is, $\sqrt{2} = -\frac{1}{2} + p/q$. But $-\frac{1}{2} + p/q$ is the sum of two rational numbers. By the Closure Law for addition of rational numbers we infer $\sqrt{2}$ is rational, but this is not so. Hence $\frac{1}{2} + \sqrt{2}$ cannot be rational.

The above statements are true if we use *any* rational number n/m in place of $\frac{1}{2}$, that is, for each rational number n/m, the numbers $n/m - \sqrt{2}$ and $n/m + \sqrt{2}$ are irrational numbers. Thus it is seen that there are as many irrational numbers of the form $n/m + \sqrt{2}$ as there are rational numbers. Also, there are as many irrational num-

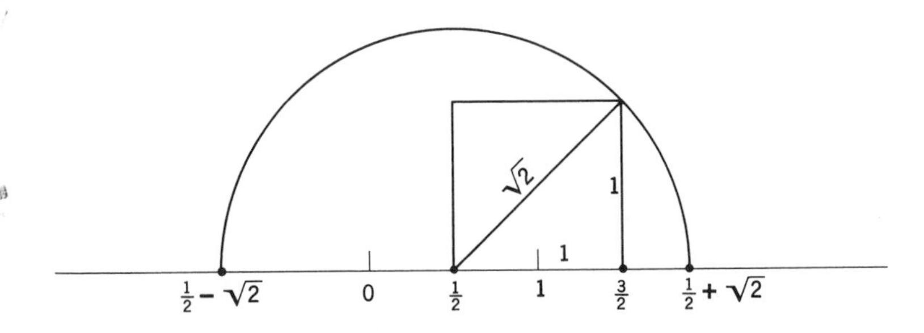

Figure 2

bers of the form $n/m - \sqrt{2}$ as there are rational numbers; the same is true for $n/m + \pi$, $n/m - \pi$, $n/m + \sqrt{3}$, and many more. Thus it is reasonable to believe that there are more irrational numbers than rational numbers.

These arguments indicate that the *rational number line* is full of "holes." These "holes" in the line correspond to the irrational numbers. The set of all numbers which correspond to the points on the line is called the *set of real numbers.* Hereafter we shall refer to the line to which the real numbers correspond as the *real line.* The irrational numbers which fill the "holes" in the line make the set of real numbers *complete.* This fact is extremely important in mathematics and will be discussed further in the next section.

Exercise 8.2a

1. Show that $5 + \sqrt{2}$ is an irrational number.
2. Show that $-\frac{2}{3} + \sqrt{2}$ is an irrational number.
3. What is the largest *integer* less than 3? Less than 0?
4. Is there a largest rational number less than 5?
5. List several upper bounds of each of the following sets:

   (a) $A = \{x \mid x \leqq 17\}$
   (b) $B = \{x \mid x = 1 - 1/n \quad \text{for } n \text{ a positive integer}\}$
   (c) $C = \{x \mid x^2 \leqq 2\}$
   (d) $D = \{x \mid x^2 \leqq 25\}$

6. State informally the meaning of the statement that the rationals are dense in the real numbers.
7. If we lived in a world in which there were no irrational numbers, it would be possible for a circle to pass through the number line without "cutting" the line

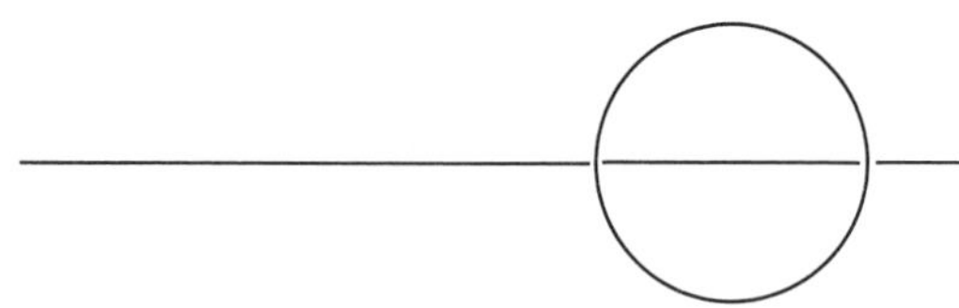

   Give an example of such a circle.

8.3 THE SET OF REAL NUMBERS

The set of real numbers was introduced loosely as consisting of the rational and irrational numbers which correspond to the points on the real line. Without proving it, we have indicated that there is a one-to-one correspondence between the points on the real line and the set of real numbers. This is a very useful idea. It is the link between arithmetic and analytic geometry. If we think of the points on the line as being indexed or addressed by the real numbers, it allows us to locate the points very conveniently. The plane can then be thought of as the Cartesian product of the real line with itself. The points in the plane will then be in one-to-one correspondence with the ordered pairs of real numbers (see Figure 3).

Rather than pursue this geometric line of thought we return to the arithmetic of the real numbers.

We remark that we have not fully attempted to answer the question, "What is a real number?" To answer this question involves "limiting processes" and operations involving infinite sets. We will discuss this informally in the section on decimal fractions later. For the present we say that the *set of real numbers* consists of the rational numbers (which include the integers) and the irrational numbers, as introduced earlier.

We indicate briefly a connection between rational numbers and irrational numbers, using $\sqrt{2}$ as an example. Recall in Section 8.2 that we showed how we could find infinitely many rational numbers $\frac{m}{n}$ such that $\left(\frac{m}{n}\right)^2$ is close to 2. Among these there are those which we write as $\frac{p}{q}$ such that $\left(\frac{p}{q}\right)^2 < 2$ and those which we write as $\frac{r}{s}$ such that $\left(\frac{r}{s}\right)^2 > 2$, that is, some are greater than $\sqrt{2}$ and some are less than $\sqrt{2}$. We denote the two sets of rational numbers as follows:

$$A = \left\{\frac{p}{q}\,\middle|\, p^2 < 2q^2\right\}$$

$$B = \left\{\frac{r}{s}\,\middle|\, r^2 > 2s^2\right\}.$$

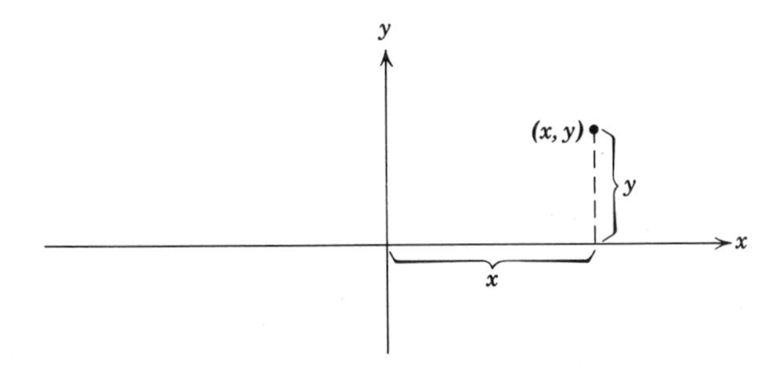

Figure 3

The number $\sqrt{2}$ is an *upper bound* of the set A and a *lower bound* of the set B. It is, in fact, the smallest or *least upper bound* of the set A. It is also the largest or *greatest lower bound* of the set B. Similarly, *every* real number may be thought of as the *least upper bound* of a set of rational numbers as it is the case here with $\sqrt{2}$. For instance, 3 can be thought of as the least upper bound of the set of all rational numbers of the form $3 - 1/n$, where n is a positive integer. When $n = 1$, $3 - \frac{1}{1} = 2$; when $n = 2$, $3 - \frac{1}{2} = \frac{5}{2}$; when $n = 3$, $3 - \frac{1}{3} = \frac{8}{3}$; and when $n = 4$, $3 - \frac{1}{4} = \frac{11}{4}$. This set looks like this

$$\{2, \tfrac{5}{2}, \tfrac{8}{3}, \tfrac{11}{4}, \tfrac{14}{5}, \ldots\}.$$

This is the concept involved in the statement that the set of real numbers is *complete.* We state this more precisely.

DEFINITION 8.3a. A set S of real numbers is *bounded* if there is a positive number b such that $|s| \leqq b$ for all s in S.

DEFINITION 8.3b. The set of real numbers is *complete* means that every nonempty bounded set of real numbers has a least upper bound.

Once we admit irrational numbers, such as $\sqrt{2}$, $\sqrt{30}$, $5 + \sqrt{7}$, $\pi, \ldots$, the following questions arise, "How are such numbers used in arithmetic computation? How are such numbers used to describe the quantitative aspects of our environment?"

Example 1

How many feet of fencing must be purchased to enclose a field in the shape of a right triangle whose legs are 1000 feet long? We see that

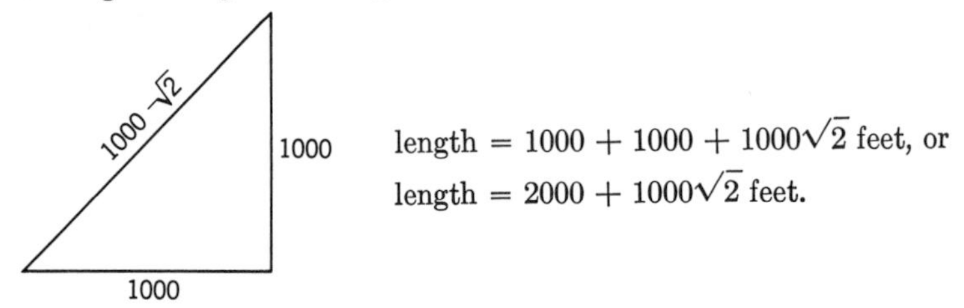

Example 2

What is the circumference of a circle whose radius is $\sqrt{2}$? $2\pi\sqrt{2}$.

8.4 DECIMAL FRACTIONS

The examples in the last section suggest that some other representation of the real numbers is needed; a representation which is amenable to arithmetic computation and which gives the user a readily understandable idea of magnitude. This is true for rational numbers as well as for irrational numbers. For instance, which of the two rational numbers listed below is the larger and what is the sum if the two are added?

$$\frac{3692846}{15496321} \qquad \frac{29487692}{58836857}$$

Without some other representation, computations using numbers of the above form would have to be, and have been, performed with not much more than brute force and perseverance. The necessary innovations in our system of numeration have occurred in relatively recent times. The use of exponents to express extremely small and extremely large numbers originated in the seventeenth century (see Eves). The idea of the decimal fraction was introduced the century before. We turn our attention to the latter.

During the middle of the sixteenth century, Simon Stevin, a Belgian, introduced the idea of *decimal fractions.* By combining the idea of using fractions whose denominators are integral powers of the base with the idea of place value, he freed the arithmetician of computations of the type indicated above.

DEFINITION 8.4. A *decimal fraction* is a rational number whose denominator is an integral power of 10.

Example 1

$$\frac{25}{100}, \quad \frac{874}{10{,}000}, \quad \frac{21}{100{,}000}, \quad \frac{337{,}601}{10{,}000}.$$

In place of writing the power of 10 in the denominator, a point called the decimal point is inserted between two digits of the numerator so that *the number of places to the right of this point tells the power of the base in the denominator.* The point serves as a "separatrix." Digits to the left of the point form the whole or integer part of the number and digits to the right of the point form the numerator of the fraction whose denominator is the power of 10 equal to the number of digits to the right of the decimal point.

Example 2

$$\frac{25}{100} = \frac{25}{10^2} = 0.25$$

$$\frac{874}{10{,}000} = \frac{874}{10^4} = 0.0874$$

$$\frac{337{,}601}{10{,}000} = \frac{337{,}601}{10^4} = 33.7601$$

The number of digits to the right of the decimal point is called the number of *decimal places* in the number.

Example 3

1. The numeral 3.1416 is given to four decimal places.

$$\frac{31{,}416}{10{,}000} = 3.1416.$$

2. The numeral 0.000163 is given to six decimal places.

$$\frac{163}{1{,}000{,}000} = 0.000163.$$

3. The numeral 0.001 is given to three decimal places.

$$\frac{1}{1000} = 0.001.$$

8.4a Computations with Decimal Fractions

There is nothing essentially new in computations involving decimal fractions. Decimal fractions are, after all, special rational numbers written in "decimal form." At most, "placement of the decimal point" in the resultant of a binary operation is the only new procedure not previously discussed. We shall consider this problem only briefly, for it can be explained as a simple consequence of the behavior of exponents and the properties of the system of rational numbers.

8.4b Addition of Decimal Fractions

The usual procedure of adding two or more decimal fractions is to add the numbers columnwise after lining up the decimal points. As in the case of columnwise addition of integers, the decimal points are "lined up" so that the Distributive Law can be applied.

Example 1

Find the sum of 3.92, 406.7273, and 0.076.

$$\begin{array}{r} 3.92 \\ 406.7273 \\ \underline{0.076} \\ 410.7233 \end{array}$$

These three numbers can also be added as rational numbers, remembering that the number of decimal places indicates the power of the base in the denominator.

$$3.92 + 406.7273 + 0.076 = \frac{392}{10^2} + \frac{4067273}{10^4} + \frac{76}{10^3}$$

Writing these rational numbers with a common denominator, we have

$$\frac{39200}{10000} + \frac{4067273}{10000} + \frac{760}{10000}$$ judicious choice of representatives of the classes

$$= \frac{39200 + 4067273 + 760}{10000}$$ by the Distributive Law

The indicated addition in the numerator of the last expression can be carried out by "column addition" (the Distributive Law again).

$$\begin{array}{r} 39200 \\ 4067273 \\ \underline{760} \\ 4107233 \end{array}$$

Notice that the digits are lined up in the same columns as they are in the decimal form. We have then

$$\frac{4107233}{10^4} = 410.7233.$$

The reason for the procedure of lining up the decimal points in the decimal numbers to be added in column addition may be more apparent if the numbers are written in the expanded form. A numeral written in a place-value system of numeration is a convenient expression for a *sum of multiples of powers of the base.* For instance, the integer 1066 can be written in "expanded form" as follows:

$$1066 = 1 \cdot 10^3 + 0 \cdot 10^2 + 6 \cdot 10^1 + 6 \cdot 10^0.$$

Using negative exponents, decimal numerals can be written in the expanded form.

Example 2

1. $2033.3906 = 2 \cdot 10^3 + 0 \cdot 10^2 + 3 \cdot 10^1 + 3 \cdot 10^0 + 3 \cdot 10^{-1} + 9 \cdot 10^{-2} + 0 \cdot 10^{-3} + 6 \cdot 10^{-4}$
2. $0.027 = 0 \cdot 10^{-1} + 2 \cdot 10^{-2} + 7 \cdot 10^{-3}$.

The addition algorithm can be extended to decimal numerals directly, and the Distributive Law applied to the "like" powers justifies the column addition as before.

8.4c Multiplication of Decimal Fractions

Multiplication is quite literally a binary operation. Indicated products of more than two numbers can be expressed because of the Associative Law but the actual computation is strictly binary. The placement of the decimal point in the product of two decimal numerals is again no problem. We illustrate with a numerical example.

Example 1

$$\begin{array}{r} 33.9 \\ \underline{4.27} \\ 2373 \\ 6780 \\ \underline{135600} \\ 144.753 \end{array}$$

To place the decimal point in the product, add the number of places in the multiplier and the multiplicand. The number of places in the product is this sum. This procedure is an immediate consequence of the behavior of exponents.

$$(33.9)(4.27) = \left(\frac{339}{10^1}\right) \cdot \left(\frac{427}{10^2}\right) = \frac{(339)(427)}{10^3} = \frac{144753}{10^3} = 144.753$$

$$(0.0339)(0.427) = \left(\frac{339}{10^4}\right)\left(\frac{427}{10^3}\right) = \frac{144753}{10^7} = 0.0144753.$$

8.4d Division of Decimal Fractions

The usual procedure in placing the decimal point in the quotient of two decimal numbers is as follows. Move the decimal point in the dividend and the divisor enough places to the right to produce whole numbers, adding zeros where needed. Carry out the division as whole numbers with the decimal point in the quotient directly above the decimal point in the new position in the dividend.

Example 1

$$60.69 \div 0.017 = ?$$

```
           .
0.017.)60.690.

  17)60690.  3000
     51000
      9690    500
      8500
      1190     70
      1190
            -----
            3570.  (Quotient)
```

Moving the decimal place in both the divisor and the dividend to produce division of integers, as we have indicated, is actually accomplished by multiplying the divisor and dividend by a high enough power of 10 to produce integers. If the indicated division is expressed in rational form, then multiplying the dividend and the divisor by a power of 10 is the same as multiplying by the multiplicative identity.

Example 2

$$\frac{60.69}{0.017} = \left(\frac{60.69}{0.017}\right) \cdot \left(\frac{10^3}{10^3}\right) = \frac{(60.69)(10^3)}{(0.017)(10^3)} = \frac{60690}{17} = 3570.$$

An alternative procedure, which is quite common, is to execute the division as a division of rational numbers. By using this procedure, the decimal points are moved just enough places to the right to produce a whole number divisor, adding zeros where necessary. Place the decimal point in the quotient directly above the decimal point in the dividend in its new position.

Example 3

$$\frac{6.069}{0.17} = \frac{\frac{6069}{10^3}}{\frac{17}{10^2}} = \left(\frac{6069}{10^3}\right)\cdot\left(\frac{10^2}{17}\right) = \left(\frac{6069}{10}\right)\cdot\left(\frac{1}{17}\right) = \frac{606.9}{17}$$

$$0.17.\overline{)6.06.9} \quad 35.7$$

Exercise 8.4

1. Add the following rational numbers:

(a) $\frac{3}{10} + \frac{2}{100}$ (b) $\frac{2}{10} + \frac{6}{1000}$

(c) $\frac{7}{100} + \frac{9}{1000}$ (d) $\frac{2}{10} + \frac{3}{100} + \frac{7}{1000}$

2. Write each of the rational numbers in problem 1 in the decimal form and verify that addition of decimal fractions in decimal form gives consistent results.

3. A number is written in expanded form when it is written multiplicatively as a sum of powers of the base 10, for example,

$$73.25 = 7\cdot 10^1 + 3\cdot 10^0 + 2\cdot 10^{-1} + 5\cdot 10^{-2}$$

Write each of the following in expanded form:

(a) 700.125 (b) 333.3333 (c) 1000.0001
(d) 27.272727 (e) 3.1416

4. Carry out the indicated operations.

(a) $(3.1416)\cdot(17.74)$ (b) $17.74 \div 3.1416$
(c) $3.1416 \div 17.74$ (d) $(293.004)(7.46)(2.917)$
(e) $1001.0102 \div 0.005$

5. Carry out the indicated operations.

(a) $(2.99776\cdot 10^{10})(1.673\cdot 10^{-24})$ (b) $(3.5\cdot 10^4)(7.69)$
(c) $(6.0228\cdot 10^{23})(1.673\cdot 10^{-24})$ (d) $(8.015\cdot 10^5) \div (0.005)$
(e) $(6.45\cdot 10^{-3}) \div (2.4\cdot 10^5)$

6. The *barn* and the *shed* referred to in Section 8.1 are extremely small units. Write each in decimal notation.

7. If we take the diameter of a silver dollar to be the unit length of a number line, how many of these units must the dollar roll in order for it to start with the head upright, turn over once, and end upright?

8. If two George Washington quarters are placed next to each other with the heads on both coins upright and one coin is rolled over the top of the other, what will be the position of the head on the rolled coin when it comes to rest on the side opposite from which it started? Try this with coins.

8.5 APPROXIMATIONS

Returning to the definition of a decimal fraction as a rational number whose denominator is a power of 10, we find that very few rational numbers can be written exactly as decimal fractions. The prime factors of 10 are 2 and 5 so that any nontrivial positive power of 10 is a product of the corresponding powers of 2 and 5.

$$\begin{aligned} 10 &= 2\cdot 5 \\ 10^2 &= 10\cdot 10 = (2\cdot 5)(2\cdot 5) = 2^2\cdot 5^2 \\ 10^3 &= 10\cdot 10\cdot 10 = 2^3\cdot 5^3 \\ &\cdots\cdots\cdots\cdots \\ 10^n &= 2^n\cdot 5^n \end{aligned}$$

This means that in order for a rational number in lowest terms to be written exactly as a decimal fraction, its denominator can include only powers of 2 and/or powers of 5 as factors.

Example 1

1. $\frac{1}{2} = \frac{1}{2}\cdot\frac{5}{5} = \frac{5}{10} = 0.5$

2. $\frac{1}{4} = \frac{1}{4}\cdot\frac{25}{25} = \frac{25}{100} = 0.25$

3. $\frac{1}{5} = \frac{1}{5}\cdot\frac{2}{2} = \frac{2}{10} = 0.2$

4. $\frac{1}{20} = \frac{1}{2^2\cdot 5} = \frac{1}{2^2}\cdot\frac{5}{5^2} = \frac{5}{(2\cdot 5)^2} = \frac{5}{10^2} = 0.05$

5. $\frac{1}{50} = \frac{1}{2\cdot 5^2} = \frac{2}{2^2}\cdot\frac{1}{5^2} = \frac{2}{(2\cdot 5)^2} = \frac{2}{10^2} = 0.02$

Thus rational numbers of the form $\frac{1}{3}, \frac{13}{11}, \ldots$, which have primes other than 2 and 5 as factors of the denominator cannot be written exactly as decimal fractions. This undoubtedly prevented the predecessors of Simon Stevin from discovering this powerful innovation in arithmetic. The *idea* essential to the discovery of decimal fractions was one of the problems of antiquity. It is embodied in such familiar problems as the frog which at each hop leaps half of the distance from itself to the end of the log. To Simon Stevin, the inspiration must have come from his realization that most numerical situations do not demand *exactness* as much as *accuracy to within an allowable error*. This is a very important idea. It is essentially the idea of approximations which we used earlier in this section.

We have referred to approximation as an *idea*. It is, in fact, a very important one. It is the idea of using a simpler, more workable, acceptable representation in lieu of something inaccessible, unknown, or inconvenient. As a mathematical idea it is related to the concept of denseness. Recall that we found that the rational numbers are densely distributed along the number line. This means that such numbers as $\sqrt{2}$, π, and other irrational numbers which lie on the number line must have many rational numbers very close to them. The rational number $\frac{22}{7}$ is bigger than the irrational number π but is close enough to π so that for many problem situations involving circles, the error involved in using $\frac{22}{7}$ instead of π is allowable. We found several rational numbers "close" to $\sqrt{2}$. Some of these may be used instead of $\sqrt{2}$ in some situations.

Exercise 8.5

1. List ten rational numbers that can be written exactly as decimal fractions. Write these numbers in decimal form.
2. List five rational numbers that can be written exactly as decimal fractions. Write them as rational numbers with powers of 10 in the denominator and in decimal form.
3. A rectangular field is 1276.32 ft long and 789.44 ft wide.
   (a) Compute the area of the field rounding given measurements to nearest foot.
   (b) Compute the area to two decimal places, using the numerals as given.
   (c) What is the difference in these two results?
4. How would you find the approximate area of a field in the shape indicated below?

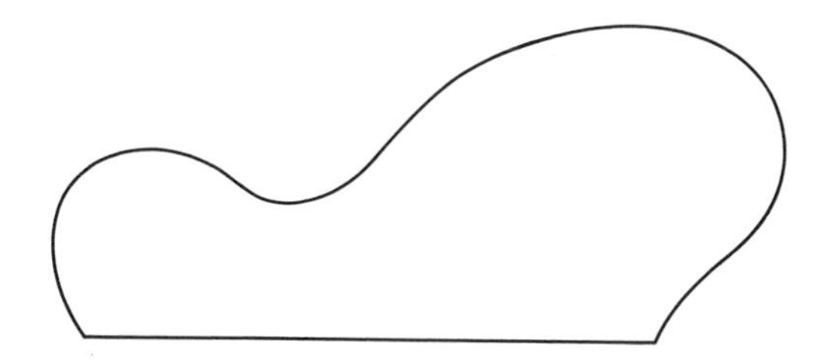

5. How would you go about getting a more accurate measure of the area? Could you justify that this would be more accurate?
6. What are some other *rational numbers* which are very close to the number π? What decimal fractions are close to π?
7. What are some rational numbers close to $\sqrt{10}$? Use the divide and average process to find five of them.
8. What are some rational numbers close to $\sqrt{5}$? Use the divide and average process to find five of them.

8.6 DECIMAL APPROXIMATION OF RATIONAL NUMBERS

We saw in Section 8.5 that we cannot express all rational numbers exactly as decimal fractions. However, we can find decimal fractions which differ from a particular rational number by an amount which we are willing to neglect, the particular amount depending on the problem situation. We find this *decimal approximation* by the simple process of division, that is, we find decimal approximations of $\frac{1}{3}$ by dividing 1 by 3 to obtain 0.3, 0.33, 0.333, and so on.

We have been careful to call the decimal fractions 0.3, 0.33, and 0.333 decimal approximations of $\frac{1}{3}$. The numerals 0.3, 0.33, and 0.333 are convenient numerals which we use instead of $\frac{3}{10}$, $\frac{33}{100}$, and $\frac{333}{1000}$, respectively. From this form it is easy to compute the error involved in using these decimal fractions in place of the rational number $\frac{1}{3}$.

$$\frac{1}{3} - \frac{3}{10} = \frac{1}{30}$$
$$\frac{1}{3} - \frac{33}{100} = \frac{1}{300}$$
$$\frac{1}{3} - \frac{333}{1000} = \frac{1}{3000}$$

The computations above indicate that $\frac{1}{3}$ is larger than any of the decimal fractions 0.3, 0.33, 0.333, and so on. If we were to continue the division process indefinitely, we would have infinitely many decimal fractions of the form 0.3333, 0.33333, ... Again $\frac{1}{3}$ is an *upper bound* of the decimal fractions of this type and, indeed, $\frac{1}{3}$ is the *least upper bound* of all such decimal fractions. This is the same idea used in looking at $\sqrt{2}$ as the least upper bound of the rational numbers of the form p/q, where $p^2 < 2q^2$. For this reason we use the convention that the rational number $\frac{1}{3}$ *is the same* as the decimal number 0.333 . . . , where the dots indicate that the 3's continue without end, that is, we write

$$\frac{1}{3} = 0.3333\ldots.$$

Any one of the numerals 0.3, 0.33, 0.333, . . . , is a decimal approximation involving an error which can be computed. This error can be made smaller by using a decimal fraction with more decimal places. At some point one must decide when the convenience of using decimal fractions outweighs the error or loss of accuracy and what is the maximum error that one is willing to accept.

Exercise 8.6

1. How much would it cost to accept 0.3 of a \$100 gift instead of $\frac{1}{3}$ of \$100?
2. How many places in a decimal approximation of $\frac{1}{3}$ would you use in order to have an error of less than one one-millionth?
3. How many places in a decimal approximation of $\frac{1}{7}$ would you use in order to have an error of less than one one-millionth?

4. What is the error involved in using a three-place decimal approximation of $\frac{1}{7}$? A four-place decimal approximation?
5. Find a ten-place decimal approximation of $\frac{1}{7}$ and of $\frac{1}{11}$.

8.7 THE REAL NUMBERS AS INFINITE DECIMALS

The decimal 0.333 . . . is called an *infinite decimal.* We indicated that $\frac{1}{3}$ can be expressed as an infinite decimal. On the other hand, decimal fractions of the form 0.5, 0.25, and so on, are called finite decimals or terminating decimals. However, if we adjoin zeros to 0.5 in an unending sequence as follows:

$$0.50000\ldots,$$

we can think of the decimal fraction representation for $\frac{1}{2}$ as an infinite decimal. We must add a note of caution. The number 1 can be written as an infinite decimal as 1.00000 . . . , but at the same time the infinite decimal 0.99 . . . is also the whole number 1 in the same sense that $\frac{1}{3} = 0.333\ldots$. If we identify 0.999 . . . with 1 as well as 3.279999 . . . with 3.28, and so on, then we can express any rational number uniquely as an *infinite decimal.* This is also true of any irrational number although it is not always easy to find the decimal representation of an irrational number. In fact, the *square root algorithm* is simply the process of finding the decimal representation of the square root of a number. We can now define the real numbers.

DEFINITION 8.7. The real numbers are the numbers named by the infinite decimals.

We first introduced the *set of real numbers* as those numbers corresponding to points on the number line. We defined the real numbers as named by the infinite decimals. We used both approaches to the real numbers in order to have a broader understanding of the nature of the real numbers. These two approaches are quite different but in no way inconsistent. The definition of the real numbers in terms of the infinite decimals is a unifying concept not inconsistent with the other approach.

8.8 THE REAL LINE

If we consider the number line again, it is a straight line along which the *integers* are evenly marked in both directions from the origin which we labeled 0.

−2 −1 0 1 2

The decimal fractions which we call tenths separate the line segment into equal segments so that ten such segments fit between any consecutive pair of integers.

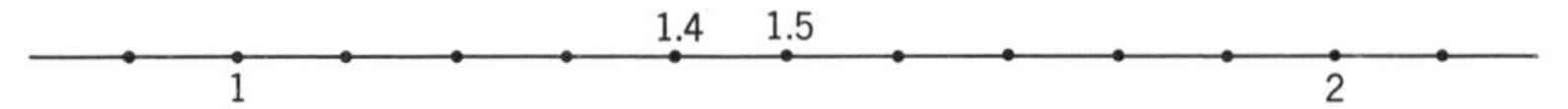

The hundredths divide each of the tenths into ten equal parts. The thousandths divide each of the hundredths segments into ten equal parts. The ten thousandths, hundred thousandths, millionths,

and so on are scattered along the number line in the same way as indicated above. If the line is divided into millionths, there would be one million such segments between any two consecutive integers. This suggests that the decimal fractions are also *dense* on the number line. This is actually the case although it requires proof. This is essentially the reason why we can use decimal fractions in any computations involving real numbers. One can imagine plotting the numbers 0.3, 0.33, 0.333 . . . indefinitely, approaching in the limit the rational number $\frac{1}{3}$. Conversely, it is plausible that if we let the letter r denote the point on the real line corresponding to the real number r, by taking successive subdivisions, tenths, hundredths, thousandths, and so forth, choosing at each successive step the nearest mark to the point r, one can approximate the real number r by a decimal fraction. By continuing indefinitely, the number r can be expressed as an infinite decimal.

Exercise 8.8

1. Plot the points 0.1, 0.14, and 0.142.
2. Find decimal approximations of $\frac{57}{40}$. Compare these to table values of $\sqrt{2}$.
3. Find decimal approximations of $\frac{6449}{4560}$ and compare these to table values of $\sqrt{2}$.
4. Find decimal approximations of $\frac{22}{7}$ and compare to table value of π.
5. Find decimal approximations of $\frac{3927}{1250}$, $\frac{754}{240}$, $\frac{355}{113}$ and compare these to π.
6. The decimal fractions are dense in the real numbers.
   (a) Interpret this statement, using $\sqrt{2}$ as an illustration.
   (b) Interpret this statement, using π as an illustration.

8.9 ORDER RELATIONS IN THE REALS

The order relations $<$ and $\leqq$ in the real numbers are defined in the same way as was done in the system of rational numbers and in the system of integers. In each instance we specified *positive* elements and defined the order relations in terms of the positive elements. We do the same now. We indicate that the real number r is positive by the notation $r > 0$ or $0 < r$. We indicate that it is non-negative by the notation $r \geqq 0$ or $0 \leqq r$.

How we determine whether a real number is positive or negative depends on the way the real numbers are introduced.

If we think of the real numbers as numbers corresponding to the points on the real line, then the real number is positive if it is associated with a point to the right of the 0 point (the origin). If r and s are any two numbers, $r < s$ or $r \leqq s$ if $s - r > 0$ or $s - r \geqq 0$, respectively.

If we think of the real numbers as infinite decimals, the decimal fraction approximation obtained by neglecting all the decimal places after a particular decimal place is a rational number. A positive real number has a positive decimal approximation. A negative real number has a negative decimal approximation. Thus the positive elements can again be determined and the order relations defined.

8.10 THE SYSTEM OF REAL NUMBERS

There are other ways of defining the real numbers. The real numbers can be defined as equivalence classes of Cantor sequences (Cauchy sequences) as is done in *Set Theory, The Structure of Arithmetic* by Hamilton and Landin. The real numbers can also be defined as "Dedekind Cuts." For a sophisticated treatment, see *Principles of Mathematical Analysis* by Rudin. Our informal treatment of the real numbers as infinite decimals on the one hand and as the least upper bounds of sets of rational numbers on the other introduces the student to both of the formal approaches indicated above in a way which makes the nature and properties of the real numbers more accessible. Each of the number systems previously studied in this book is a subsystem of the system of real numbers. The natural numbers are real numbers. The integers are real numbers. The rational numbers are real numbers. Without formally listing the properties as was done with the other number systems, we define the *system of real numbers* as a number system which satisfies the same laws as the system of rational numbers and which has an order relation with respect to which the set is *complete.* A mathematical system which satisfies the same laws as the system of rational numbers is called a *field.* In this language, the real numbers are specified as a *complete ordered field.* Rather than pursue the discussion in this direction further, we make a few comments regarding computations with real numbers. Arithmetic at the elementary level is primarily concerned with the five arithmetic processes, addition, subtraction, multiplication, division, and estimating square roots. Arithmetic computations are limited to these operations involving rational numbers except in a few isolated instances, such as $\sqrt{7} \cdot \sqrt{7} = 7$.

Computations using irrational numbers involve infinite processes; hence, in actual numerical calculations, the irrational numbers are replaced by decimal fractions.

Awareness of this situation is important and has been stressed in this book.

8.11 REPEATING DECIMALS

We were careful to distinguish between rational numbers and irrational numbers, rational numbers being of the form m/n, where m and n are integers and $n \neq 0$. Irrational numbers cannot be expressed in this form. We now ask, Can these numbers be distinguished when expressed in decimal form? The answer is Yes. Some rational numbers are finite or terminating decimals; the other rational numbers turn out to be those infinite decimals which "repeat," that is, a certain block of consecutive digits will be repeated over and over in an unending sequence.

Example 1

0.825 0.75	Finite or terminating decimals
$0.272727\overline{27}\ldots$ $0.46314631\overline{4631}\ldots$ $29.37854854\overline{854}\ldots$	Infinite repeating or non-terminating repeating decimals. The bar indicates the repeating "blocks."

That such is the case can be easily verified by using the "division" interpretation on a few rational numbers, such as $\frac{5}{7}$, $\frac{2}{9}$, $\frac{4}{11}$, and so on. We are interested more in *why* the rational numbers have representations as infinite repeating decimals.

In examining the division process which yields the decimal representation of a rational, such as $\frac{5}{7}$, we see that we are actually dividing repeatedly by the same number 7.

$$\begin{array}{r} 0.7 \\ 7\overline{)5.0} \\ \underline{49} \\ 1 \end{array} \qquad 50 = 7 \cdot 7 + 1$$

The next step is to divide 7 into 10.

```
   0.71
 7)5.00
   490          10 = 7·1 + 3
    10
     7
     3
```

The next step is to divide 7 into 30.

```
   0.714
 7)5.000
   4900         30 = 7·4 + 2
   1000
    760
     30
     28
      2
```

Notice that at each step we are dividing 7 into the remainder from the previous division times a power of 10. But, how many different remainders can we have when we divide all possible numbers by 7? We saw in Section 6.8 that the only possible remainders when dividing by 7 are 0, 1, 2, 3, 4, 5, 6. Now let us continue the division

$$0.714285\overline{714285}$$

```
   0.714285714285
 7)5.000000000000
   49
    10
     7
     30
     28
      20
      14
       60
       56
        40
        35
         50
```

It is quite obvious now that "714285" will repeat endlessly. Can you look at the above division and tell what the decimal expansion of $\frac{1}{7}$, $\frac{2}{7}$, $\frac{3}{7}$, and so on will be?

The reason that rational numbers are infinite repeating decimals is actually embodied in what we have previously called the *division algorithm.* To reiterate, if m and n are any two positive integers, then there are positive integers q and r such that $m = n \cdot q + r$ and $0 \leqq r < n$.

Since there are only n distinct integral values that the remainder r can assume, the above argument implies that the decimal numeral for m/n will be repeating. This is not to be interpreted as saying that the number of digits in the repeating sequence will be equal to the divisor n. It does say that it can be less than *or* equal to the divisor but never greater.

It can be shown that, conversely, every repeating decimal is the decimal representation of a rational number, that is, given a repeating decimal, we can find a rational number whose repeating decimal is the given one. We indicate how this is done. Let us use the letter N to denote an infinite repeating decimal. Suppose

$$N = 0.273273273\overline{273}\ldots$$

We multiply by that power of 10 whose exponent is equal to the number of digits in the repeating block and subtract N from this product. Thus

$$\begin{array}{rcl} 10^3N = 1000N &=& 273.273273\overline{273}\ldots \\ N = \quad 1N &=& 0.273273\overline{273}\ldots \\ \hline 999N &=& 273 \end{array}$$

$$N = \frac{273}{999}$$

Modifications of this procedure must be made for those infinite repeating decimals which do not start repeating immediately, for example,

$$N = 32.49631631631\overline{631}\ldots$$

We want the repeating blocks to "match up" so that subtraction will eliminate the decimal fraction. Hence we multiply first by 10^5 and then by 10^2.

$$\begin{array}{rcl} 10^5N = 100{,}000N &=& 3249631.631631\overline{631}\ldots \\ 10^2N = \quad 100N &=& 3249.631631\overline{631}\ldots \\ \hline 99900N &=& 3246382 \end{array}$$

$$N = \frac{3246382}{99900}$$

The previous argument indicates that every rational number is a repeating decimal and the above examples suggest that every infinite repeating decimal is a rational number. This leaves but one conclusion. *The irrational numbers are the infinite nonrepeating decimals.* If one reflects about this for a moment, it seems reasonable that there are many more irrationals than rationals.

Exercise 8.11

1. (a) How many possible remainders are there when 11 is the divisor? List them.
(b) Write $\frac{1}{11}$ as an infinite repeating decimal.
(c) Write $\frac{2}{11}$ as an infinite repeating decimal.
(d) Write $\frac{3}{11}$ as an infinite repeating decimal.

2. (a) How many possible remainders are there when 12 is the divisor?
(b) Write $\frac{1}{12}$ as an infinite repeating decimal.
(c) Write $\frac{2}{12}$ as an infinite repeating decimal.
(d) Write $\frac{3}{12}$ as an infinite repeating decimal.

3. (a) How many possible remainders are there when 13 is the divisor?
(b) Write $\frac{1}{13}$ as an infinite repeating decimal.
(c) Write $\frac{2}{13}$ as an infinite repeating decimal.

4. Each of the infinite repeating decimals is a rational number. Find the rational numbers.

(a) $0.17721772\overline{1772}\ldots$
(b) $0.314314314\overline{314}\ldots$
(c) $0.29353535\overline{35}\ldots$

5. Find a decimal fraction which approximates each of the rational numbers of problem 4 to within an error of one part in 10,000.

6. Find the rational number represented by each of the following infinite repeating decimals.

(a) $4.99999\overline{9}\ldots$
(b) $0.100100100\overline{100}\ldots$
(c) $0.009009009\overline{009}\ldots$

8.12 ROUNDING OFF DECIMAL APPROXIMATIONS

Since it is physically impossible to write down an infinite decimal, the decimals after a certain finite number of places are dropped. The part that is retained is a decimal fraction, and the part that is dropped constitutes the error involved in using the approximation:

$$\tfrac{5}{7} = 0.714285\overline{714285}\ldots$$
$$\tfrac{1}{3} = 0.333\overline{3}\ldots$$
$$\tfrac{5}{7} = \underbrace{0.7142}_{\substack{\text{decimal fraction}\\ \text{approximation}}} + \underbrace{0.000085\overline{714285}\ldots}_{\text{error}}$$
$$\tfrac{1}{3} = \underbrace{0.333}_{\substack{\text{decimal fraction}\\ \text{approximation}}} + \underbrace{0.00033333\overline{3}\ldots}_{\text{error}}$$

The usual purpose of "rounding off" a decimal fraction is to reduce the error involved in the approximation. There are several conventions used in rounding off numbers. The procedure we shall use is to look at the first digit dropped. If this digit is 0, 1, 2, 3, or 4, the last digit in the approximation is retained. If the first digit dropped is 5, 6, 7, 8, or 9, the last digit of the approximation is increased by 1. Thus we would use 0.333 as a three-place decimal approximation of $\frac{1}{3}$ and 0.7143 as a four-place decimal approximation of $\frac{5}{7}$.

Decimal numerals, in general, are often rounded off to a certain number of significant digits. A digit of a numeral naming an approximate number is *significant* unless its only function is to help place the decimal point. Whenever digits to the right of the decimal point are dropped, they must never be replaced by zeros, whereas digits to the left of the decimal point must be replaced by zeros in keeping with the meaning of *significant digits.* All nonzero digits in a number are significant. All zeros between significant digits are significant. A zero following a nonzero digit may be significant.

Example 1

673,924 has six significant digits.
674,000 as a rounding of 673,924 has three significant digits. As an independent numeral it has three or more, possibly six, significant digits.
0.07003 has four significant digits.
0.07 has one significant digit.
1.2370 has five significant digits.
200,001 has six significant digits.

Example 2

The population of Montana is listed as 670,000. This is to be interpreted as a number of two significant digits. The population at the time of the census might have been any number, such as 673,924, or any other number between 665,000 and 675,000, but because the population is constantly changing as a result of people moving into the state and people moving out for one reason or another, it is meaningless to list 673,924 exactly. For most purposes the approximate figure 670,000 is accurate enough.

8.13 DECIMAL APPROXIMATIONS OF IRRATIONAL NUMBERS

The full significance of characterizing the rational numbers as terminating decimals or infinite repeating decimals and irrational numbers as infinite nonrepeating decimals may not have been realized. Finding the decimal representation of a rational number involves only a simple division process, and as soon as the repeating block of digits has been determined, the division process does not have to be continued, that is, it is always possible to determine the exact digit in any decimal place in an infinite repeating decimal.

Example 1

What digit is in the 105th decimal place of the infinite repeating decimal of the rational number $\frac{1}{7}$? Since there are six digits in the repeating block of digits and since $105 \equiv 3 \pmod{6}$, the digit in the 105th place is the same as the digit in the third place of the repeating block.

It is also possible to compute the *exact* error involved in using a decimal fraction as an approximation to a rational number. We illustrated this in Section 8.6. Such is not the case when decimal fractions are used to estimate irrational numbers. Without actually computing the decimal, there is no known way of predicting the digit in the fifth decimal place of π, or the digit in the seventh decimal place of $\sqrt{3}$, or the digit in any decimal place of any irrational number. This means we cannot compute the *exact* error involved in using decimal fractions in place of irrational numbers. It is possible to give *bounds* on the error. We can do this using only the properties of the place-value system and what we mean by rounding off a number. We illustrate our remarks with some examples.

Example 2

What does it mean to say 1.4 is a one-place decimal approximation of $\sqrt{2}$? This means that $\sqrt{2}$ is a number which is between 1.35 and 1.45.

$$1.35 \leqq \sqrt{2} \leqq 1.45.$$

The error involved in using 1.4 as an approximation to $\sqrt{2}$ is less in absolute value than 0.05, that is, 0.05 is a *bound* on the error. By extracting the square root of 2 to two decimal places we get 1.41. The error in using 1.41 as an approximation to $\sqrt{2}$ is less in absolute value than 0.005. Similarly, the error in using 3.1416 in place of π is less in absolute value than 0.00005 or five parts in one hundred thousand.

Exercise 8.13

1. In what sense is 3.14 an approximation of π? Is 3.142 an approximation of π? Is 3 an approximation of π?
2. Which is the better approximation of π, 3.142 or $\frac{22}{7}$?
3. What is the error in using 0.6666667 for $\frac{2}{3}$?

8.14 SQUARE ROOTS

Before we consider the problem of finding decimal approximations of the square roots of numbers (square root algorithms), we shall discuss more fully the meaning of the square root of a number. It was carefully pointed out in the last chapter that the symbol $\sqrt{2}$ is a numeral, that is, a name for that number which when multiplied by itself gives the number 2. It was also pointed out at that time that many people do not distinguish $\sqrt{2}$ from some complicated arithmetic operation. Indeed, many people do not think of $\sqrt{2}$ as a number at all. Unfortunately there are many teachers in the elementary and secondary schools who think of $\sqrt{2}$ not as a number but as something to do. This is partly because of the existence of certain natural numbers which are perfect squares. The perfect squares are the squares of the natural numbers.

$$1, 4, 9, 16, 25, 36, 49, \ldots$$

These numbers are part of the real number system, so there is a natural answer to the question, "What number multiplied by itself is 4, or 9, or 16, etc.?" This is indicated by

$$\begin{aligned} \sqrt{4} &= 2 \\ \sqrt{9} &= 3 \\ &\cdots\cdots\cdots \\ \sqrt{144} &= 12 \\ \sqrt{625} &= 25 \\ &\cdots\cdots\cdots \\ \sqrt{2401} &= ? \\ &\cdots\cdots\cdots \\ \sqrt{82369} &= ? \end{aligned}$$

When the number N^2 becomes unfamiliarly large, such as 2401 or 82,369, the question naturally arises whether these numbers are perfect squares or not and, if they are, how does one find their square roots? One way, of course, is to write down the squares of the natural numbers to see if these numbers occur among the squares. That there is actually an algorithm which can be used to answer this question is part of the reason for the confusion between the number and the algorithm.

The square root of a number a is actually a solution of the equation

$$x^2 = a.$$

We noted repeatedly that the solvability of equations, in general, depends on the number system in which the coefficients lie, that is, if the letter "a" denotes a perfect square and we require the solution to be a *natural number*, there is only *one* solution. If we allow *integer* solutions, there are *two* solutions, for example, if

$$x^2 = 25,$$

then $$x = 5 \quad \text{or} \quad x = -5.$$

If we allow a to be any positive rational number and require *rational* solutions, we may have no solution or two solutions, depending on the nature of a, that is, *if* a is the square of a rational number, we will have two solutions. If a is not the square of a rational number, we will have no rational solutions. The equation

$$x^2 = \tfrac{25}{64}$$

has two rational solutions,

$$x = \tfrac{5}{8} \quad \text{and} \quad x = -\tfrac{5}{8},$$

while

$$x^2 = 2$$

has no rational solutions, for there is no rational number whose square is the number 2.

If we allow a to be a non-negative real number and allow the solutions of $x^2 = a$ to be real numbers, there will be exactly two solutions when $a \neq 0$. We indicate the two square roots of the number a by the symbols $\sqrt{a}$ and $-\sqrt{a}$. The square roots of 3 will be written $\sqrt{3}$ and $-\sqrt{3}$. The $\sqrt{3}$ is the positive number which when multiplied by itself gives the number 3, whereas $-\sqrt{3}$ is the additive inverse of $\sqrt{3}$ and is the negative number which when multiplied by itself gives 3. In order to avoid any confusion about the square roots of those numbers written as squares, we use the absolute value to define $\sqrt{a^2}$.

DEFINITION 8.14. For every real number a, $\sqrt{a^2} = |a|$ and $-\sqrt{a^2} = -|a|$.

Example 1

$$\sqrt{(-3)^2} = |-3| = 3.$$

There is one situation that we have not yet discussed and that is the case when a is allowed to be a negative number in the equation $x^2 = a$, that is, do the equations

$$x^2 = -1,$$
$$x^2 = -5,$$
$$\cdots\cdots$$

have solutions? These equations do not have solutions which are *real* numbers. In the same way that we introduced the negative integers as solutions of the equation

$$a + x = b,$$

and the rational numbers as solutions of the equation

$$ax = b,$$

and the irrational numbers as solutions of the equation

$$x^2 = a \quad \text{when} \quad a > 0,$$

we now introduce the number i as the solution of the equation

$$x^2 + 1 = 0$$

or

$$x^2 = -1.$$

Hence $$i^2 = -1.$$

It follows that $$i^3 = i^2 \cdot i = -i,$$
and $$i^4 = i^2 \cdot i^2 = 1.$$

In general, numbers of the form $2 + 3i$, $1 + i$, $7i$, $\frac{1}{2} + \frac{\sqrt{2}}{3}i$, $\pi - i$ are called *complex numbers*. Numbers of the form $7i$, $2i$, $\sqrt{3}i$ are called *pure imaginary* numbers. The terms *complex* and *pure imaginary* are used here simply as the names of sets of numbers. The reader is cautioned about attaching any literal meaning to these terms. The system of complex numbers is a number system which is very much a part of the scientific world, but we will not discuss it further in this book.

Exercise 8.14

1. Is $3 + \sqrt{5}$ a number?
2. What are the sum, difference, and product of $3 - \sqrt{5}$ and $3 + \sqrt{5}$?
3. What are the sum, difference, and product of $\sqrt{a} + \sqrt{b}$ and $\sqrt{a} - \sqrt{b}$?
4. $\sqrt{10}$ is approximately 3.162. Give a decimal approximation for $1/\sqrt{10}$.
5. $\sqrt{2}$ is approximately 1.4142. Give a decimal approximation for $1/\sqrt{2}$.
6. Give a decimal approximation for $1/(2 + \sqrt{2})$.
7. Give a decimal approximation for $1/(\sqrt{10} - \sqrt{2})$.
8. Give a decimal approximation for $\sqrt{10}/10$, $\sqrt{2}/2$, $(2 + \sqrt{2})/2$, $(\sqrt{10} + \sqrt{2})/8$.
9. Give a decimal approximation for $\sqrt{2}/\sqrt{2}$, $\sqrt{10}/\sqrt{10}$, $(2 + \sqrt{2})/(2 - \sqrt{2})$.
10. Express the following, using the number i: (For example, $\sqrt{-5} = i\sqrt{5}$, since $(i\sqrt{5})^2 = i^2(\sqrt{5})^2 = -5$.)

$$\sqrt{-4},\quad \sqrt{-9},\quad \sqrt{-7},\quad \sqrt{-1},\quad \sqrt{-50} + \sqrt{-32}.$$

8.14a The Square Root Algorithm

The square root algorithm is the arithmetic process of finding or approximating the square root of a number. We review the process for the benefit of those who may have forgotten it.

Example 1

Find $\sqrt{82369}$.

Step 1. Mark off the digits in pairs to the left, starting from the decimal point. Each pair determines a *place* in the square root.

```
   *  *  * .
 √ 8'23'69.
```

Step 2. Find the largest whole number whose square is less than or equal to the number in the left-hand pair or single digit:

$$2^2 = 4 < 8 < 9 = 3^2$$

```
   2  *  * .
 √ 8'23'69.
   4
   ---------
   4
```

Write 2 above this "pair." Square 2 and subtract from 8. Bring down the two digits of the next pair.

Step 3. Double the number 2 in the root and place an asterisk as indicated to the right of the 4.

```
         2  *  * .
       √ 8'23'69.
         4
   4(*)  4 23
```

Step 4. Estimate how many times 40 divides 423. We try 9. Replace the asterisk with 9 and multiply by 9. 9 is too large. We try 8. Replace the asterisk with 8 and multiply by 8. Place 8 above the pair brought down.

```
         2  9  * .
       √ 8'23'69.
         4
   4(9)  4 23
      9  4 41
```

Step 5. Repeat steps 3 and 4.

```
         2  8  7.
       √ 8'23'69.
         4
   4(8)  4 23
      8  3 84
  56(7)   39 69
      7   39 69
```

$\sqrt{82369} = 287$

We now consider what takes place at each step. Recall that multiplying a number by 100 moves the decimal point *two* places to the right. But multiplying a number by 100 only multiplies the square root of the number by 10. This follows from the fact that the square root of a product is equal to the product of the square roots.

$$\sqrt{M \cdot N} = \sqrt{M} \cdot \sqrt{N}$$
$$\sqrt{36} = \sqrt{4 \cdot 9} = \sqrt{4} \cdot \sqrt{9} = 2 \cdot 3 = 6$$
$$\sqrt{100 \cdot N} = \sqrt{100} \cdot \sqrt{N} = 10\sqrt{N}.$$

This is the reason that the digits in the number are marked off in pairs. The number of pairs determines the number of digits in the square root.

At each step of the algorithm we are interested in finding the largest whole number whose square is less than or equal to the number determined by those pairs directly concerned. In step 2, for instance, we estimate the largest whole number whose square is less than or equal to 8. In the next step we seek the largest whole number whose square is less than or equal to 823. At this point we are working with two pairs, so the square root of 823 is a two-digit number of which the first digit is 2. We can write this as $20 + x$. We want to estimate the largest integer x so that the square of the number $20 + x$ is less than or equal to 823, that is, we would like the largest x which satisfies

$$(20 + x)^2 \leqq 823.$$

Squaring $(20 + x)$, we get

$$400 + 2 \cdot 20x + x^2 \leqq 823.$$

Subtracting 400 from both sides of this inequality, we see that

$$2 \cdot 20x + x^2 \leqq 423.$$

This step corresponds to subtracting 4 from 8 and bringing down the next pair of digits. (Note this step in the example.)

$$(2 \cdot 20 + x)x \leqq 423$$
$$(40 + x)x \leqq 423.$$

This accounts for doubling the digit in the root and leaving a place for a digit as indicated by the * in the example. We divided 423 by 40 to get an estimate of x. This procedure is based on the observation that 40 is much larger than the digit x so that dividing by 40 is almost like dividing by $40 + x$. This is the reason that we often overestimate x. We saw in the example that 9 was too large so 8 is the number we sought.

The next step is a repetition of the last step. We want the largest whole number whose square is less than or equal to 82369. This is a 3 digit number whose first two digits are known. That is, we seek the largest whole number x such that

$$\begin{aligned}
&(280 + x)^2 \leqq 82369 \\
&78400 + 2 \cdot 280x + x^2 \leqq 82369 \\
&560x + x^2 \leqq 3969 \\
&(560 + x)x \leqq 3969 \\
&x = 7 \\
&\underline{280 + 7 = 287}
\end{aligned}$$

We extracted the square root of the square of a natural number. The algorithm is valid for any positive real number and the process may be continued beyond the decimal point. We need to add zeros to make as many pairs to the right of the decimal point as we want decimal places in the square root. We illustrate:

Example 2

Find $\sqrt{3.4}$ to three decimal places.

$$\begin{array}{r|l}
 & \;\;1.\;8\;\;4\;\;3 \\
 & \sqrt{3.40'00'00} \\
 & \;\;1 \\
\hline
28 & 2\;40 \\
\underline{8} & \underline{2\;24} \\
364 & 16\;00 \\
\underline{4} & \underline{14\;56} \\
3683 & 1\;44\;00 \\
\underline{3} & \underline{1\;10\;49}
\end{array}$$

If we carry the work out one place further, we would find that $\sqrt{3.4}$ is closer to 1.844 than to 1.843. This extra step is less troublesome than worrying about "least absolute remainders." We point out instead that we can greatly improve the approximation by a simple division process which is discussed in the next section.

Exercise 8.14a

1. Find $\sqrt{502.3}$ rounded to 3 decimal places.
2. Find $\sqrt{50.23}$ rounded to 3 decimal places.
3. Find $\sqrt{1000.}$ rounded to 4 decimal places.
4. Find $\sqrt{5.023}$ rounded to 4 decimal places.
5. Find $\sqrt{0.5023}$ rounded to 4 decimal places.

8.14b Newton's Method of Approximating Square Roots

The method of approximating the square root of a number by the "divide and average" process discussed earlier is actually *Newton's method of approximation.* (Sir Isaac Newton, 1642–1727, an Englishman, was one of the very great scientists of all time. Newton made many contributions to mathematics and physics, many of which still bear his name. At about the same time as—but independently of Gottfried Wilhelm Leibnitz, 1646–1716—he originated the calculus.)

Newton's method is based on the calculus and is a powerful method for approximating roots of very general equations. In the particular case of approximating square roots, the method reduces to a very simply *iterative* or *repetitive* process. The repetitive nature of the process, "divide and take the average, divide and take the average" makes this method well suited to our modern high-speed electronic computers. Another important feature of Newton's method is the fact that the first "guess" or approximation does not have to be very accurate, that is, making a "poor guess" the first time does not mean the work has to be abandoned and the process begun all over again. It means that another one or two repetitions of the process will be needed to yield an accurate approximation. We illustrate the method by finding a decimal approximation to $\sqrt{300}$. We label our first "guess" A_1 and successive approximations A_2, A_3, ...

Example 1

Find $\sqrt{300}$.

Step 1. Since $17^2 = 289 < 300 < 324 = 18^2$, we choose 17 as a reasonable first guess.

$$A_1 = 17 \qquad \text{(first approximation)}$$

Step 2. Divide the number N by A_1, that is, 300 by 17, and carry out the division to twice as many digits as in the previous approximation and round off the last digit to an even number. To get the second approximation A_2, take the average of this quotient and the previous approximation.

$$\frac{300}{17} = 17.64$$

Rounding to the nearest even digit we get 17.64 to twice as many digits as in A_1.

$$A_2 = \frac{17.64 + 17.00}{2} = 17.32 \qquad \text{(second approximation)}$$

Notice that A_2 *verifies* our first guess as being a good guess because when we round off 17.32 to a two-digit number we get $A_1 = 17$.

Repeating the process, we have

$$A_3 = \frac{\frac{300}{17.32} + 17.320000}{2} = \frac{17.321016 + 17.320000}{2}$$

$$= 17.320508 \qquad \text{(third approximation)}$$

The fact that A_3 verifies A_2 implies A_2 is accurate to two decimal places. A_3 is accurate to within 1 in the last place.

To show that a poor guess yields the same decimal fraction after a few more repetitions of the process, suppose we let

$$A_1 = 10$$

$$A_2 = \frac{\frac{300}{10} + 10}{2} = 20$$

Notice that A_2 does not verify A_1 because A_2 rounded to two digits is not equal to A_1. We carry out the division to one less than twice as many digits in the previous approximation when the verification fails.

$$A_3 = \frac{\frac{300}{20} + 20.0}{2} = 17.5$$

$$A_4 = \frac{\frac{300}{17.5} + 17.5000}{2} = \frac{17.142 + 17.500}{2} = 17.321$$

$$A_5 = 17.320508$$

Newton's method can be used to approximate cube roots as well as square roots. (For an excellent account, see Swain.)

The various corrective measures in those cases where the approximation fails to verify the previous approximation were presented as "rules to follow." The reasons for the validity of these measures as well as the method itself have their roots in the calculus. The method was presented here as another method of estimating square roots, a method adaptable to electronic computers.

Exercise 8.14b

1. Find $\sqrt{3}$ rounded to 7 decimal places.
2. Find $\sqrt{30}$ rounded to 7 decimal places.
3. Find $\sqrt{3000}$ rounded to 6 decimal places.
4. Find $\sqrt{5}$ rounded to 6 decimal places.
5. Find $\sqrt{50}$ rounded to 7 decimal places.
6. Find $\sqrt{500}$ rounded to 6 decimal places.
7. Find $\sqrt{3.4}$ rounded to twice as many digits as in Example 2 of the previous section.

REFERENCES

Eves, Howard, *An Introduction to the History of Mathematics*, Rinehart and Co., New York, 1953.

Hamilton, Norman T. and Joseph Landin, *Set Theory, The Structure of Arithmetic*, Allyn and Bacon, Boston, 1961.

Rudin, W., *Principles of Mathematical Analysis*, McGraw-Hill Book Co., New York, 1953.

Swain, Robert L., *Understanding Arithmetic*, Rinehart and Co., New York, 1952.

*
*
*

CHAPTER NINE

Topics from Geometry

9.1 INTRODUCTION

In this chapter we shall be discussing points, lines, plane figures bounded by straight lines, plane figures bounded by curved lines, figures in three-space bounded by planes, and figures in three-space bounded by curved surfaces. We think of these objects as "sets of points," and we deal with these sets of points much as we dealt earlier with sets of numbers. We use "point," "line," and "plane," relying on the intuitive ideas that these terms convey. They are descriptive of the objects of a particular set. We symbolize these objects by marks, figures, and diagrams in the same sense that we use numerals to symbolize numbers.

It is our objective to present some of the notions of lengths, areas, and volumes without the formality of a geometric development. We shall rely on the conventional interpretations rather than on formal definitions of some of the terms used. For a more formal treatment see any recently published textbook in plane geometry (e.g., Brumfiel, Eicholz, and Shanks).

9.2 LENGTHS OF LINE SEGMENTS

The length of a straight-line segment has been discussed indirectly in Section 6.12. There we spoke of the "distance" between two points on the number line where the integers were used to label the points. Using the set of real numbers to label the points, the *distance* from a point labeled "a" to a point labeled "b" is defined to be $|b - a|$. This can be defined as the *length of the line segment* from the point labeled a to the point labeled b.

Hereafter we shall use capital letters to label points and lower-case letters to designate lines in conformity with the usual practice in geometry. We shall use $\overline{AB}$ to denote the line segment from a point A to a point B. Here A and B have no particular numerical association but are simply names of the endpoints of the straight-line segment.

In the naive sense, the *length of the straight-line segment denoted* AB can be interpreted as the minimum number of *unit segments* it takes to "cover" the line segment completely without "overlapping." The unit segment is chosen to suit the situation. It may be an inch, a foot, a mile, a millimeter, and so forth. We may say a line segment is 6 in. long, $6\frac{1}{2}$ miles long, 22.3 cm long, and so on.

Length is one of the measures referred to earlier (see Section 8.1). The length of a line segment is a real number associated with that segment. We are, in effect, setting up a correspondence between line segments and positive real numbers. The number associated with the segment is information about the line segment. The usefulness of this information will depend on the precision of the measuring instrument and the care exercised in its use.

It is interesting to note that many of the words associated with measurements have a "physical" origin. For example, the "foot" was initially the length of a man's foot and, as you might guess, varied considerably from time to time and from locale to locale. The "inch" was initially the distance from the last knuckle to the tip of a man's thumb. The "hand," a unit of measure used in designating the height of a horse, was the distance across the palm of a man's hand. Of course, these measures were not very "standard." Gradually measures of various kinds have become "standardized" as evidenced by the "standard" tables of weights and measures. (For additional historical information see Larsen, Swain, or Newman.)

The length of a segment of a curve is not easily defined, and when the length is defined, the task of determining it generally requires the use of calculus. We shall look at the special case of the arc of a circle. With the help of a little imagination and by proceeding carefully step by step, we arrive at a suitable definition of the length of an arc of a circle.

Consider the circular arc, which we denote $\widehat{AB}$, as in Figure 1. We wish to define the length of $\widehat{AB}$. We shall use the length of straight-line segments, the triangular inequality, and the concepts of least upper bound and greatest lower bound to arrive at the definition.

Let C be the point on the arc (Figure 2) midway between A and B (C can be found by construction). Then, considering the straight-line segments $\overline{AC}$ and $\overline{CB}$, we can regard the sum of the lengths of the

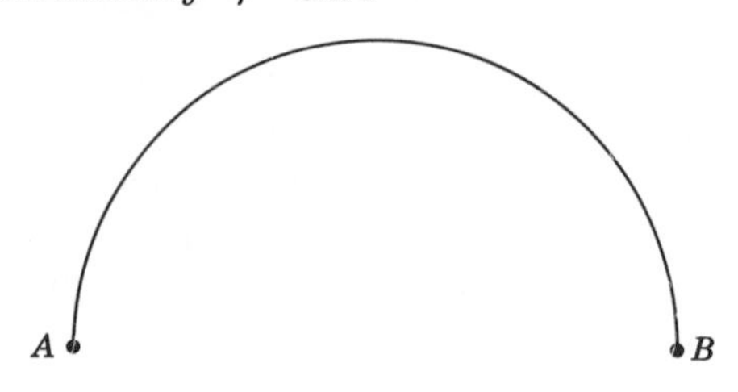

Figure 1

straight-line segments as an approximation to the length of $\widehat{AB}$. Let AC denote the length of the straight-line segment $\overline{AC}$. (Note that AC is a real number.) Then our first approximation to the length of $\widehat{AB}$, denoted by l_2, (the "2" for two segments), is

$$l_2 = AC + CB.$$

For a second approximation, choose points D and E such that D is on the arc midway between A and C and E is on the arc midway between C and B (see Figure 3).

Then a second approximation, l_4, to the length of $\widehat{AB}$ is given by

$$l_4 = AD + DC + CE + EB.$$

Notice that $l_2 \leqq l_4$ by the triangular inequality (see Section 6.12c, 3), that is,

$$AC \leqq AD + DC$$

and

$$CB \leqq CE + EB,$$

so

$$l_2 = AC + CB \leqq AD + DC + CE + EB = l_4.$$

Continuing in this manner we can obtain *inscribed polygonal paths* from A to B of 2, 4, 8, 16, etc., sides. Let us designate the approximation obtained by using a path of 2^n sides by l_{2^n}.

Associated with each inscribed polygonal path is a circumscribed polygonal path obtained by constructing the tangents at the endpoints

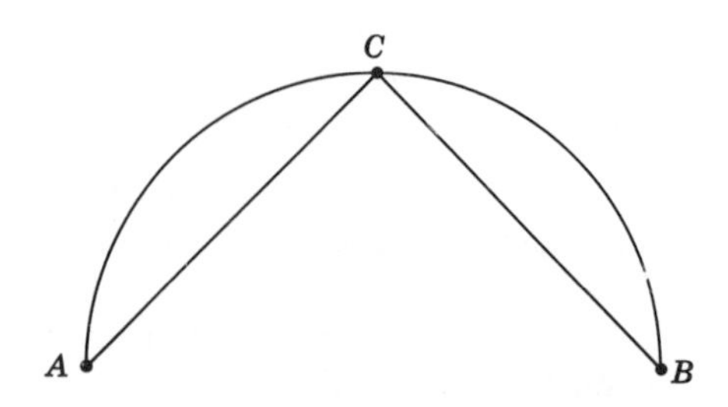

Figure 2

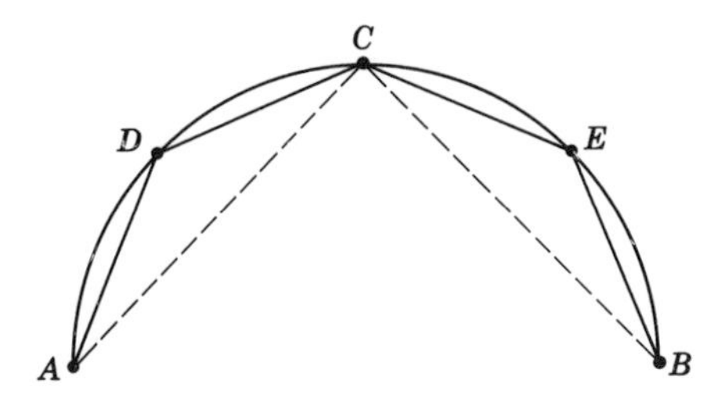

Figure 3

of the arc and at each point selected. These tangents meet to form polygonal paths as indicated in Figure 4.

Let us designate by L_2 the length of the circumscribed path associated with the inscribed path l_2. Using the triangular inequality, it can be shown that

$$l_{2^n} < L_2 \qquad \text{for every } n,$$

and

$$l_{2^n} < l_{2^{n+1}} \qquad \text{for every } n.$$

The sequence of numbers $l_2, l_4, l_8, \ldots l_{2^n}, \ldots$ is an increasing sequence of real numbers bounded above by the number L_2. By the property of *completeness* (see Section 8.3) this sequence has a least upper bound. Similarly, the lengths of the circumscribed paths form a decreasing sequence bounded below by the length of the chord $\overline{AB}$. Again by the property of completeness this sequence has a greatest lower bound. If the least upper bound of the increasing sequence is equal to the greatest lower bound of the decreasing sequence, the common value is defined to be the *length* of the circular arc $\widehat{AB}$.

Example 1

To illustrate this procedure let us use successive approximations as outlined above to estimate the length of a semicircular arc of a circle of diameter 2, which we know has length π.

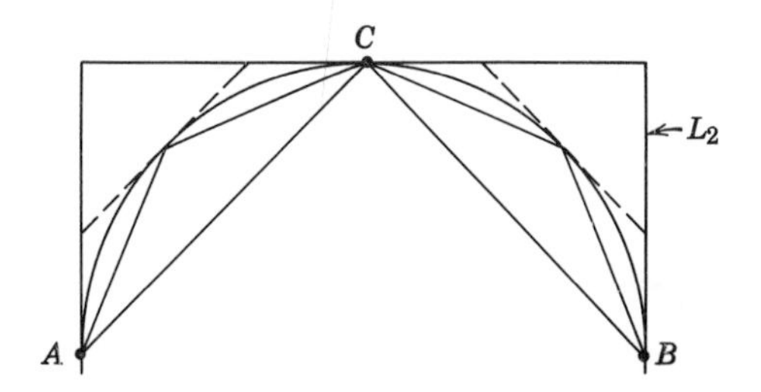

Figure 4

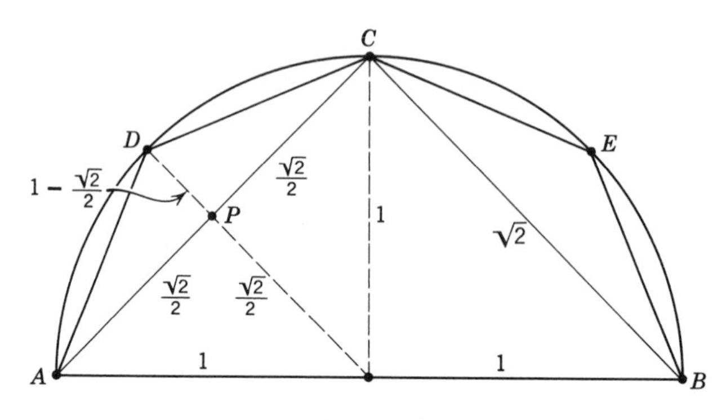

Figure 5

$AB = 2$ Length of $\widehat{AB} = \pi \cong 3.14$

$l_2 = AC + CB = \sqrt{2} + \sqrt{2} \cong 2(1.4142) \cong 2.83$

$l_4 = AD + DC + CE + EB$, but since AD, DC, CE, and EB are equal by construction,

$l_4 = 4(AD)$, where AD can be computed from $\triangle APD$, Figure 5.

$$AD = \sqrt{\left(1 - \frac{\sqrt{2}}{2}\right)^2 + \left(\frac{\sqrt{2}}{2}\right)^2} = \sqrt{1 - \sqrt{2} + \tfrac{1}{2} + \tfrac{1}{2}}$$

$$= \sqrt{2 - \sqrt{2}} \cong \sqrt{2 - 1.41421356} \cong 0.76537$$

$l_4 = 4(AD) \cong 4(0.76537) \cong 3.06$

$l_8 = AF + FD + DG + GC + CH + HE + EI + IB$, but, by construction, these are all equal, so

$l_8 = 8(AF)$, where AF can be computed from $\triangle AQF$, Figure 6.

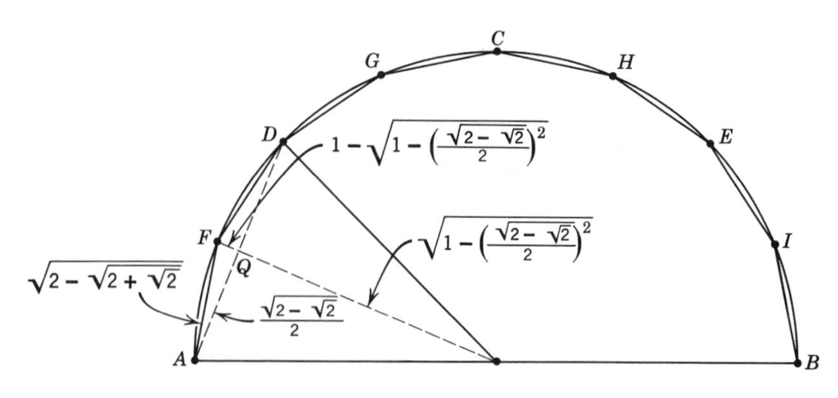

Figure 6

$$AF = \sqrt{\left(\frac{\sqrt{2-\sqrt{2}}}{2}\right)^2 + \left(1 - \sqrt{1 - \left(\frac{\sqrt{2-\sqrt{2}}}{2}\right)^2}\right)^2}$$

$$= \sqrt{2 - \sqrt{2+\sqrt{2}}}$$

$$\cong \sqrt{2 - \sqrt{3.41421356}} \cong \sqrt{2 - 1.8477}$$

$$\cong \sqrt{0.1523} \cong 0.39$$

$$l_8 \cong 8(0.39) = 3.12$$

$$2.83 < 3.06 < 3.12 < 3.14$$

$$l_2 < l_4 < l_8 < \pi$$

Notice that the third approximation yields accuracy to two significant figures.

Exercise 9.2

1. Show that $l_2 \leqq l_4$, using Figure 3.
2. Show that $l_{2^n} \leqq l_{2^{n+1}}$.
3. Find l_4 for a semicircular arc of diameter 3.
4. Estimate the length of the following curved path consisting of two semicircles by
   (a) using a ruler to estimate the measure of each segment of polygonal paths on a full size drawing.
   (b) using the calculations from problem 3.

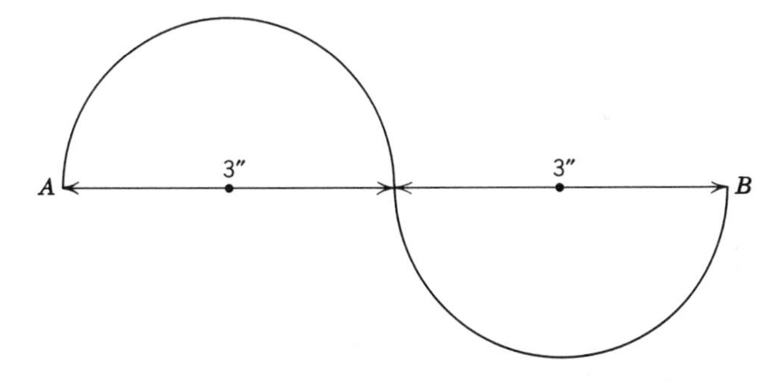

5. In Section 9.2 we used the triangular inequality to show that $AC \leqq AD + DC$. Sketch the triangle involved and verify the validity of our argument.
6. What is the exact length of the arc of problem 4?
7. Sketch the triangles referred to in Figure 4 and verify that $l_2 < L_2$.
8. Label the figure properly and verify that $l_4 < L_2$.

9.3 AREAS

In this section we shall present derivations of the standard formulas for the areas of a few selected plane figures.

As with the length of a line segment, the *area* of a plane figure is also a *measure,* that is, the area of a plane figure is a non-negative real number such that if a plane figure P is contained in a plane figure Q, then the area of P, denoted $A(P)$, is less than or equal to the area of Q, $A(Q)$. If the plane figures P and Q are disjoint, then the area of the union of the two plane figures is equal to the sum of the area of P and the area of Q. The "length" of a line segment, as a measure, has these properties. The "volume" of an object in space, which will be discussed briefly in a later section, is also a measure and has these properties. Since we use these properties implicitly in what follows, we list them in the language of *area* and refer to them briefly.

Let P denote a plane figure and $A(P)$ its area; then

1. $A(P) \geqq 0$. (Non-negative)
2. If $P \subseteq Q$, then $A(P) \leqq A(Q)$. (Monotone)
3. If $P \cap Q = \emptyset$, then $A(P \cup Q) = A(P) + A(Q)$. (Finitely additive)

Since we are interested in how to determine the area of a plane figure, we review what is meant by the area of a rectangle.

First choose a unit of length. Then a *square* one unit of length on a side is said to have *one square unit of area.* From Figure 7 we see that if we had three unit squares side by side we would want to count the area 3 square units. Similarly, if we have a rectangle with sides of length 2 and 4, by counting squares we would want to call its area 8 square units. A square $\frac{1}{2}$ unit length on each side is $\frac{1}{4}$ square unit in area, since four such squares precisely fill a unit square. A rectangle whose sides are 2 and $2\frac{1}{2}$ units in length has area 5 square units as we see by counting.

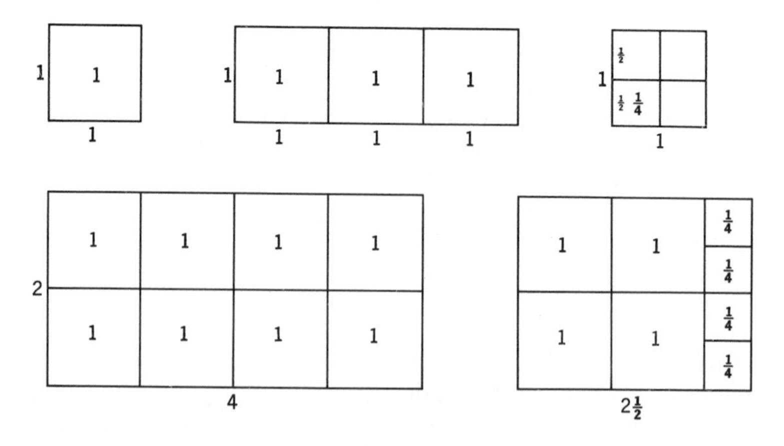

Figure 7

By using our imagination we can see how this idea of counting could be extended to any rectangle whose *length* and *width* were given in terms of rational numbers, and we find that the counting procedure gives us the same result as multiplying length by width. (See problem 4, Exercise 7.11c.)

We therefore *define* the area of a rectangle with length l and width w to be lw square units, where the real numbers l and w are given in the same units of length. If we use A to designate the area, then

$$A = lw.$$

For a square, which is just a special case of the rectangle with $l = w$, we usually use the symbol s to denote the length of a side. Then the area of a square is given by

$$A = s^2.$$

The area of plane figures, in general, can be defined in terms of the areas of rectangles. (See Section 9.7 for an example of the general procedure.) For our purposes we derive the formula for the area of a triangle and use this information to derive the formulas for the area of other plane figures.

9.3a Area of Triangles

The diagonal of a rectangle divides the rectangle into two equal parts. (See if you can recall enough of plane geometry to prove this. Try the theorem, "Two right triangles are congruent if the hypotenuse and a side of one are equal, respectively, to the hypotenuse and a side of the other.")

Each of these parts is a right triangle (see Figure 8). If the area of the rectangle is lw, then the area of the right triangle is $\frac{1}{2}lw$. We usually designate the length of the two legs of a right triangle by b and h, b for the base and h for the height. Then the area of a right triangle is the product of $\frac{1}{2}$, the base, and the height

$$A = \tfrac{1}{2}(bh).$$

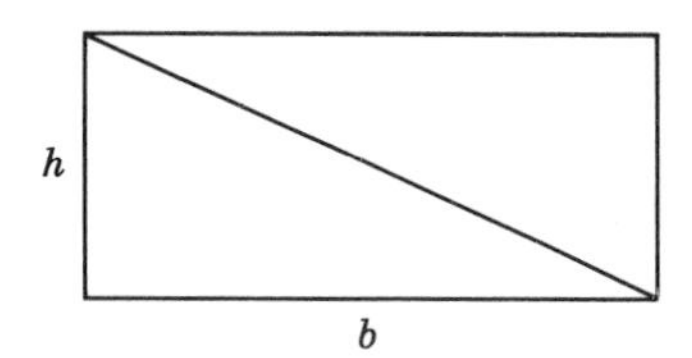

Figure 8

Notice that we are using the *additive property* of area, that is, the area of the rectangle is equal to the sum of the two equal numbers which represent the area of the right triangles.

To obtain the area of a general triangle, drop a perpendicular from a vertex to the opposite side (see Figure 9).

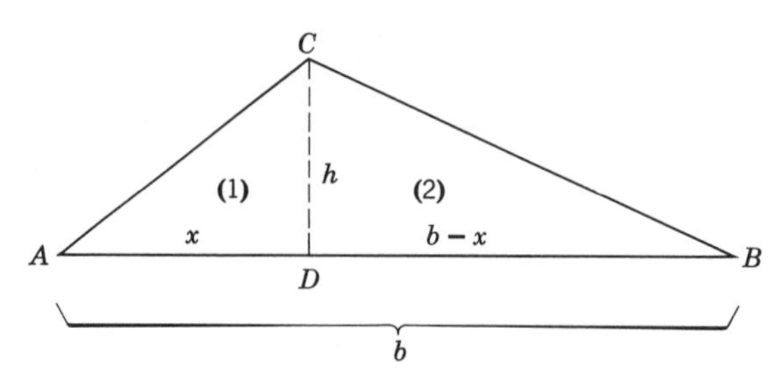

Figure 9

The length of this segment, $\overline{CD}$, is designated as an altitude or height of the triangle and denoted h. The segment $\overline{CD}$ divides the triangle into two triangles, (1) and (2), each of which is a right triangle. Let us denote the length of the base of (1) by x and the length of the base of (2) by $b - x$. They both have height h. Applying the known information about right triangles, we have

$$\text{Area of (1)} = \tfrac{1}{2}(xh),$$

$$\text{Area of (2)} = \tfrac{1}{2}(b - x)h = \tfrac{1}{2}(bh) - \tfrac{1}{2}(xh),$$

and

$$\text{Area (1)} + \text{Area (2)} = \tfrac{1}{2}(xh) + \tfrac{1}{2}(bh) - \tfrac{1}{2}(xh) = \tfrac{1}{2}(bh).$$

Hence the area of the general triangle is also given by the product of $\frac{1}{2}$, the base, and the height

$$A = \tfrac{1}{2}(bh).$$

Notice again that we rely on the additive property of area.

9.3b Area of Parallelogram

Next let us turn to the parallelogram, a plane figure whose opposite sides are parallel and equal (see Figure 10).

Here we designate the length of the perpendicular line segment between two parallel sides, called the "altitude" of the parallelogram, h, and

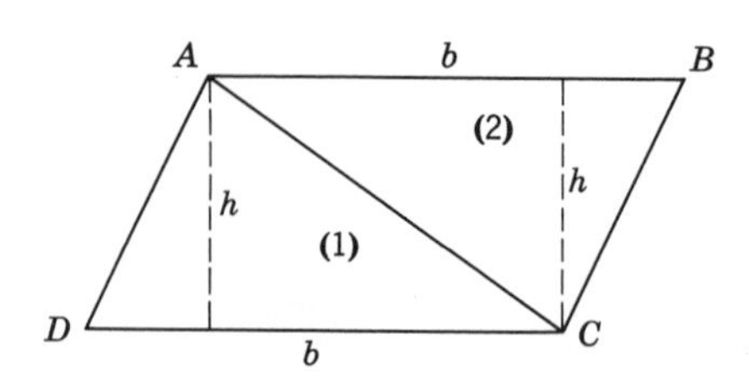

Figure 10

the length of one of these parallel sides, called the base, b. If we draw the diagonal, $\overline{AC}$, we note that this divides the parallelogram into two triangles, each of which has base of length b and height of length h. Thus

$$\text{Area of triangle (1)} = \tfrac{1}{2}(bh),$$
$$\text{Area of triangle (2)} = \tfrac{1}{2}(bh),$$

and

$$\text{Area (1)} + \text{Area (2)} = \tfrac{1}{2}(bh) + \tfrac{1}{2}(bh) = bh.$$

Hence the area of a parallelogram is the product of the lengths of the base and the height

$$A = bh.$$

9.3c Area of the Trapezoid

The trapezoid is a plane figure bounded by four straight line segments, two of which are parallel (see Figure 11).

Again we will designate the length of the perpendicular line segment between the two parallel sides by h and call it the height. We will denote the length of one of the parallel sides b and the other a. By drawing a diagonal as indicated in Figure 11, we see that the trapezoid is divided into two parts, each of which is a triangle. One triangle has base of length b and height of length h and the other has base of length a and height of length h. We have

$$\text{Area of triangle (1)} = \tfrac{1}{2}(bh),$$

and

$$\text{Area of triangle (2)} = \tfrac{1}{2}(ah).$$

Then

$$\begin{aligned}\text{Area of trapezoid} &= \text{Area (1)} + \text{Area (2)} = \tfrac{1}{2}(bh) + \tfrac{1}{2}(ah)\\ &= \tfrac{1}{2}(b + a)h \qquad \text{(Distributive Law)}\end{aligned}$$

This is usually written

$$A = \tfrac{1}{2}h(a + b).$$

In words, we would say that the area of a trapezoid is found as the product of $\frac{1}{2}$, the height, and the sum of the two "bases." Notice that we again rely on the additive property of area.

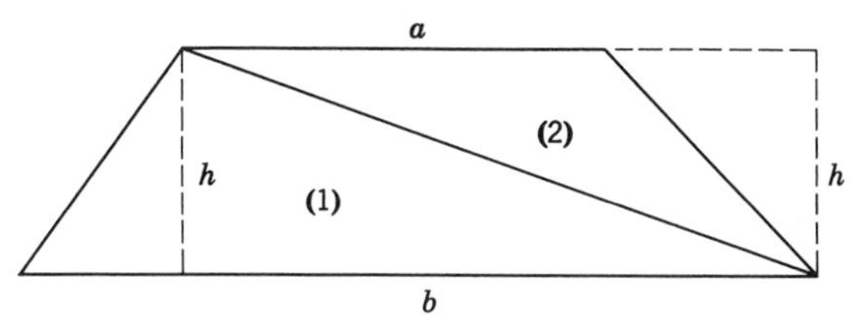

Figure 11

9.3d The Area of Regular Polygons

Next we establish the formula for the area of a regular n-gon, a regular polygon of n sides. This is a plane figure that has equal sides and equal angles. The simplest plane figures of this type are the equilateral triangle and the square. In establishing a formula that yields the area of any regular n-gon we will picture the regular hexagon for reference (see Figure 12). Associated with each regular polygon is a circumscribed circle. Let us designate the center of this circle as the center of the regular polygon. Then if we draw straight lines from the center to each of the vertices, we will have constructed a triangle for each of the sides of the polygon. The distance from the center of a regular polygon to one of its sides (that is, perpendicular distance) is called the *apothem*. We shall designate its length by the letter a. This is also the altitude of the triangle formed by one of the sides of the polygon and the lines from its endpoints to the center. Let us designate the length of one of the sides of the polygon by the letter s; then the area of one of the triangles is $\frac{1}{2}(as)$. If the polygon has n sides, then there are n such triangles in the polygon. Using the additive property of area, we have

$$A = \tfrac{1}{2}a(ns).$$

But ns is the "perimeter" (distance around) the regular polygon; hence

$$A = \tfrac{1}{2}(ap).$$

In words, this says that the area of a regular polygon is the product of $\frac{1}{2}$, the apothem, and the perimeter.

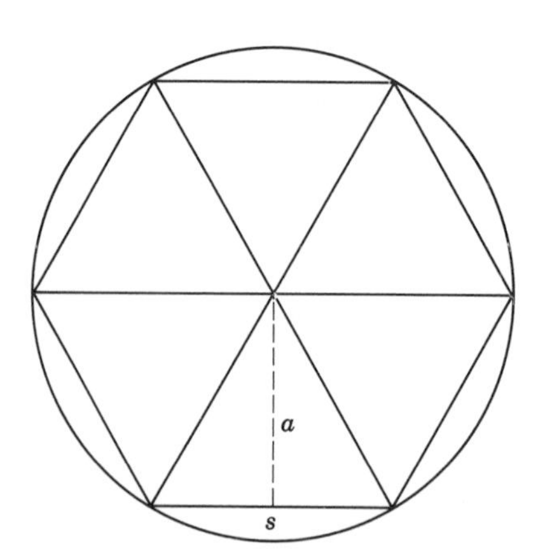

Figure 12

Exercise 9.3

1. Find the areas of the triangles shown, using the dimensions given.

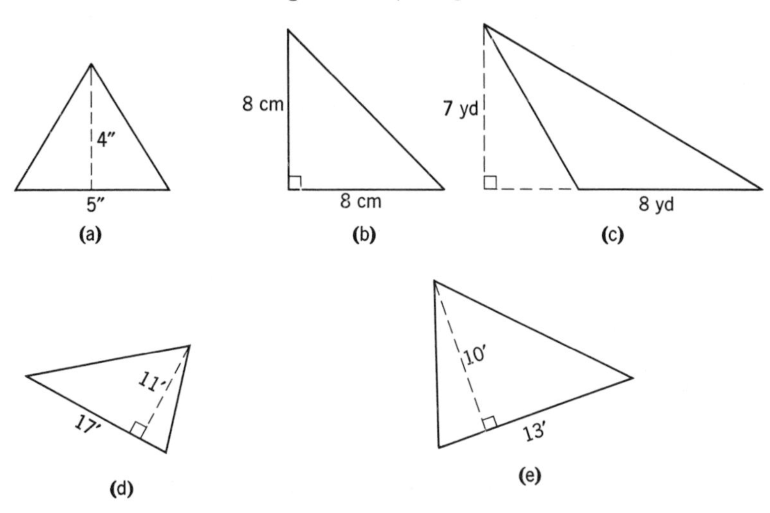

2. Find the areas of the parallelograms shown, using the dimensions given.

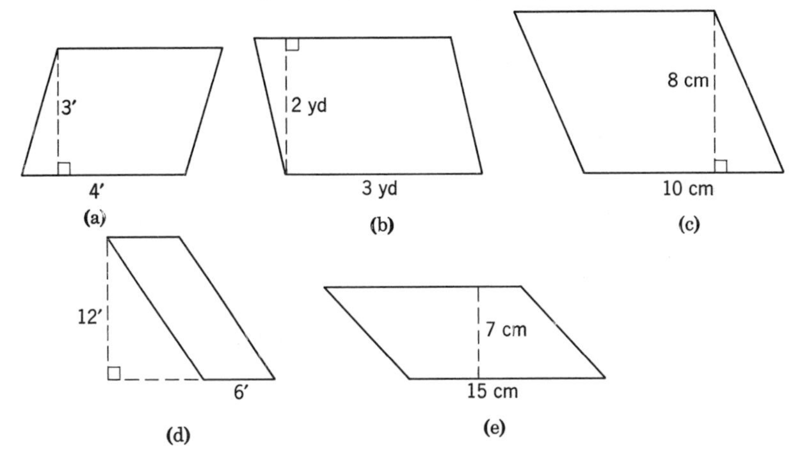

3. A man owned a rectangular lot 150 ft by 100 ft. From one corner, A, a fence is placed to a point M in the center of the longer opposite side as shown.

(a) Find the area of $ABCD$.
(b) Find the area of AMB.
(c) Find the area of $AMDC$.

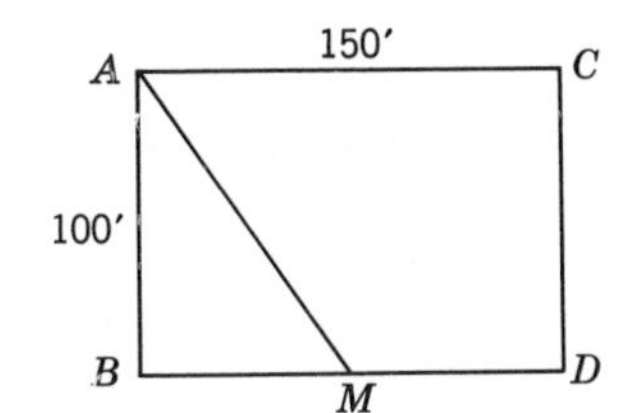

4. (a) In the drawing below, measure $\overline{AB}$ and $\overline{DS}$. Using these measures, find the area of the parallelogram.
   (b) Measure $\overline{AD}$ and $\overline{RB}$. Using these measures, find the area of the parallelogram.
   (c) Do your results in (a) and (b) agree? Since measurement is approximate, they may not be exactly the same, but they should be close.

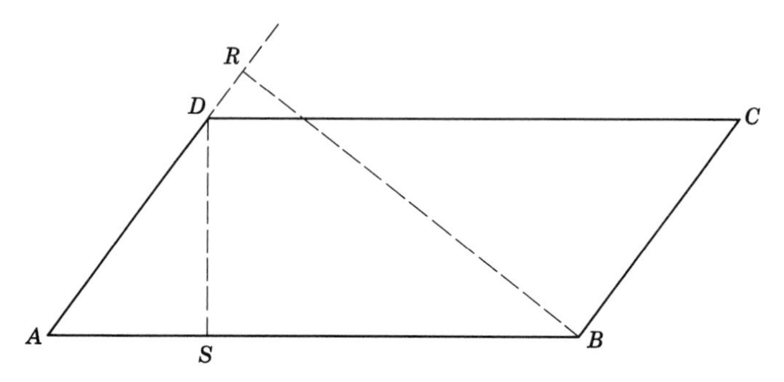

5. Find the area of the following trapezoids, using the dimensions given.

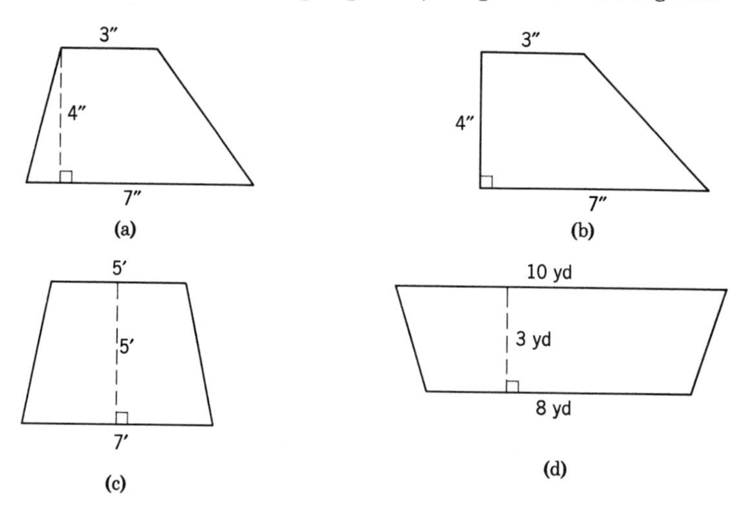

6. Using rational approximations for the irrational numbers, find an approximation to the area of a rectangle whose length is $\sqrt{2}$ ft and whose width is $\sqrt{3}$ ft.

9.4 VOLUMES AND SURFACE AREA

In this section we shall present some of the standard formulas for volume. First we define a *unit of volume*. As with area, choose a unit of length. A *cube* one unit of length on each edge is said to have *one cubic unit of volume.* From Figure 13 we see that if we had 3 cubes side by side, we would want to count this 3 cubic units. Similarly, by counting, we see that if we had a rectangular solid 2 units by 3 units by 2 units, we would want to call this 12 cubic units. A cube $\frac{1}{2}$ unit on an edge would be counted as $\frac{1}{8}$ cubic unit, for it takes precisely 8 of them to "fill" one cubic unit.

As with area, if the units of measure of the dimensions of the rectangular solid are given in terms of rational numbers, we can obtain the number of units of volume by "counting," and we see that the result is the same as if we multiplied "length" by "width" by "height." If we designate the length, width, and height by l, w, and h, respectively, l, w, and h real numbers, then the volume, V, of the rectangular solid is *defined* by

$$V = lwh.$$

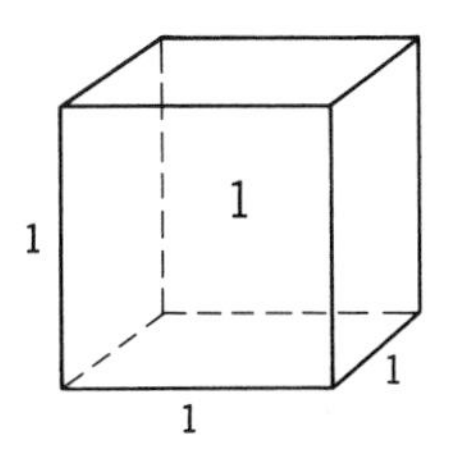

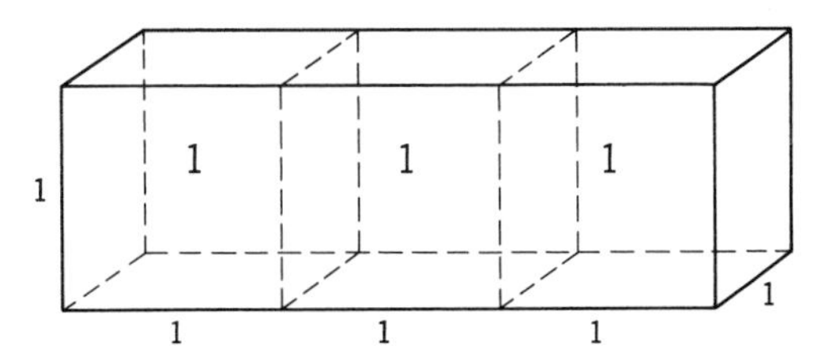

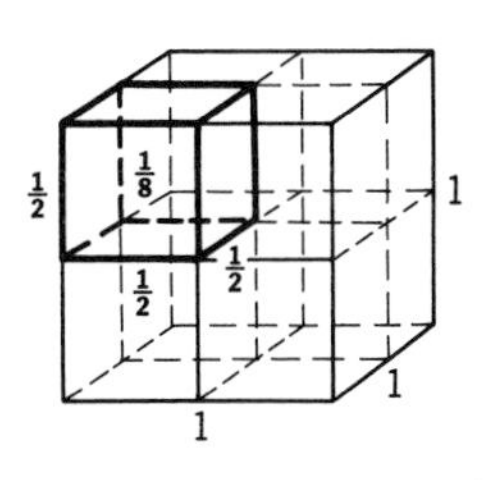

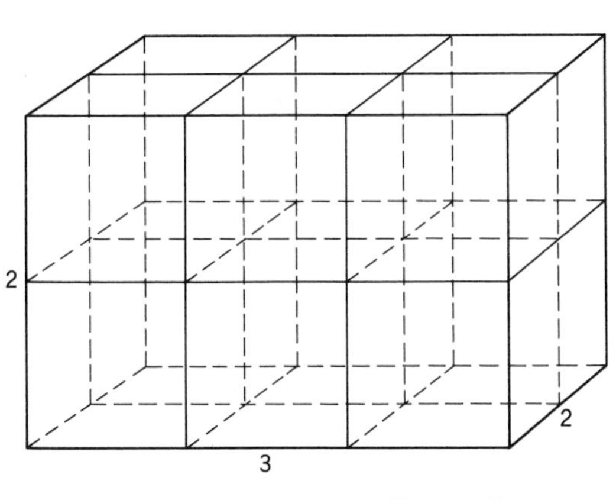

Figure 13

The derivation of the formulas for each of the solids given in the following paragraphs can be made precise with the use of calculus. We shall simply describe the type of figures under discussion and present the formula for that figure.

9.4a Prism

In the same sense that we referred to a two-dimensional figure bounded by straight lines as a polygon, we speak of a three-dimensional figure bounded by planes as a *polyhedron.*

A *prism* is a polyhedron two of whose faces (called bases) are congruent polygons (exactly the same size and shape), in parallel planes, and whose remaining faces (called lateral faces) are parallelograms (see Figure 15).

A prism, each of whose faces and bases is a rectangle, is called a *rectangular solid* or a *rectangular parallelepiped.* The volume of a parallelepiped (box-shaped figure) is given by the product of the lengths of three concurrent edges. (Concurrent means "meeting at one point.") (See Figure 14.)

$$V = lwh$$

The *total area* of such a figure is the sum of the areas of the faces and bases. The *lateral area* is the total area less the area of the bases. Letting T denote the total area and S the lateral area, we have

$$T = 2(lw + lh + wh),$$

and $$S = 2(lw + wh).$$

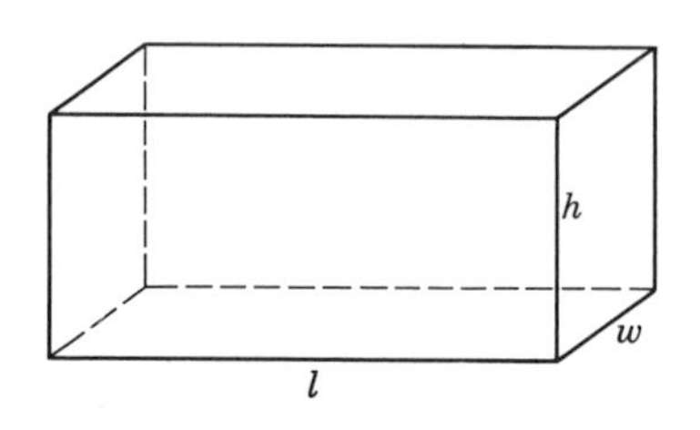

Figure 14

To speak in general of prisms it is convenient to define what is meant by a "right section." A *right section* of a prism is the polygon formed by the intersection of the prism with a plane which is perpendicular to each of the lateral faces (see Figure 15).

Then, in general, for a prism we have

$$T = \text{(perimeter of a right section)} \times \text{(lateral edge)} + \text{(area of the bases)},$$

$$S = \text{(perimeter of a right section)} \times \text{(lateral edge)},$$

and

$$V = \text{(area of a right section)} \times \text{(lateral edge)},$$

or $$V = \text{(area of the base)} \times \text{(altitude)}.$$

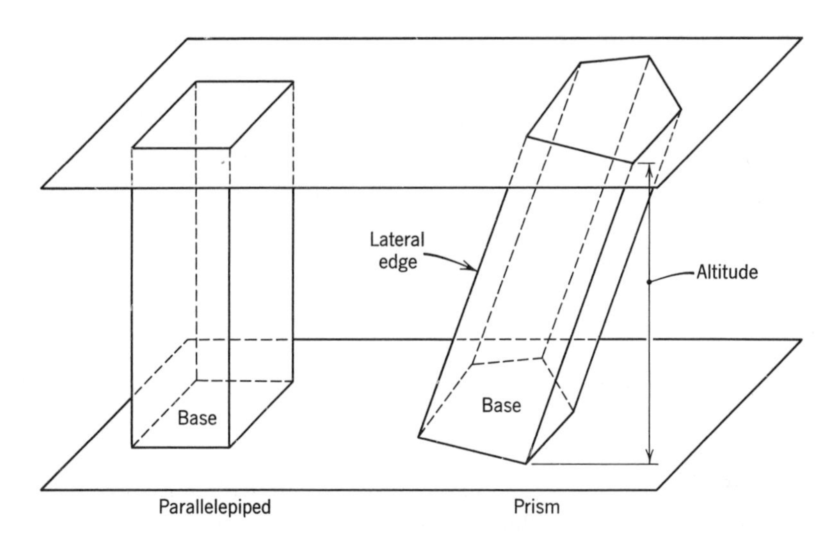
Lateral edge
Altitude
Base
Base
Parallelepiped
Prism

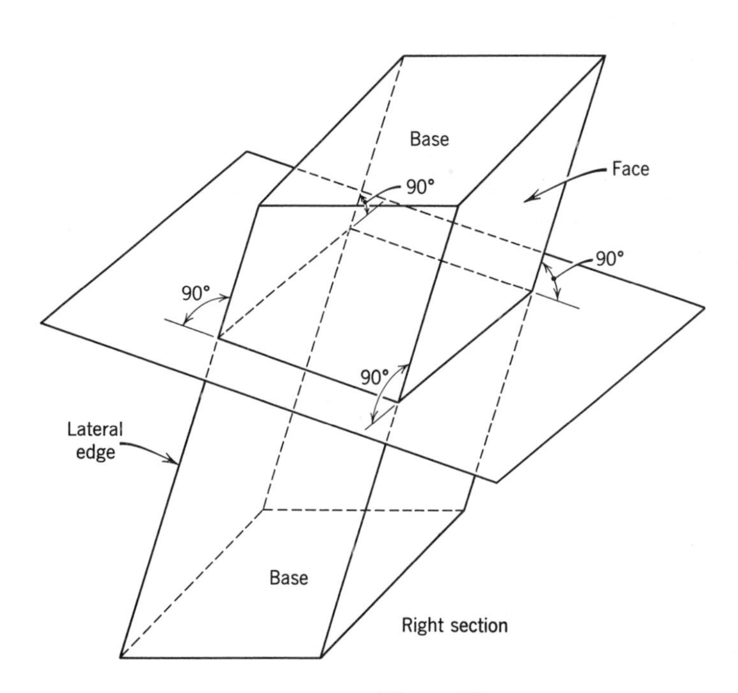
Base
Face
90°
90°
90°
90°
Lateral edge
Base
Right section

Figure 15

9.4b Circular Cylinder

A *right circular cylinder* is like a prism whose bases are right sections except that the bases are circles rather than polygons. The formulas for the prism also hold true for the right circular cylinder, but they may be stated in language involving π (see Figure 16).

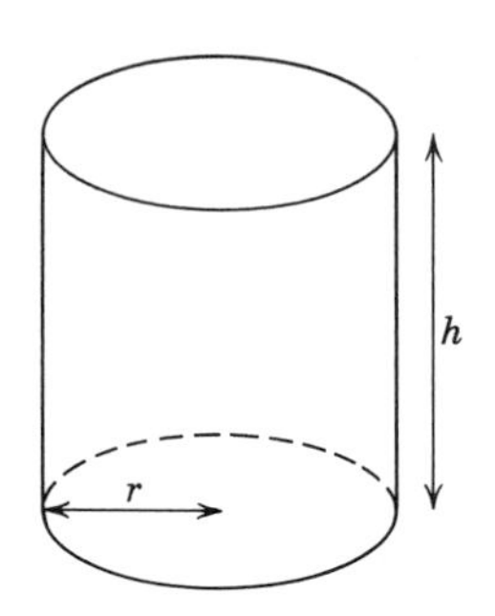

Figure 16

If r is the radius of the base and h the altitude, then

$$S = 2\pi rh,$$
$$T = 2\pi rh + 2\pi r^2,$$
and
$$V = \pi r^2 h.$$

9.4c Pyramid

A *pyramid* is a three-dimensional figure whose base is a polygon and whose lateral faces are triangles. If the base is a regular polygon and a line from the vertex of the pyramid to the center of the base is perpendicular to the base, then the pyramid is called a *regular pyramid* (see Figure 17).

For a regular pyramid, Figure 17,

$$V = \tfrac{1}{3} \text{ (area of base)} \times \text{(altitude)},$$
and
$$S = \tfrac{1}{2} \text{ (perimeter of base)} \times \text{(slant height)}.$$

For the general pyramid this formula for the volume holds true, but the given formula for lateral surface area does not.

9.4d Cone

The *right circular cone* is like a regular pyramid except that the base is a circle. Formulas for the regular pyramid will also serve for the

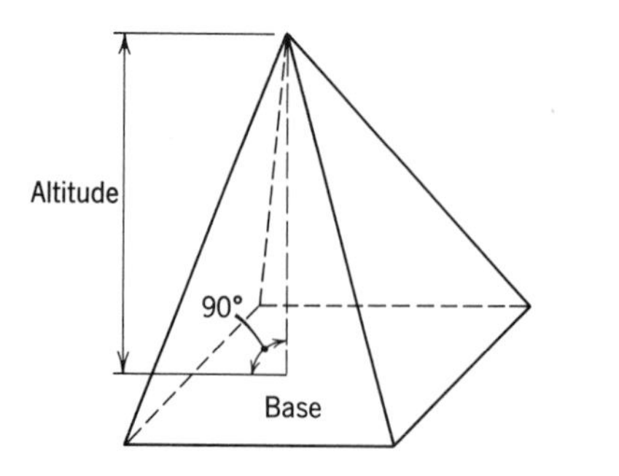

Figure 17

cone. As with the cylinder, we can express these formulas in terms of π, namely (Figure 18),

$$S = \pi r\sqrt{r^2 + h^2},$$

and $$V = \tfrac{1}{3}\pi r^2 h.$$

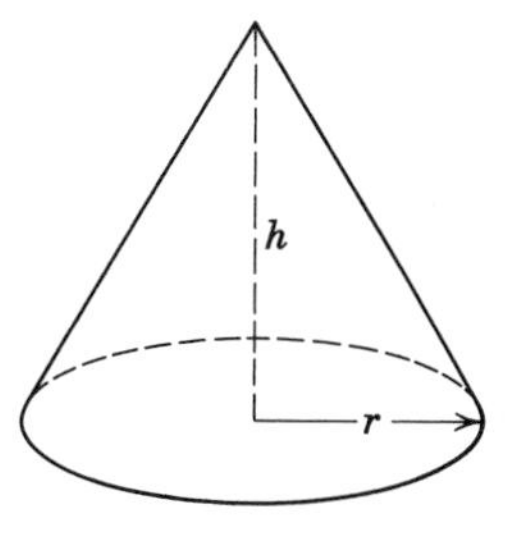

Figure 18

A *frustrum* of a regular pyramid or cone, or a truncated pyramid or cone, is illustrated in Figure 19.

Let b, b' denote the areas of the bases and h the altitude (see Figure 19); then

$$S = \tfrac{1}{2}\text{ (sum of perimeters of bases)} \times \text{(slant height)},$$

and $$V = \tfrac{1}{3}h(b + b' + \sqrt{b \cdot b'}).$$

9.4e Regular Polyhedra

A *regular polyhedron* is one whose faces are congruent regular polygons.

There are but five (except for size) *regular polyhedra*, as shown in Figure 20.

Although the argument required to show that there are five and only five regular polyhedra is not difficult, it will not be given here. For further reference, the reader may consult *What is Mathematics* by Courant and Robbins.

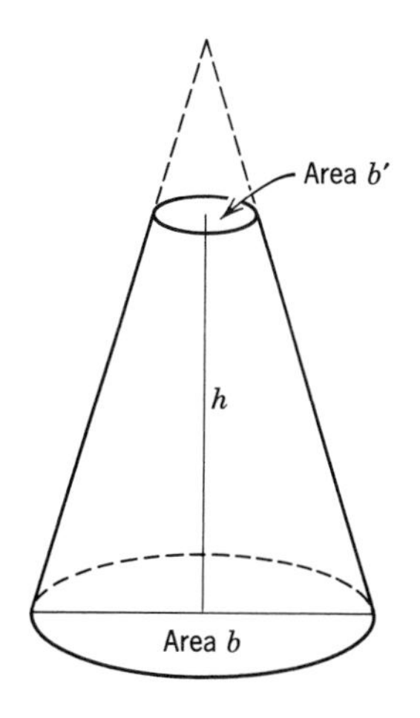

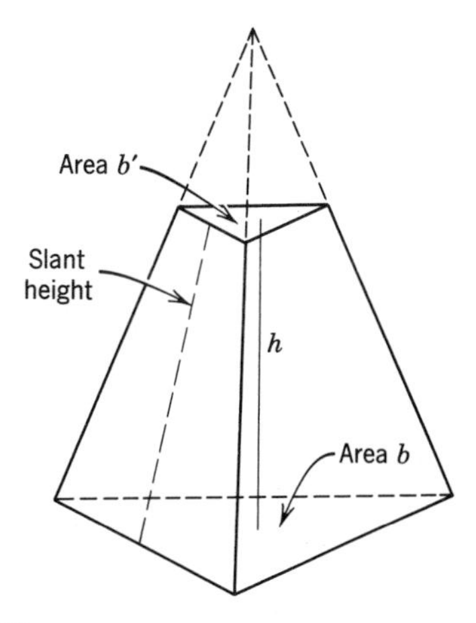

Figure 19

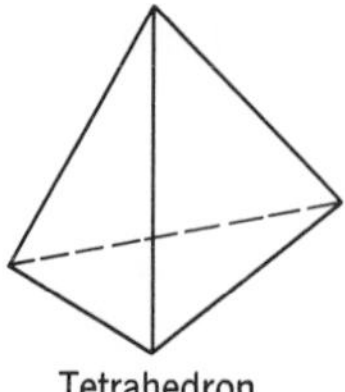

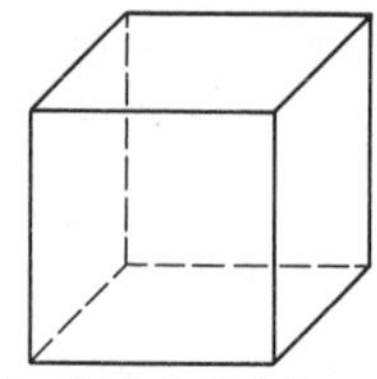

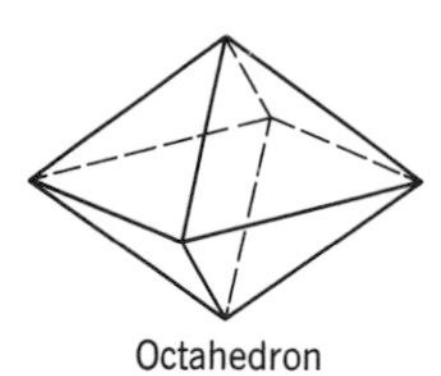

Dodecahedron

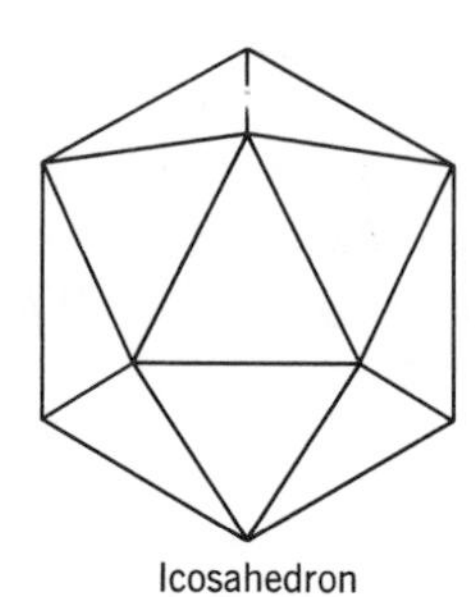

Figure 20

TABLE 1

REGULAR POLYHEDRA

(Let "a" denote the length of an edge.)

Name	Nature of Surface	Total Area	Volume
Tetrahedron	4 equilateral triangles	$1.73205a^2$	$0.11785a^3$
Hexahedron	6 squares	$6.00000a^2$	$1.00000a^3$
Octahedron	8 equilateral triangles	$3.46410a^2$	$0.47140a^3$
Dodecahedron	12 pentagons	$20.64573a^2$	$7.66312a^3$
Icosahedron	20 equilateral triangles	$8.66025a^2$	$2.18170a^3$

9.4f Sphere

For a *sphere* (see Figure 21) let r represent the radius, d the diameter; then

$$S = 4\pi r^2 = \pi d^2,$$
$$\text{and } V = \tfrac{4}{3}\pi r^3 = \tfrac{1}{6}\pi d^3.$$

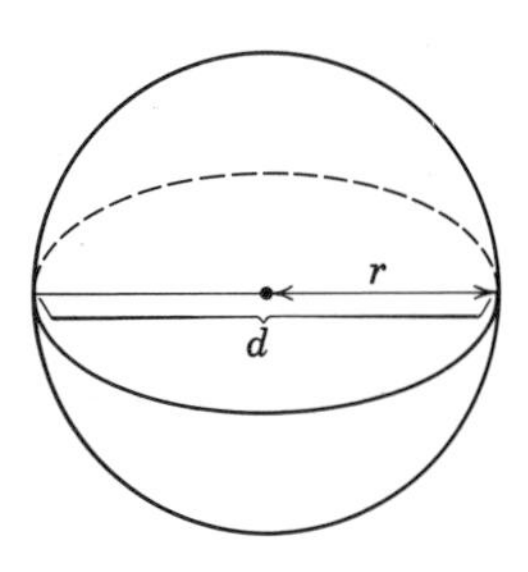

Figure 21

9.4g Circular Torus

Consider a line segment, $\overline{OA}$, of length a and a circle with center O and radius r, where $r < OA$. Fix the point A and cause the line segment, with the circle, to rotate in a plane perpendicular to the plane of the circle. The circle will "sweep out" a dough-nut-shaped figure called a *circular torus* (see Figure 22).

$$S = 4\pi^2 ar$$
and
$$V = 2\pi^2 ar^2.$$

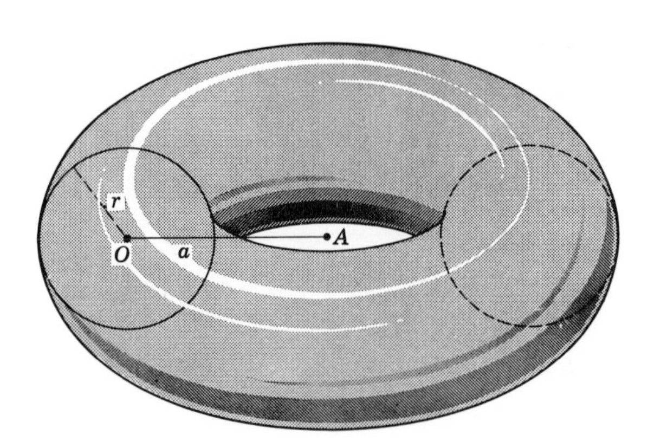

Figure 22

Exercise 9.4

1. Find the volume and total surface area of rectangular solids of the following dimensions:

   (a) 4 in. by 5 in. by 12 in.
   (b) 3.5 ft by 7.2 ft by 8.6 ft.
   (c) 3 ft by 5 ft by 18 in.
   (d) $4\frac{1}{2}$ yd by $2\frac{2}{3}$ yd by 8 yd.

2. Find the total surface area, lateral surface area, and volume of the following:

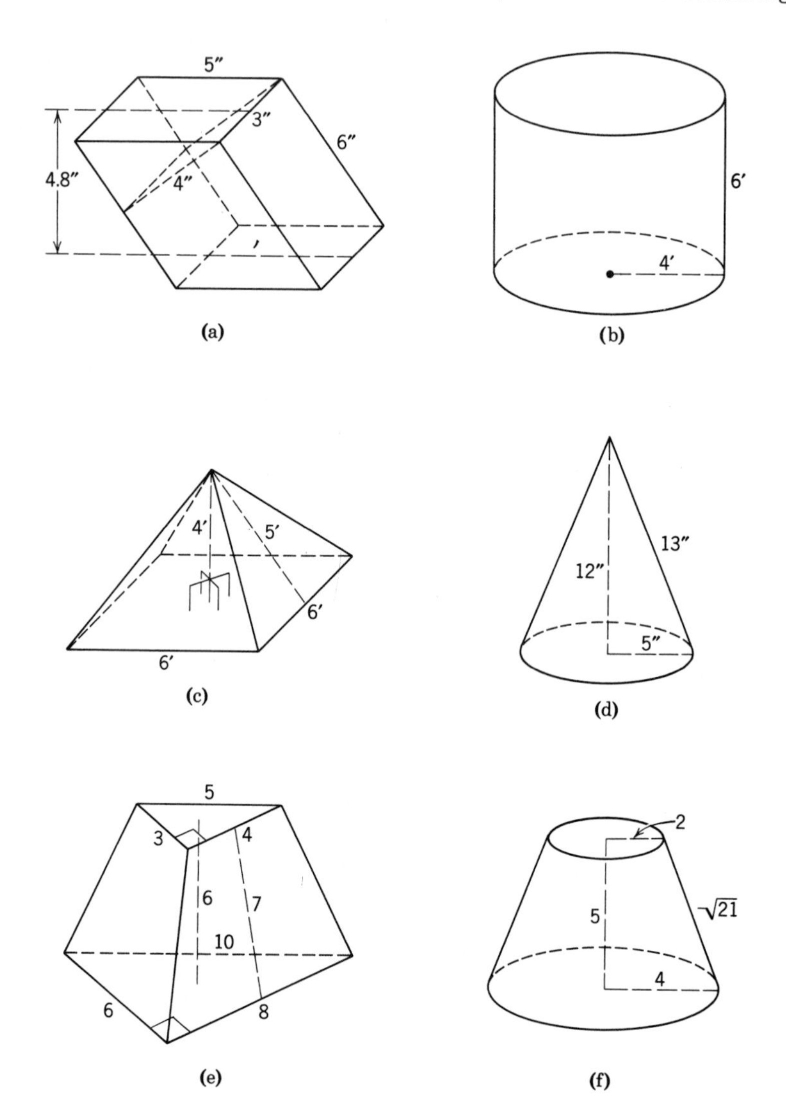

(a) (b) (c) (d) (e) (f)

3. Find the surface area and volume of a sphere whose radius is

(a) 3 in. (b) 4 ft
(c) 14 in. (d) $4\frac{1}{2}$ cm

(Use 3.14 or $\frac{22}{7}$ as an approximation to π.)

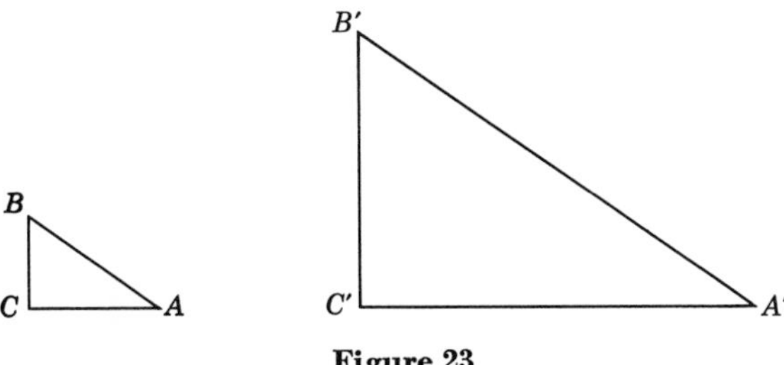

Figure 23

9.5 SIMILAR PLANE FIGURES

In this section we wish to discuss what is meant by similar plane figures with the primary objective of using similar right triangles in indirect measurement.

Two triangles are said to be *similar* to each other if corresponding angles are equal and corresponding sides are proportional. This relation is symbolized $\sim$ (see Figure 23).

$$\triangle ABC \sim \triangle A'B'C'$$

$$\angle A = \angle A', \quad \angle B = \angle B', \quad \angle C = \angle C'.$$

$$\frac{AB}{A'B'} = \frac{AC}{A'C'} = \frac{BC}{B'C'} \quad \text{or} \quad \frac{AB}{AC} = \frac{A'B'}{A'C'}, \text{ and so on.}$$

Two polygons are *similar* to each other if their corresponding angles are equal and their corresponding sides are proportional (see Figure 24). Polygons $ABCDE$ and $A'B'C'D'E'$ are similar.

$$\angle A = \angle A', \quad \angle B = \angle B', \quad \angle C = \angle C', \quad \angle D = \angle D', \quad \angle E = \angle E'$$

$$\frac{AB}{A'B'} = \frac{BC}{B'C'} = \frac{CD}{C'D'} = \frac{DE}{D'E'} = \frac{EA}{E'A'}.$$

As a special case it can be shown that if an acute angle of one right

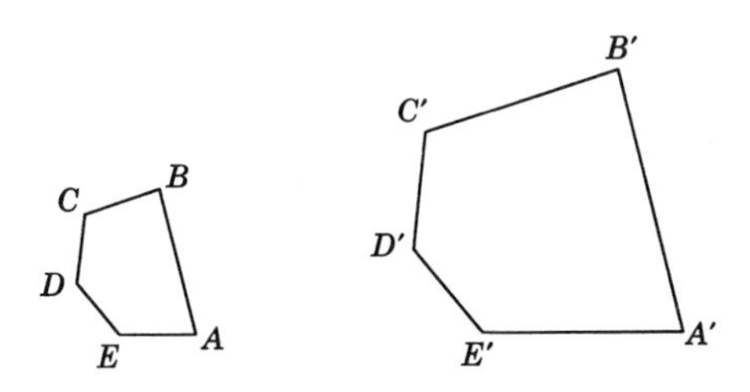

Figure 24

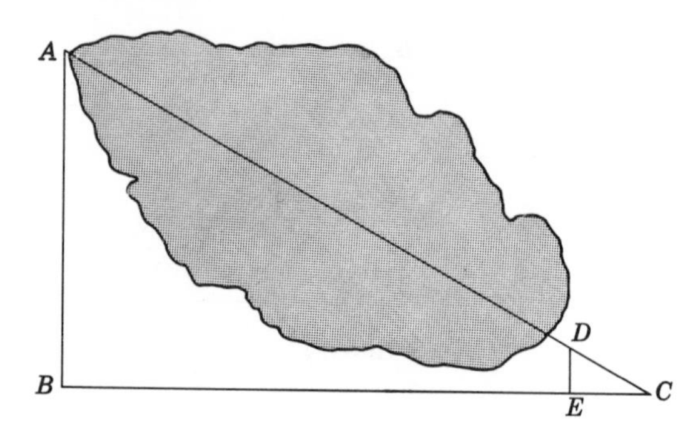

Figure 25

triangle is equal to an acute angle of another right triangle, then the triangles are similar. This simple criterion for determining similarity of right triangles leads to their use in indirect measurement.

Example 1

A lake lies between points A and C (Figure 25). The problem is to determine the distance from A to C by using the properties of similar right triangles.

First we locate a point B such that $\overline{AB}$ and $\overline{BC}$ are at right angles to one another, and we pick a point D on $\overline{AC}$ and a point E on $\overline{BC}$ such that $\overline{DE}$ is perpendicular to $\overline{BC}$. Then triangles ABC and DEC are right triangles and are similar right triangles because $\angle C$ is common to both. Also we measure and find $EC = 4$ units of length, $BC = 52$ units of length, and $DC = 5$ units of length. From the properties of similar triangles we have

$$\frac{AC}{DC} = \frac{BC}{EC},$$

or

$$\frac{AC}{5} = \frac{52}{4},$$

so

$$AC = \frac{260}{4} = 65 \text{ units of length.}$$

Exercise 9.5

1. Find the height of the tree in the accompanying diagram.

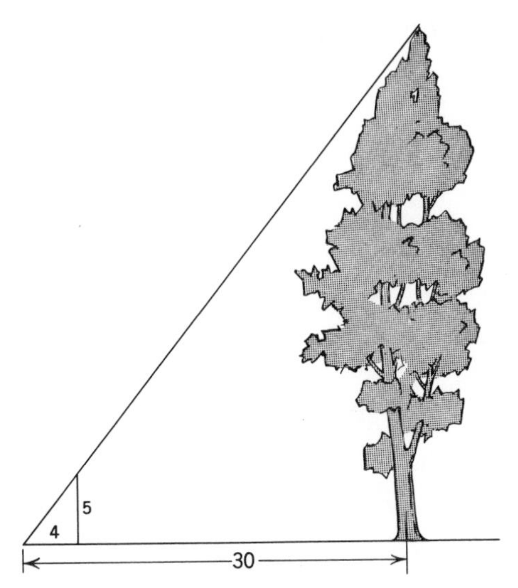

2. A man 6 ft tall cast a shadow of 9 ft when standing 24 ft away from a point directly under a street lamp. How high above the ground is the street lamp?
3. In the diagram, if $\triangle ABC \sim \triangle DCE$ and $AC = 12$ yd, $AB = 20$ yd, $CE = 100$ yd. Find DE, the length of the lake.

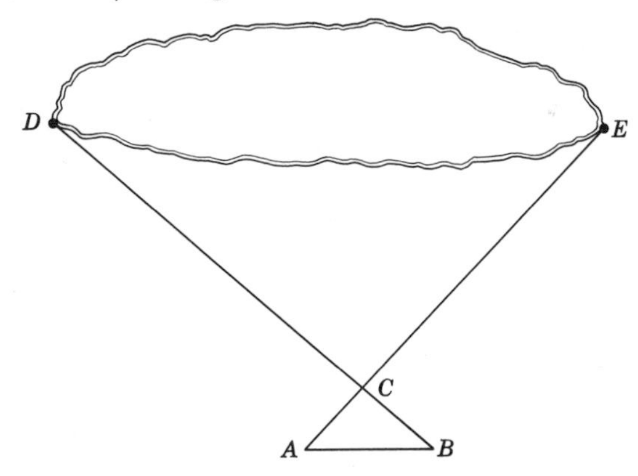

4. In the diagram, $\triangle ABC \sim \triangle ADE$. Find x.

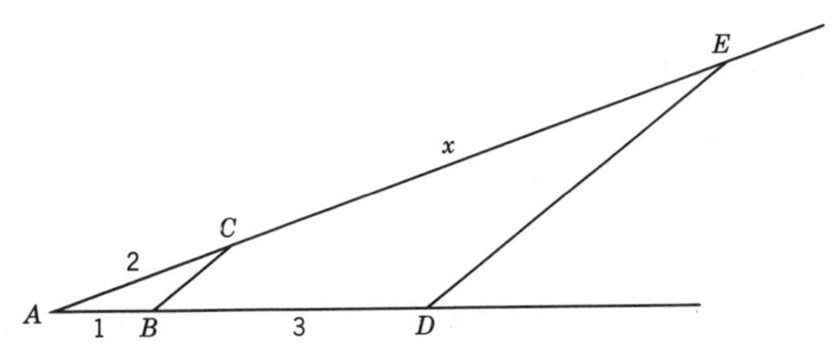

5. In the diagram, $\triangle ABC \sim \triangle ADE$. Find x.

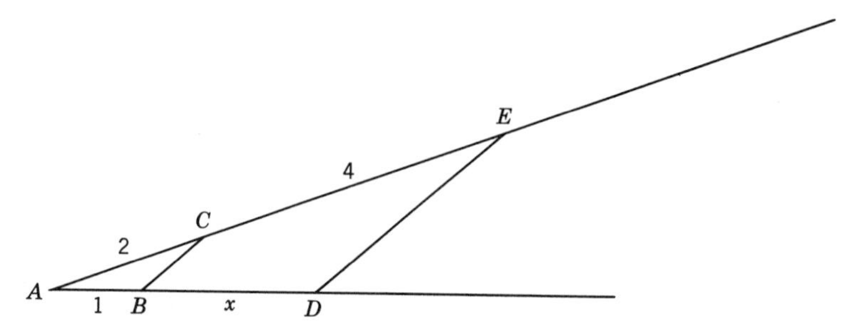

6. In the diagram, $\triangle ABC \sim \triangle ADE$. Find x.

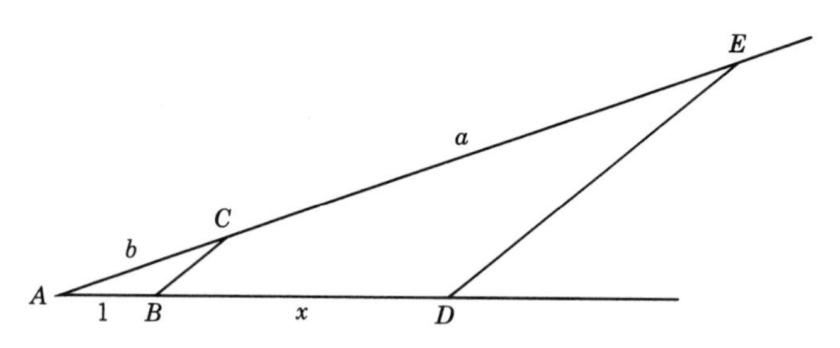

7. In the diagram, $\triangle ABC \sim \triangle ADE$. Find x.

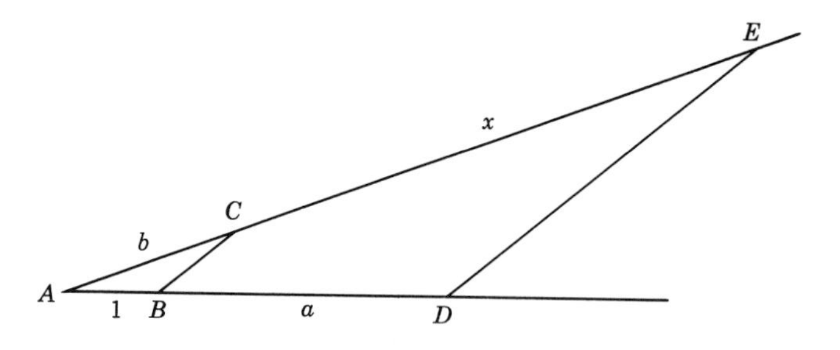

8. Examine your results of problems 4, 5, 6, and 7 and give a general geometric interpretation of multiplication and division.

9. Give a geometric interpretation of addition and subtraction.

9.6 THE PYTHAGOREAN THEOREM

PYTHAGOREAN THEOREM. The square of the length of the hypotenuse of a right triangle is equal to the sum of the squares of the lengths of the legs.

Before we give any proofs of the Pythagorean Theorem we state a theorem about right triangles for which the reader can supply a proof.

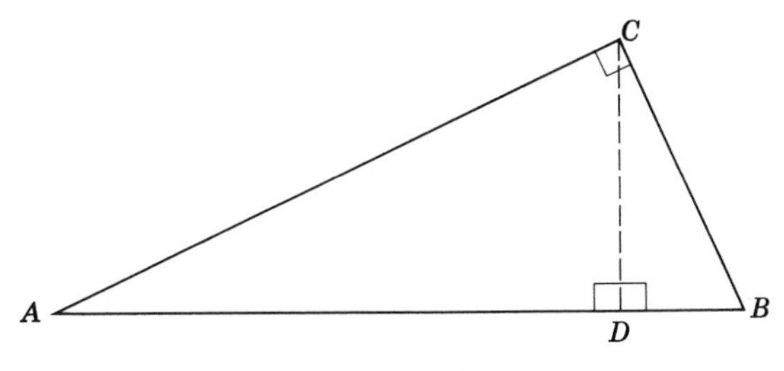

Figure 26

THEOREM. The altitude to the hypotenuse of a right triangle forms two right triangles which are similar to the given triangle (see Figure 26):

$$\triangle ADC \sim \triangle ABC \sim \triangle BDC$$

From this and by using the properties of similar triangles, we have (see Figure 27)

1. The length of the altitude $\overline{CD}$ to the length of the hypotenuse is a mean proportional between the lengths of the two segments $\overline{AD}$ and $\overline{DB}$ formed on the hypotenuse. (*Mean proportional:* x is a mean proportional between a and b if $a/x = x/b$, or $x^2 = ab$.)

2. The length of leg $\overline{AC}$ of a right triangle ABC is the mean proportional between the length of the hypotenuse $\overline{AB}$ and the length of an adjacent segment $\overline{AD}$ on the hypotenuse formed by the altitude $\overline{CD}$ from the right angle (see Figure 27).

(1) $\dfrac{AD}{CD} = \dfrac{CD}{DB}$ (2) $\dfrac{AD}{AC} = \dfrac{AC}{AB}$ or $AC^2 = AD \cdot AB$

Let us now consider the theorem of Pythagoras.

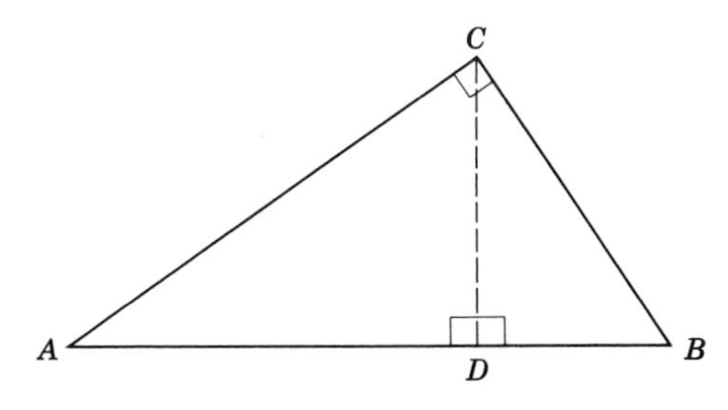

Figure 27

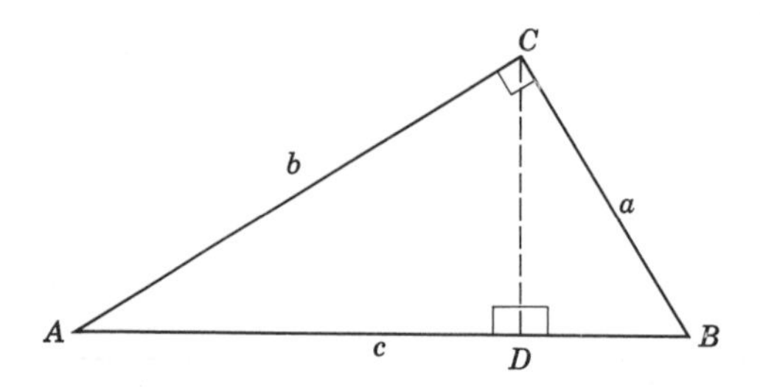

Figure 28

Let $\overline{CD}$ be the altitude from the right angle to the hypotenuse $\overline{AB}$ (see Figure 28). Let AD, DB, a, b, and c be the lengths of $\overline{AD}$, $\overline{DB}$, $\overline{BC}$, $\overline{AC}$, and $\overline{AB}$, respectively. Then $AD/b = b/c$, or $AD = b^2/c$, and $DB/a = a/c$, or $DB = a^2/c$. But $AD + DB = c$. By substitution

$$AD + DB = c,$$

or

$$\frac{b^2}{c} + \frac{a^2}{c} = c,$$

so that

$$b^2 + a^2 = c^2 \quad \text{or} \quad a^2 + b^2 = c^2.$$

Interpreting the Pythagorean Theorem in terms of "area" (Figure 29) we have:

For every right triangle the square on the hypotenuse has an area equal to the sum of the areas of the squares on the other two sides (see Section 7.13).

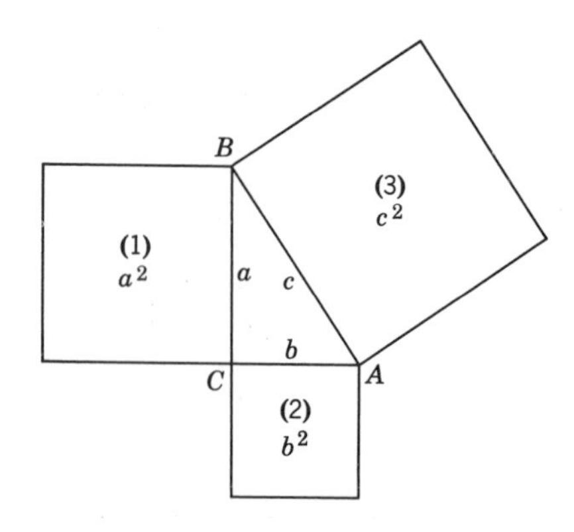

Figure 29. Area (1) + Area (2) = Area (3).

For a proof of the theorem based on this interpretation, consider the diagram of Figure 30.

The area of the large square of side $a + b$ is equal to the area of the small square of side c plus the area of the four right triangles with legs a and b.

$$(a + b)^2 = c^2 + 4(\tfrac{1}{2}ab)$$
$$a^2 + 2ab + b^2 = c^2 + 2ab$$
$$a^2 + b^2 = c^2.$$

A demonstration involving areas which may be used at the elementary level involves cutting and matching. First construct the diagram shown in Figure 31 in relation to any right triangle ABC.

Cut the figure on the line $DABE$ and compare the two sections by matching. Carefully done, this will illustrate that the areas are identical. By pairing like areas on opposite sides of this line and "subtracting" them from the original equal areas, we are left with

$$a^2 + b^2 = c^2.$$

The reader is to be cautioned that this does not form a "proof." It is merely a demonstration to add credibility to the statement of the theorem.

As an example of how "proofs" by cutting and fitting may be misleading, consider Figure 32.

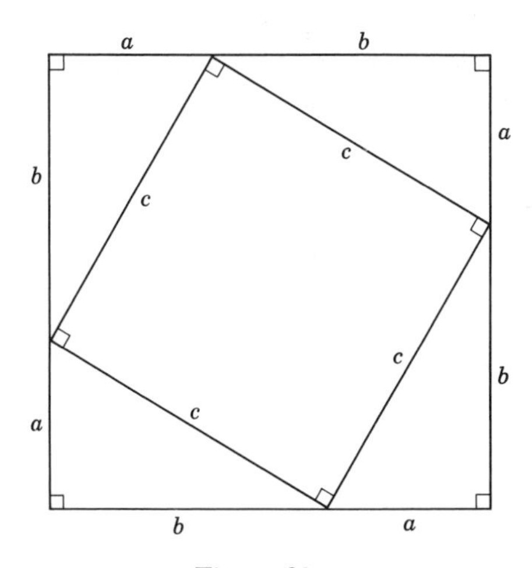

Figure 30

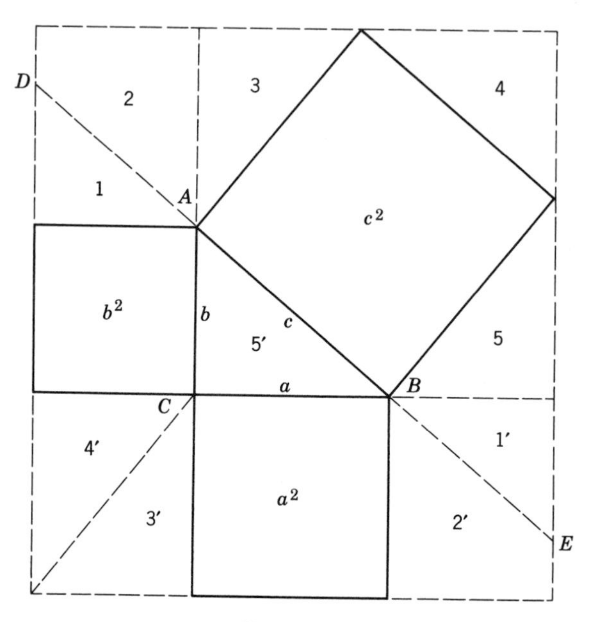

Figure 31

The square is 8 by 8, hence has area 64. The rectangle is 5 by 13, hence has area 65. Where did the additional unit of area come from? Before reading further, see if you can develop an explanation.

The angles at C and F are right angles, which means that the "fit" along the lines $\overline{HF}$ and $\overline{CG}$ is perfect. This leaves only the diagonal $\overline{AD}$ as a possible place for the extra square unit to hide. It may be that $\overline{AGHD}$ is not a straight line as it appears to be, or we might in-

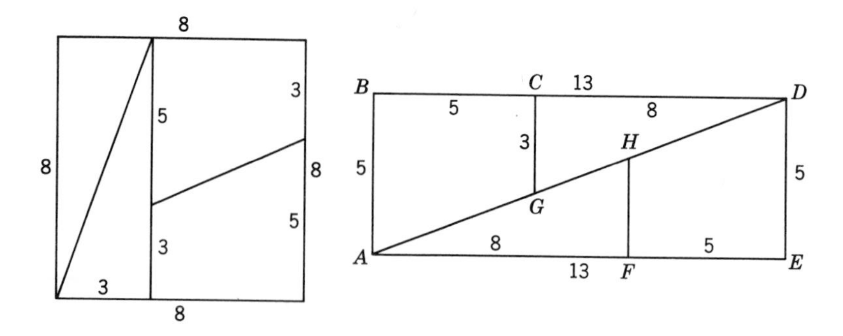

Figure 32

vestigate angles BAF and CDE to make sure that they are right angles.

Let us use the properties of similar triangles. We know that $\overline{AFE}$ is a straight line. Why? Looking at the figure we see that $\overline{HF}$ is parallel to $\overline{DE}$ and *if* $\overline{AGHD}$ is a straight line, then $\triangle AFH \sim \triangle AED$. *If* these triangles are similar, then their corresponding sides are proportional. But $\frac{8}{3} \neq \frac{13}{5}$; hence these triangles are *not* similar. If the triangles are not similar, then $\overline{AGHD}$ is not a straight line. A slight bend in the line at G and H would account for the extra unit of area (see Figure 33).

Exercise 9.6

1. Find the area of a square inscribed in a circle of radius

(a) 1 in. (b) 5 ft.

2. Find the area of a regular polygon of six sides (regular hexagon) inscribed in a circle of radius

(a) 10 in. (b) 8 ft.

3. Find the area of an equilateral triangle inscribed in a circle of radius

(a) 10 in. (b) 18 in.

4. In a 30, 60, 90° right triangle, the side opposite the 30° angle is equal to one-half the hypotenuse.

(a) What is the area of a parallelogram with sides 20 and 16 and included angle of 30°?
(b) What is the area of a parallelogram with sides 20 and 16 and included angle of 60°?

5. (a) The length of the diagonal of a square is 18. Find its area.
(b) The length of the diagonal of a square is 50. Find its area.

6. Prove that if two triangles are similar, the ratio of their areas is equal to the ratio of the squares of the lengths of two corresponding sides.

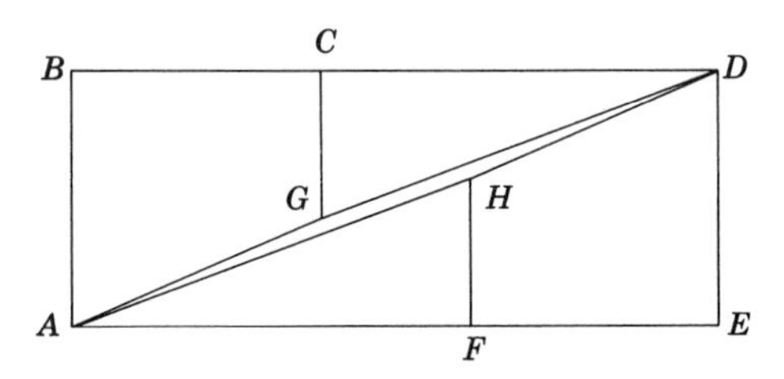

Figure 33. A square unit of area "hiding in a crack."

7. An alternate proof of the Pythagorean Theorem based on the area concept can be developed from the following figure:

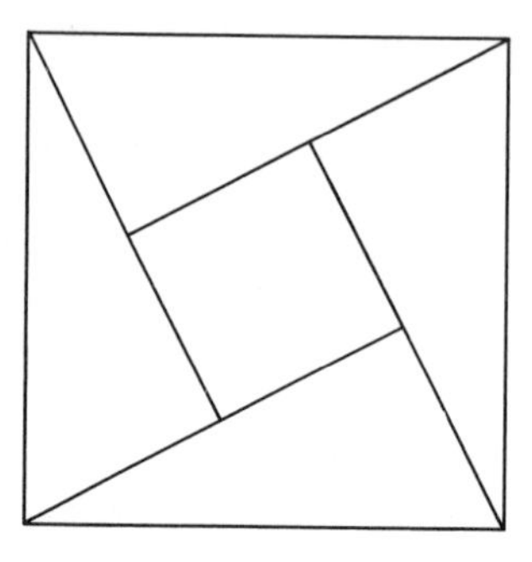

Label the figure and complete the proof.

9.7 THE NUMBER π

The symbol π is much misunderstood. Many people think that it is something used in arithmetic to "stand for" $3\frac{1}{7}$, or 3.1416, and it comes as quite a surprise to learn that π is a symbol for a particular number just as 3 and $\sqrt{5}$ are symbols for numbers. π is an *irrational number* and as such would be an *infinite nonrepeating decimal.* The numbers symbolized by $3\frac{1}{7}$, 3.14, and 3.1416 are *rational approximations* to π.

The number, which is symbolized by the Greek letter π, has a very interesting history. We will present a brief chronology of this number later in this section. First let us see if we can establish the *existence* of such a number.

9.7a The Existence of π

Consider *any* two circles, with centers O and O' of radii r and r', respectively, and $r < r'$ (see Figure 34).

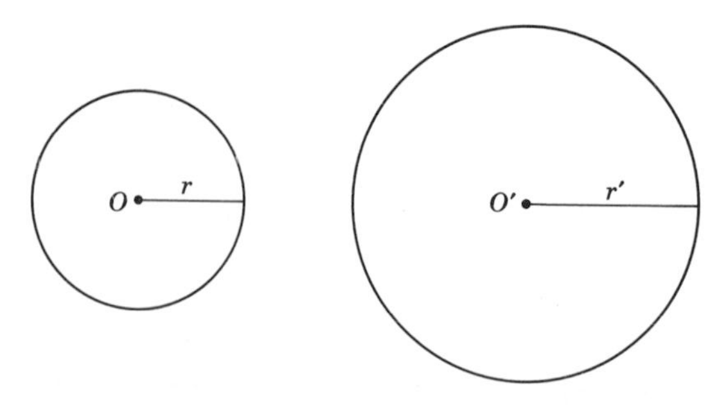

Figure 34

For simplicity let us reconstruct the circle with center O' so that it will be concentric with the circle with center O, that is, have the same center. From the common center O draw a line cutting the smaller circle at A and the larger circle at A'. From O draw a second line, different from $\overline{OA'}$, cutting the smaller circle at B and the larger circle at B'. Draw the segments $\overline{AB}$ and $\overline{A'B'}$. It is easy to show that $\triangle OAB \sim \triangle OA'B'$ (see Figure 35). Using the properties of similar triangles, we have

$$\frac{AB}{AO} = \frac{A'B'}{A'O}.$$

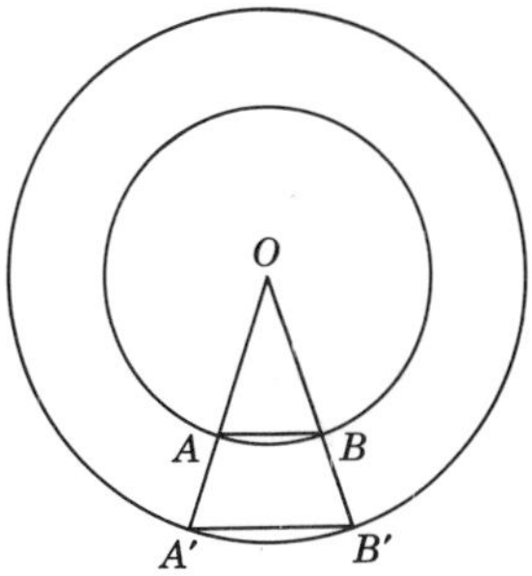

But this is an equality of ratios of real numbers; hence for any number n

$$\frac{(n)(AB)}{AO} = \frac{(n)(A'B')}{A'O},$$

or

$$\frac{(n)(AB)}{(2)(AO)} = \frac{(n)(A'B')}{(2)(A'O)}.$$

Figure 35

If the circle is divided into n equal arcs and triangles formed by drawing in the chords and radii, then $(n)(AB)$ would be the perimeter of the inscribed polygon and $(2)(AO)$ would be the diameter of the smaller circle. Similarly, $(n)(A'B')$ and $(2)(A'O)$ would be the perimeter of the inscribed polygon and diameter of the larger circle. Then the equation

$$\frac{(n)(AB)}{(2)(AO)} = \frac{(n)(A'B')}{(2)(A'O)}$$

means that the ratio of the perimeter of a regular inscribed polygon of n sides to the diameter of the circle is the same regardless of the size of the circle.

Now let us suppose n is allowed to become very, very large. The perimeters of the inscribed polygons come closer and closer to the circumference of the circle. In fact, the least upper bound of the sequence of real numbers denoting the perimeters is the length of the circumference of the circle (see Section 9.2). We would then have

$$\frac{\text{Circumference of smaller circle}}{\text{Diameter of smaller circle}} = \frac{\text{Circumference of larger circle}}{\text{Diameter of larger circle}}$$

This means that the ratio of the circumference of a circle to its diameter is the same regardless of the size of the circle, that is, this ratio is a *constant*. The name given to this constant is pi and it is symbolized π.

DEFINITION 9.7a. The number π is the ratio of the circumference of any circle to its diameter.

Let c represent the circumference of any circle and d its diameter; then

$$\pi = \frac{c}{d}.$$

This approach to the existence of pi also leads to a reasonable explanation of the formulas $c = 2\pi r$ or $c = \pi d$ for the circumference and $A = \pi r^2$ for the area of a circle of radius r. Recall the formula developed for the area of a regular polygon with n sides of length s, namely,

$$A = (\tfrac{1}{2}ap) \quad \text{or} \quad A = \tfrac{1}{2}a(ns),$$

where a denotes the apothem and p the perimeter ns. As n becomes very large, the apothem a approaches the radius r of the circle and the perimeter ns approaches the circumference c of the circle. In fact, the least upper bounds of the sequences representing a and p are r and c, respectively. Then

$$A = \tfrac{1}{2}(rc).$$

But from the definition of π, $c = \pi d$ or $c = 2\pi r$, and

$$A = \tfrac{1}{2}r(2\pi r),$$

or

$$A = \pi r^2.$$

9.7b Calculation of π

The classical method of computing a numerical approximation to π makes use of inscribed and circumscribed regular polygons. Since $\pi = c/d$, the circumference of a circle of unit diameter is π. The computation may be begun by using an equilateral triangle or a square as the initial polygon; then, by doubling the number of sides, obtain polygons of 6, 12, 24, 36, . . . , or 8, 16, 32, 64, . . . , sides, respectively. Let us examine the procedure, using the square as the initial polygon.

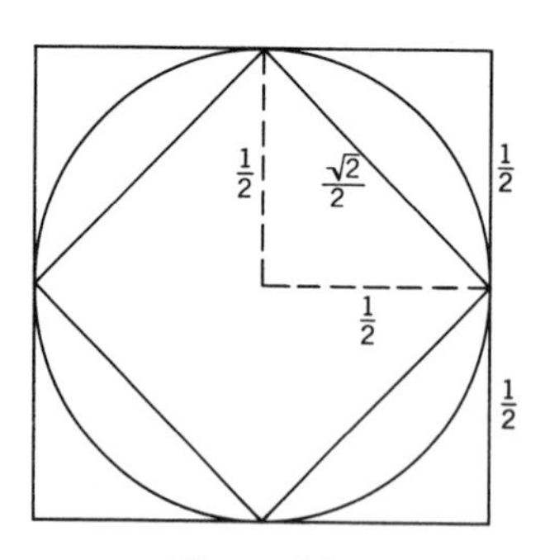

Figure 36

As our first approximation we have (see Figure 36),

$$2\sqrt{2} < \pi < 4,$$

or

$$2.82 < \pi < 4.$$

For our second approximation let us double the number of sides of the inscribed polygon and the circumscribed polygon (see Figure 37). The length of a side of the inscribed octagon is

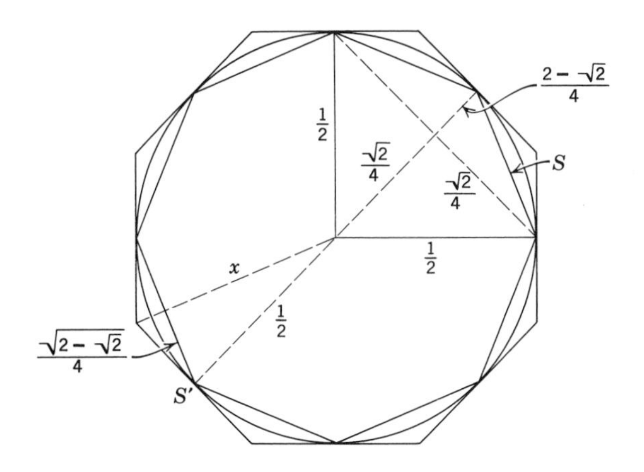

Figure 37

$$s = \sqrt{\left(\frac{\sqrt{2}}{4}\right)^2 + \left(\frac{2-\sqrt{2}}{4}\right)^2} = \sqrt{\frac{2}{16} + \frac{4 - 4\sqrt{2} + 2}{16}}$$

$$= \sqrt{\frac{2-\sqrt{2}}{4}} = \frac{1}{2}\sqrt{2 - \sqrt{2}}.$$

The perimeter is then $8(\frac{1}{2}\sqrt{2-\sqrt{2}})$ or approximately

$$4(0.7654) \cong 3.06.$$

For the circumscribed polygon of side s',

$$\frac{s'/2}{\frac{(\sqrt{2-\sqrt{2}})}{4}} = \frac{1/2}{x},$$

where
$$x = \sqrt{\left(\frac{1}{2}\right)^2 - \left(\frac{\sqrt{2-\sqrt{2}}}{4}\right)^2}.$$

Solving for s' and using approximate square roots yields

$$\frac{s'}{2} \cong 0.2071.$$

Then the perimeter of the circumscribed polygon is

$$(16)\left(\frac{s'}{2}\right) \cong 16(0.2071) \cong 3.31.$$

Hence, for our second approximation, we have

$$3.06 < \pi < 3.31.$$

This method can be continued indefinitely. Each successive computation yields a closer approximation to π.

The method of using inscribed polygons is called the "classical method" for computing π. It dates back to the time of Archimedes, about 240 B.C. (see Section 9.7c and Eves).

A method for computing π that involves area is based on the fact that a circle of radius 1 will have area π.

Considering just one quadrant to simplify calculations, we have, from the trapezoid and triangle, our first "lower" approximation to the area of the circle (see Figure 38).

4 (area of trapezoid + area of triangle)

$$= 4\left[\frac{1}{2}\left(\frac{1}{2}\right)\left(1 + \frac{\sqrt{3}}{2}\right) + \left(\frac{1}{2}\right)\left(\frac{1}{2}\right)\left(\frac{\sqrt{3}}{2}\right)\right]$$

$$= 4\left[\frac{2+\sqrt{3}}{8} + \frac{\sqrt{3}}{8}\right] = 4\left(\frac{2+2\sqrt{3}}{8}\right),$$

which is approximately 2.732.

Using the rectangles, we have as our first "upper" approximation

$$4\left[1\left(\frac{1}{2}\right) + \frac{1}{2}\left(\frac{\sqrt{3}}{2}\right)\right] = 2 + \sqrt{3},$$

which is approximately 3.732.

Then $$2.732 < \pi < 3.732.$$

By dividing the radius into four equal parts we have three trapezoids and a triangle approximating the area (see Figure 39).

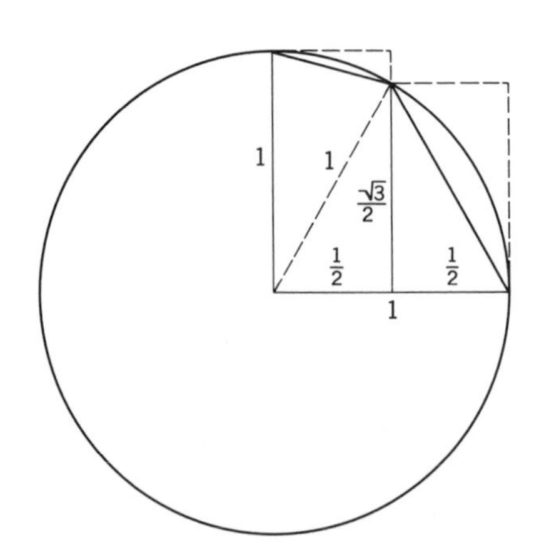

Figure 38

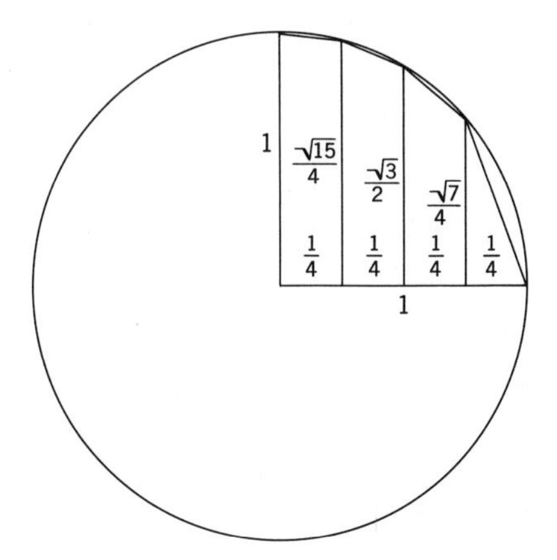

Figure 39

"Lower" approximation:

$$4\left[\frac{1}{8}\left(\frac{4+\sqrt{15}}{4}\right)+\frac{1}{8}\left(\frac{\sqrt{15}+2\sqrt{3}}{4}\right)\right.$$
$$\left.+\frac{1}{8}\left(\frac{2\sqrt{3}+\sqrt{7}}{4}\right)+\frac{1}{2}\left(\frac{1}{4}\right)\left(\frac{\sqrt{7}}{4}\right)\right]$$
$$=\frac{1}{2}\left[\frac{4+\sqrt{15}}{4}+\frac{\sqrt{15}+2\sqrt{3}}{4}+\frac{2\sqrt{3}+\sqrt{7}}{4}+\frac{\sqrt{7}}{4}\right]$$
$$=\frac{1}{8}(4+2\sqrt{15}+4\sqrt{3}+2\sqrt{7}),$$

which is approximately 2.9957.

"Upper" approximation:

$$4\left[1\left(\frac{1}{4}\right)+\left(\frac{\sqrt{15}}{4}\right)\left(\frac{1}{4}\right)+\left(\frac{\sqrt{3}}{2}\right)\left(\frac{1}{4}\right)+\left(\frac{\sqrt{7}}{4}\right)\left(\frac{1}{4}\right)\right]$$
$$=1+\frac{\sqrt{15}}{4}+\frac{\sqrt{3}}{2}+\frac{\sqrt{7}}{4},$$

which is approximately 3.4957.

Our second approximation is then

$$3.00 < \pi < 3.50.$$

As with the inscribed polygons, this procedure can be continued indefinitely, each successive computation yielding a closer approximation to π.

There are other geometric procedures that may be used at elementary levels which do not involve so much computation. Many experiments are suggested in standard texts to give the pupil information about π beyond the definition. One simple one is to construct a unit circle on squared paper (graph paper) and count squares to obtain an approximation to the area. This will be left as an exercise for the student.

9.7c Chronology of π

This will not be a true "chronology" of π in that it will not be a date-by-date itemizing of the history of π. It is, rather, an informal discussion of selected items in the chronology of π.

We are led to believe that in ancient times the ratio of the circumference to the diameter of a circle was taken to be 3 (see the Biblical references: I Kings 7:23; II Chronicles 4:2). The Rhind papyrus gives us $\pi = (4/3)^4 = 3.1604 \ldots.$ It is believed the first scientific attempt to compute π was made by Archimedes about 240 B.C. Using the classical method, he determined that π was between 223/71 and 22/7. This represents remarkable accuracy in approximating square roots with rational numbers.

About 400 years later Ptolemy of Alexandria in his famous *Syntaxis Mathematica* developed a table of chords of a circle subtended by central angles of each degree and half degree. From this, using a regular inscribed polygon of 360 sides, he obtained a value, given in sexagesimal notation, as $3\,8'30''$. Transcribed to decimal language this would be 377/120 or 3.1416 rounded to four places.

About 480 A.D. Tsu Ch'ung-chih, a Chinese, gave the rational approximation 355/113. In decimal language this is 3.1415929 . . . , which is accurate to six places. About 1150 A.D. the Hindu mathematician Bhaskara gave 3927/1250 as an accurate value of π, 22/7 as an inaccurate value, and $\sqrt{10}$ for ordinary work.

In the late 1500's and early 1600's the following computations of π were carried out.

François Vieta, a French mathematician, found π correct to 9 decimal places by the classical method, using polygons having $6(2^{16}) = 393{,}216$ sides.

Adriaen van Roomen of the Netherlands found π correct to 15 decimal places by the classical method, using polygons having $2^{30} = 1{,}073{,}741{,}824$ sides.

Ludolph van Ceulen of Germany computed π to 35 decimal places by the classical method, using polygons having $2^{62} = 4{,}611{,}686{,}018{,}427{,}387{,}904$ sides. This was considered such an unusual accomplishment that for a time in Germany this 35-place approximation to π was called the Ludolphian Number.

One is led to wonder why so much time and effort were spent in the computation of π. One reason might be that these men were looking for a repeating sequence in the decimal approximation to π. If it could be found, they would then know that π was a rational number.

Later computations were based on infinite series:

Abraham Sharp—71 correct places. 1699.
De Lagny—112 correct places. 1719.

Much speculation came to an end when in 1767 Johann Heinrich Lambert proved that π is irrational. This did not stop the "π computers," however. William Shanks of England computed π to 707 places. For a long time this remained the most fabulous piece of calculation ever performed. It occupied Shanks for more than 15 years. In 1946 D. F. Ferguson of England found errors in Shanks' value of π. He published a corrected value to 710 places. In the same month J. W. Wrench, Jr. of the United States, published an 808-place value of π, but Ferguson found an error in the 723rd place. In January 1948 they jointly published a corrected and checked value for π to 808 places.

To conclude this summary on the calculations of π, we turn to the electronic calculator. The ENIAC (Electronic Numerical Integrator and Computer) at the Army Ballistic Research Laboratories in Aberdeen, Maryland, in about *70 hours* gave π to *2035 places*, checking the Ferguson-Wrench result of 808 places. (Compare this with the efforts of Shanks.)

Among the curiosities connected with π are various mnemonics that have been devised for the purpose of remembering π to a large number of decimal places. In the following, by A. C. Orr, one has merely to replace each word by the number of letters it contains to obtain π correct to 30 decimal places.

Now I, even I, would celebrate
In rhymes unapt, the great
Immortal Syracusan, rivaled nevermore
Who in his wondrous lore,
Passed on before,
Left men his guidance
How to circles mensurate.

Another similar mnemonic is

See, I have a rhyme
Assisting my feeble brain,
Its tasks ofttimes resisting.

For a more complete chronology of π see Eves and Schepler.

Exercise 9.7

1. Draw a circle of radius 10 units ($\frac{1}{4}$ in.) on graph paper of $\frac{1}{4}$ in. squares.
   (a) Cross out all squares the circle passes through.
   (b) Count all squares inside the circle not crossed out.
   (c) Count the number of crossed out squares.
   (d) From the above draw some conclusions about the value of π.
2. Calculate the third approximation for π, using the "area" method.
3. If a is the side of a regular polygon inscribed in a circle of radius r, then

$$b = \sqrt{2r^2 - r\sqrt{4r^2 - a^2}}$$

   is the side of a regular inscribed polygon having twice the number of sides.
   (a) Use this information to calculate the third approximation to π with an inscribed polygon of 16 sides.
4. A common approximation in the Middle Ages for a square root was

$$\sqrt{n} = \sqrt{a^2 + b} \cong a + \frac{b}{2a + 1}.$$

   By taking $n = 10 = 3^2 + 1$, show why it may be that $\sqrt{10}$ was so frequently used for π.
5. Find the perimeter of a regular 12-sided polygon inscribed in a circle of radius 1, thus finding an approximation for π.
6. What does the irrationality of π imply about its decimal representation?
7. A *radian* is the measure of the central angle in a circle subtended by an arc equal in length to the radius of the circle.
   (a) If θ is the measure of a central angle of a circle given in radian measure, show that the length of the arc cut off by the sides of this angle is given by $r\theta$.
   (b) How many radians are equivalent to 360°?

9.8 INTRODUCTION TO COORDINATE GEOMETRY

We have used the concept of the number line to strengthen the concept of numbers themselves. There is also an interesting relation between the concept of the number line and geometry. When the terms "point" and "line" are used in plane geometry, they are undefined objects endowed with certain properties determined by the axioms. In order to have some intuitive idea of how these terms might be interpreted in the physical world, expressions such as "a point is like the tip of a pin" or "a straight-line segment is like the edge of a ruler" are used. Postulates such as "there is one and only one line through two distinct points" and "two distinct lines are parallel or meet in a point" sharpen our concept of "point" and "line." The "plane" can be discussed informally in the same way and made precise by a set of postulates. Since the points and lines are undefined, we might have a geometry in which the "line" is the number line for the integers or the number line for the rational numbers. We discussed the *number line* for the *integers*, the *rational numbers*, and the *real numbers*. The number "line" for the integers should be depicted as the set of points equally spaced with no points between consecutive pairs:

$$\ldots \; \dot{-5} \quad \dot{-4} \quad \dot{-3} \quad \dot{-2} \quad \dot{-1} \quad \dot{0} \quad \dot{1} \quad \dot{2} \quad \dot{3} \quad \dot{4} \quad \dot{5} \; \ldots$$

The rational number "line" is difficult to depict because the rational numbers are *dense*, that is, between any two distinct rational numbers there are an infinite number of distinct rational numbers. Furthermore, the set of rational numbers is *not* complete. This would imply there are "holes" in the rational number "line."

The real number line is the "continuous" line one usually visualizes. This is the "line" referred to in plane geometry. We indicated in problem 7, Exercise 8.2a, that the *rational number "line"* has too many "holes" for the purposes of ordinary geometry. It is possible to have two rational number "lines" in a plane which are not parallel and which do not have a point in common (see Figure 40).

9.8a The Euclidean Plane

The pictorial representation of $R \times R$, where R is the set of real numbers, is called the *Euclidean Plane.* Just as we labeled the points on the real number line with the real numbers, so also we label the points in the plane with the ordered pairs of $R \times R$. We use the ordered pair (x, y) to denote an arbitrary ordered pair of real numbers and refer to it as the point (x, y) in the geometric representation. To establish

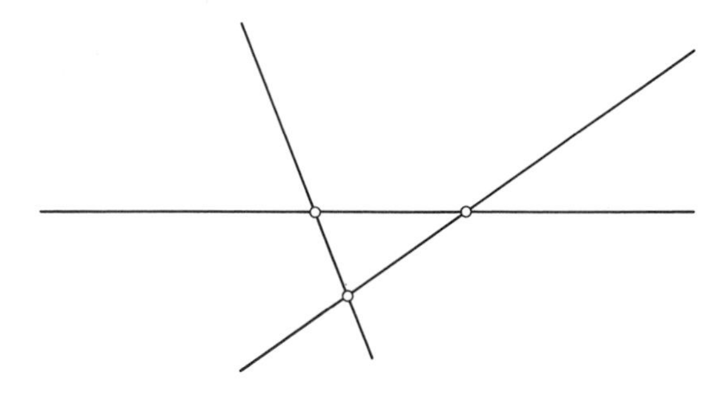

Figure 40

this one-to-one correspondence between the set of ordered pairs of real numbers and the points in the plane, we choose a pair of perpendicular lines (usually horizontal and vertical) and call these the *axes* of the system. The horizontal line is called the x-axis and the vertical line the y-axis. Their point of intersection is called the origin and the ordered pair $(0, 0)$ is made to correspond to this point. The ordered pairs $(x, 0)$ are made to correspond to points on the x-axis in the same manner as the real numbers x were made to correspond to the points on the real number line. The ordered pairs $(0, y)$ are made to correspond to the points on the y-axis in a similar manner with the upward direction taken as the positive direction.

We obtain the point corresponding to the ordered pair (x, y) by drawing a line parallel to the y-axis through the point $(x, 0)$ and a line parallel to the x-axis through the point $(0, y)$. The point of intersection of these lines corresponds to the ordered pair (x, y) (see Figure 41).

Exercise 9.8a

1. Describe the set $J \times J$, where J is the set of integers.
2. If the set $J \times J$ was represented pictorially as in Section 2.6, indicate what this would look like by plotting a few points. Circle those points in the pictorial representation of $J \times J$ whose distance from the origin $(0, 0)$ is less than or equal to 5.

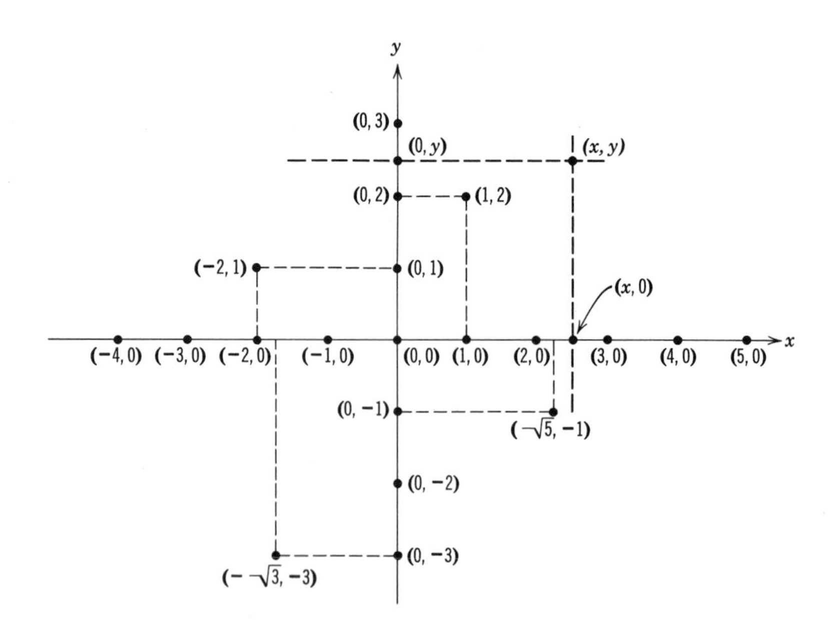

Figure 41

3. Plot several of the points in the pictorial representation of $R \times R$ whose coordinates are related as follows:

(a) The second coordinate is twice the first coordinate (i.e., (0, 0), (1, 2), (2, 4), etc.). This relation can be described by the equation $y = 2x$. The set of points in the pictorial representation is called the *graph* of $y = 2x$ and is a straight line.

(b) The second coordinate is the same as the first. This relation can be described by the equation $y = x$.

4. Plot the points (x, y) whose coordinates are given by the following equations:

(a) $y = 2x + 3$ (b) $y = x + 4$
(c) $y = -x$ (d) $y = -3x + 5$

5. Indicate, by shading, the set of points (x, y) satisfying the following inequalities:

(a) $x \leqq 3$ (b) $y \leqq 0$
(c) $-3 \leqq x \leqq 3$ (d) $|x| \leqq 3$
(e) $0 \leqq x \leqq 4$ *and* $0 \leqq y \leqq 3$ (f) $x + y \leqq 5$

9.8b Point Sets in the Plane

In problems 3, 4, and 5, Exercise 9.8a, we discussed particular *point sets* in the plane. The circle in plane geometry can also be described as a point set. It is usually defined as the set of points equidistant from a given point. What can we say about the coordinates of those points equidistant from the origin (0, 0)? We saw earlier that there are many ways of defining "distance." We saw examples of distance "following the streets" and "as the crow flies." The "distance" in ordinary geometry is the latter, the "straight-line distance." Since the coordinates of a point in the plane are given by the ordered pair of real numbers (x, y), we can compute the distance "as the crow flies" from (0, 0) to (x, y) (see Figure 42).

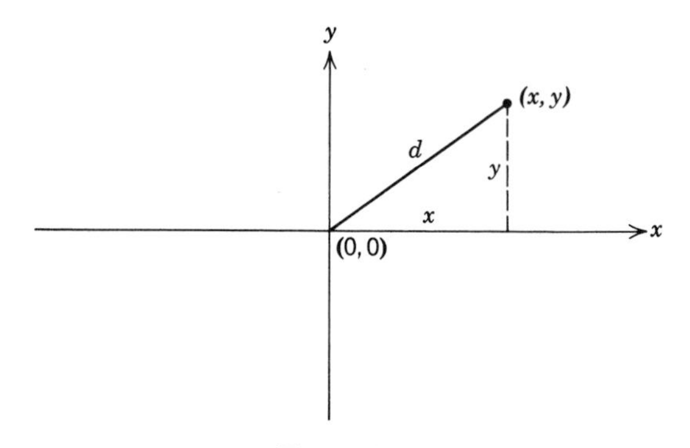

Figure 42

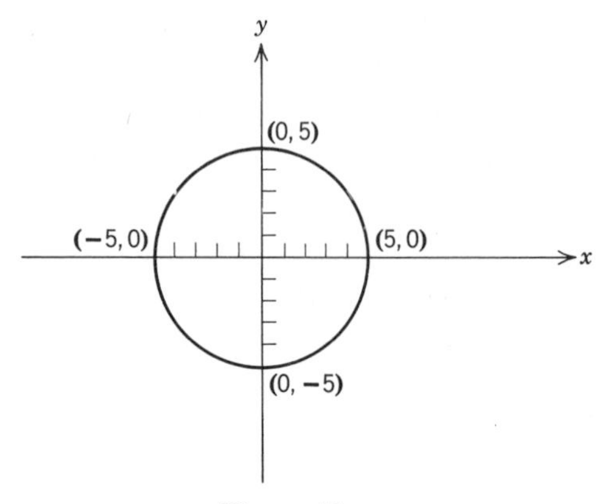

Figure 43

If we let d denote the distance from (0, 0) to (x, y), then

$$d = \sqrt{x^2 + y^2}.$$

Let us consider the circle centered at (0, 0) with radius 5 (see Figure 43). What are the coordinates of some of the points on the circle? We list a few: (0, 5), (0, −5), (5, 0), and (−5, 0). Notice that each of these points is five units from the origin along one of the axes.

Any other point (x, y) on the circle must also be at a distance of 5 units from the origin, that is, its coordinates must satisfy the relation

$$\sqrt{x^2 + y^2} = 5.$$

We can write this equation without the radical sign by squaring both sides. We get the equation whose graph is a circle of radius 5, centered at the origin (Figure 44):

$$x^2 + y^2 = 25$$

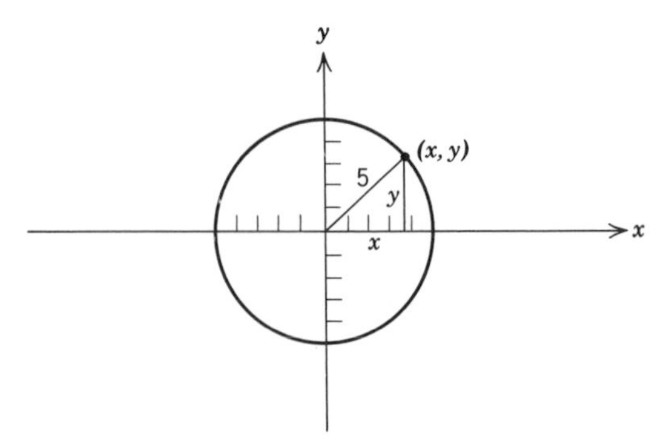

Figure 44

The relation of the algebra of real numbers to the study of point sets in the plane (plane geometry) leads to the investigation of geometry by analytic methods. This is formally called analytic geometry and further development of the concepts involved is beyond the scope of this book. (See any recent textbook in introductory college mathematics.)

Exercise 9.8b

1. (a) How far is the point (5, 12) from the point (0, 0) in straight line distance?
   (b) How far is the point (−12, 5) from the point (0, 0) in straight line distance?
   (c) Plot these points and two other points whose distance from (0, 0) is the same as the points in (a) and (b).
   (d) Write the equation describing the set of *all* points whose distance from (0, 0) is the same as in (a), (b), and (c).
2. Write the equation of a circle of radius r centered at (a) the origin, (b) the point (a, b).
3. (a) What would be the distance from the point (0, 0) to the point (3, 4), using the "along the street" distance?
   (b) What would be the distance from the point (0, 0) to the point (x, y), using the "along the street" distance?
   (c) Using the "along the street" distance, plot several points whose distance from (0, 0) is equal to 7.
4. If we retain the definition of circle as the set of points equidistant from a fixed point, and use the "along the street" interpretation of distance as in problem 3(c), describe this new "circle."

REFERENCES

Brumfiel, Charles F., Robert E. Eicholz, and Merril E. Shanks, *Geometry*, Addison-Wesley Publishing Co., Reading, Mass., 1960.

Courant, R., and H. Robbins, *What is Mathematics*, Oxford University Press, New York, 1941.

Eves, Howard, *An Introduction to the History of Mathematics*, Rinehart and Co., New York, 1953.

Larsen, Harold D., *Arithmetic for Colleges*, The Macmillan Company, New York, 1958.

Newman, James R., *The World of Mathematics*, Simon and Schuster, New York, 1956.

Schepler, H. C., "The Chronology of Pi," *Mathematics Magazine*, January–February, March–April, and May–June issues, 1950.

School Mathematics Study Group, *Mathematics for Junior High School*, vols. I, II, and III.

Swain, Robert L., *Understanding Arithmetic*, Rinehart and Co., New York, 1952.

Answers to Selected Exercises

EXERCISE 1.4a

1. (a) 𓎆𓎆𓎆𓎆𓎆𓎆𓎆 𓏺𓏺𓏺𓏺𓏺𓏺𓏺 (c) 𓂭𓂭𓂭𓂭𓂭𓂭𓂭𓂭𓂭 𓍢𓍢𓍢𓍢𓍢𓍢𓍢𓍢𓍢 𓏺𓏺𓏺𓏺𓏺𓏺𓏺𓏺𓏺

(e) 𓆼𓆼𓍢 𓎆𓎆 𓏺𓏺𓏺𓏺 (g) 𓍢𓍢𓍢𓍢𓍢𓍢𓍢𓍢 𓏺𓏺𓏺𓏺𓏺𓏺𓏺𓏺

2. (a) 1,220,453 (c) 1,033,306

3. (a) 𓁨𓁨𓆐𓆐𓆐𓆐𓆐𓂭𓂭 𓍢𓍢𓍢𓍢𓍢𓍢 𓏺𓏺𓏺𓏺𓏺𓏺

EXERCISE 1.4b

1. (a) XXVI (c) XLIX (e) CDXXXI (g) MDLI (i) MMCDIX
2. (a) 37 (c) 94 (e) 457 (g) 1151 (i) 2999
4. (a) MMVI (c) DXLIII

EXERCISE 1.4c

1. (a) λd (c) $\mu\theta$ (e) $\upsilon\lambda\alpha$ (g) $\alpha'\phi\nu\alpha$ (i) $\beta'\upsilon\theta$
2. (a) 44 (c) 653 (e) 172 (g) 6435 (i) 54,567

EXERCISE 1.5a

1. (a) 四十二 (c) 三十六 (e) 二百四十六 (g) 三千一百四十六 (i) 五千四百六十九

2. (a) 36 (c) 208 (e) 2535

EXERCISE 1.7

1. (a) 25 = △□□I; 100 = ⊡△△□; 197 = ⊡⊡⊡□I (b) 25 = I⊡L□I; 100 = I⊡L△□; 197 = F⊡I□I (c) 25 = ILI; 100 = $ILIO$; 197 = $FOII$
2. (a) 360 = $EEFFFFLL$ (b) 360 = $LELO$

EXERCISE 1.9

1. 385 (a) 999 ∩∩∩∩∩∩∩∩ ||||| (b) |||||| < |||||| (c) τπε (d) 三百八十五 (e) : —
2. (a) 27 (c) 2

2. (a) 27 (c) 2
4. (a) 1, 10, 11, 100, 101, 110, 111, 1000, 1001, 1010, 1011, 1100, 1101, 1110, 1111, 10000, 10001, 10010, 10011, 10100, 10101, 10110, 10111, 11000, 11001 (b) $10101)_2 = 21)_{10}$; $1110011)_2 = 115)_{10}$

EXERCISE 2.2

1. (a) set (b) object (c) set
3. (a) Well defined; {April, June, Sept., Nov.} (c) Well defined; {44, 46, 48, 50, . . .} (e) Well defined; {0} (g) Not well defined (i) Not well defined

EXERCISE 2.3

1. Subsets: $Z \subseteq N; F \subseteq N; F \subseteq Z; R \subseteq N; R \subseteq Z; R \subseteq F; S \subseteq N; S \subseteq Z; S \subseteq F; S \subseteq R; R \subseteq S$. Proper subsets: $Z \subset N; F \subset N; F \subset Z; R \subset N; R \subset Z; R \subset F; S \subset N; S \subset Z; S \subset F$.
3. $X = \{1, 2, 3\}$; Subsets: $\{1, 2, 3\}$; ϕ; $\{1, 2\}$; $\{1, 3\}$; $\{2, 3\}$; $\{1\}$; $\{2\}$; $\{3\}$; The proper subsets are the last six.
5. (a) e.g., $S_{(\text{even})} = \{0, 2, 4, 6, 8\}$; $S_{(\text{odd})} = \{1, 3, 5, 7\}$ (c) $\{2\}$; ϕ; $\{0, 1, 2, 3, 4, 5\}$; S itself; $\{5, 6, 7, 8\}$ (e) $\{0, 1\}$
6. $S = \{x|x \text{ is an even number.}\}$; $T = \{x|x \text{ is an odd number.}\}$
7. (a) $s \in Q$ (c) $z \in Q$ (e) $h \notin Q$ (g) $h' \in Q$ (i) $f \notin Q$
8. (a) No (c) Yes

EXERCISE 2.4

1.

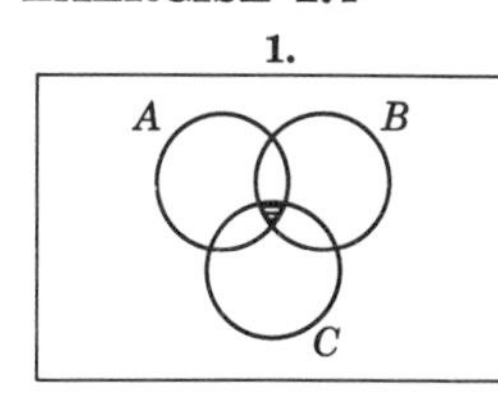

3.

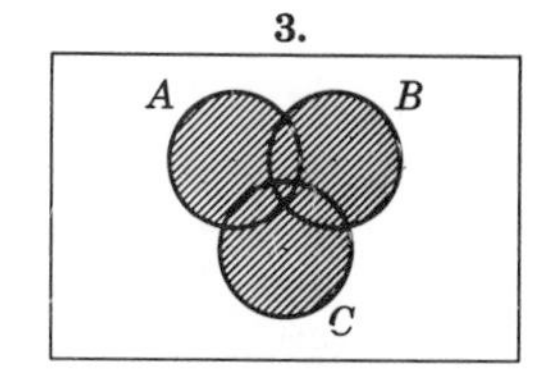

5.

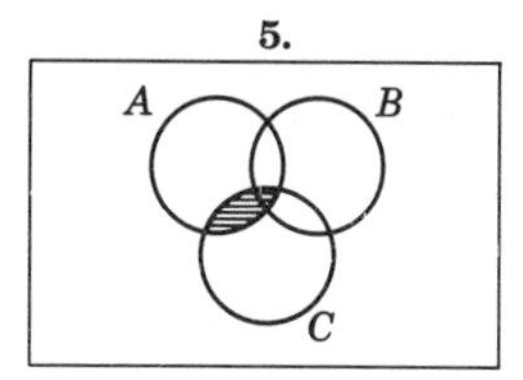

7.

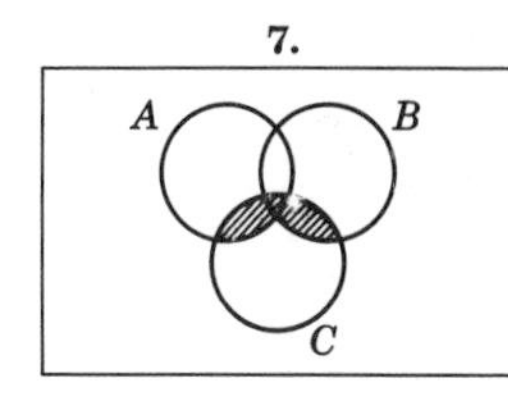

9.

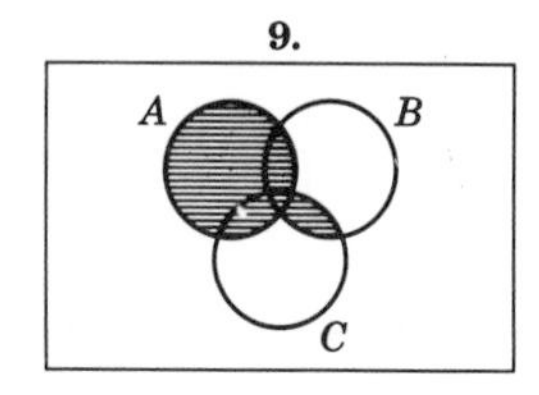

11.

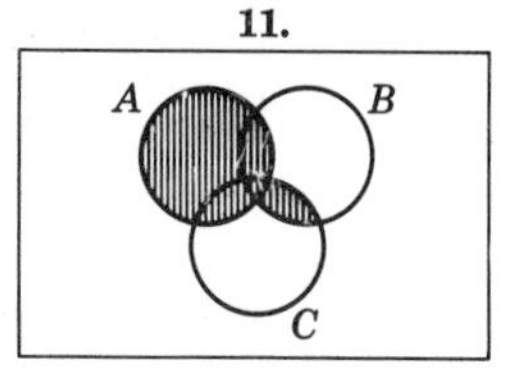

13. (a) Ted, Tim (c) Ted, Tim, John, Jill

EXERCISE 2.5

1. (a) The union of a set with itself is the set itself. The union of a set with the empty set is the set itself. The union of a set with the universal set is the universal set. (c) If a set is a proper subset of each of two other sets then it is a proper subset of their union. (e) The intersection of a set with itself is the set itself. The intersection of a set with the universal set is the set itself. The intersection of a set with the empty set is the empty set. (g) If a set is a proper subset of each of two others, then it is a subset of their intersection.

2. (a) $A \cup B = \{1, 2, 3, 4, 5\}$; $A \cap B = \phi$ (c) $A \cup B = \{1, 2, 3, 5\}$; $A \cap B = \{1, 3\}$ (e) $A \cup B = \{1, 2, 3\}$; $A \cap B = \{2, 3\}$

3. (a) $E \cup U = U$ (c) $A \cup B$ is the set of odd natural numbers and 2, 4, and 6. (e) $E \cap U = E$ (g) $A \cap B$ is the first three odd natural numbers; $\{1, 3, 5\}$ (i) $(A \cup B) \cap E$ is the first three even natural numbers; $\{2, 4, 6\}$ (k) $(E \cap A) \cup B = B$; $\{1, 2, 3, 4, 5, 6\}$

4. (a) ϕ (c) A (e) $A \cap B$

5. (a) $A \cup B$ (c) B (e) $A \cup B$

6. (a) $A = \{2, 3, 4, 5\}$ (c) $A = \{3, 4\}$; $B = \{2, 3\}$

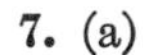
7. (a)

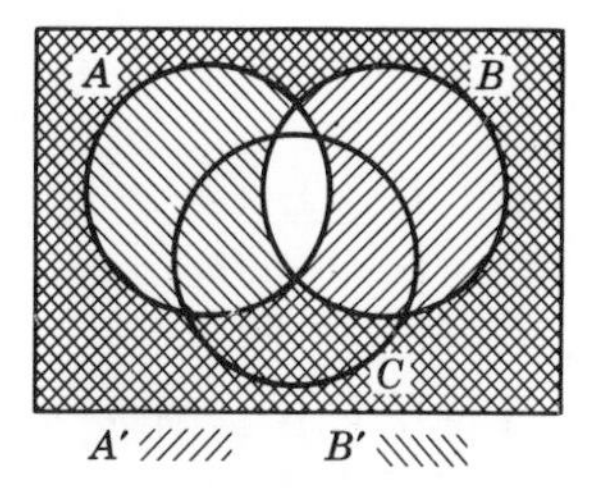

A' ////// B' \\\\\\

$A' \cap B'$ ×××××

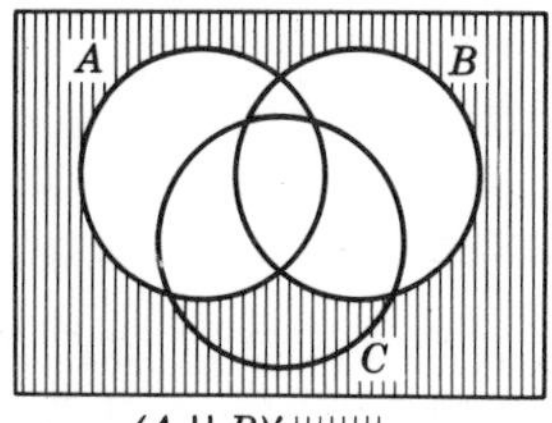

$(A \cup B)'$ ||||||||

9. $2^5 = 32$ subsets; 31 proper subsets.

EXERCISE 2.6

1. $\{(a, 0), (a, 1), (a, 2), (b, 0), (b, 1), (b, 2)\}$.

3. (a) $\{a, b, c, d, e, 1, 2, 3\}$. (c) $\{1, a, 2, b, 3, c, 5, 7, 9\}$. (e) ϕ. (g) $\{1, 3\}$. (i) ϕ. (k) $\{1, 2, 3, 5, 7, 9\}$. (m) $\{1, 2, 3, 4, 5, 6, 7, 8, 9, 0\}$.

4. (a)

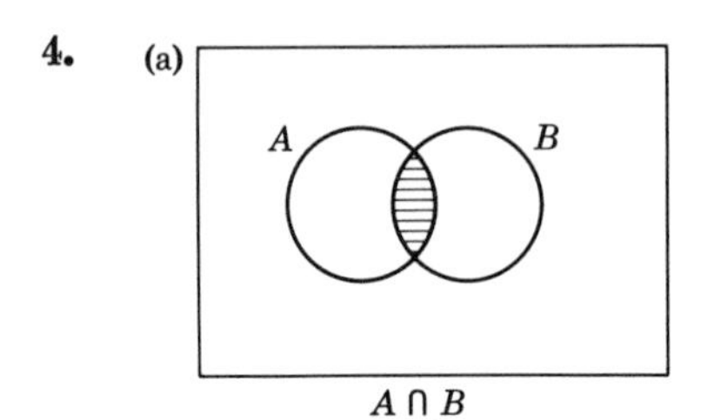

$A \cap B$

(c)

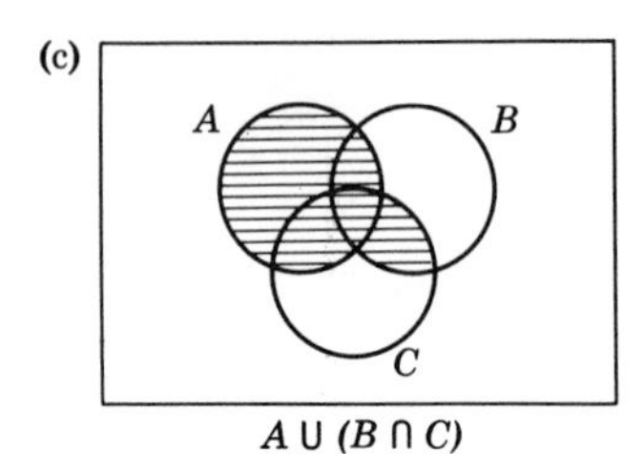

$A \cup (B \cap C)$

5. $2^{16} = 65{,}536$ subsets.

6. (a) $\{2, 3\}$. (c) $\{3\}$. (e) ϕ. (g) $\{(3, 3)\}$.

7. (a) $A \cap C$. (c) A. (e) $A \cap B$.

9.

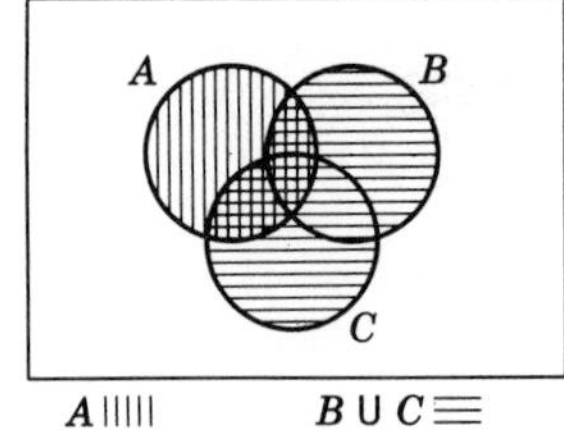

A ||||| $B \cup C$ ≡

$A \cap (B \cup C)$ ⊞

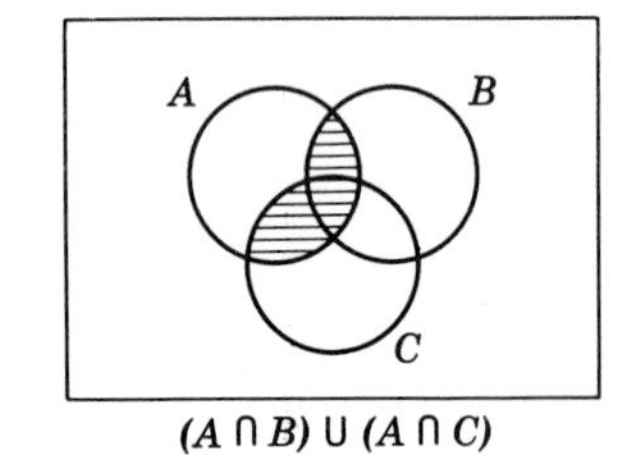

$(A \cap B) \cup (A \cap C)$

10. (a) Ted, Tim, Jack, June. (c) Ted, Tim. (e) Ted, Tim. (g) Tom, Tim, Ted, Tobe, Jim, Joan, Jack, June, John, Jill, Jane, Jan, Sam, Sono, Sue, Sara; 16 attended party.

11. Total 932.

EXERCISE 3.2

1. E.g., "was (is) the wife of."

3. "Is less than."

5. "Is the capital of."

EXERCISE 3.5

1. (a) $A \cap B = \{2, 5\}; B \cap A = \{2, 5\}$

(c) $(A \cup B) \cup C = \{1, 2, 3, 4, 5, 6\} \cup \{4, 5, 6, 7\} = \{1, 2, 3, 4, 5, 6, 7\}$

$A \cup (B \cup C) = \{1, 2, 4, 5\} \cup \{2, 3, 4, 5, 6, 7\} = \{1, 2, 3, 4, 5, 6, 7\}$

(e) e.g., $A \cap (B \cup C) = (A \cap B) \cup (A \cap C)$;
$A \cup (B \cap C) = (A \cup B) \cap (A \cup C)$

2. (a) Yes, $J = F$. Yes, $A = G$. Yes, $D = K$. (c) A, G, L.
4. Yes; Yes.

EXERCISE 3.9

1. Ⓣ is not reflexive, not symmetric, but is transitive.
3. Ⓒ is not reflexive, not symmetric, and not transitive.
5. They are all multiples of 7, or exactly divisible by 7.

EXERCISE 3.10

2. 120 ways
3. (a) $7 \mid 35$ because $35 = 7 \cdot 5$ (c) $3 \mid 51$ because $51 = 3 \cdot 17$
5. Let $n \leftrightarrow 2n$ for $n = 1, 2, \ldots$
7. 5040 ways
8. 1,307,674,368,000 possible permutations. At the rate of 6 per min (360/hr) the time required is 3,632,428,800 hr, or 454,053,600 8-hr days, or 1,816,214.4 250-working-day years.

EXERCISE 3.12

1. "1–1" is reflexive since a set may be placed in one-to-one correspondence with itself. "1–1" is symmetric by the definition of the relation, i.e., "1–1" means "both ways." A "1–1" B implies there is a 1–1 correspondence of A to B and B to A; hence B "1–1" A. "1–1" is transitive. Consider sets A, B, and C. For $a \in A$, $b \in B$, and $c \in C$, let $a \leftrightarrow b$, $b \leftrightarrow c$; then from $a \leftrightarrow b \leftrightarrow c$ we can obtain $a \leftrightarrow c$. Hence A 1–1 B and B 1–1 C implies A 1–1 C.
3. Reflexive since any student is "same sex as" himself. Symmetric since if student A is the same sex as student B, then student B is the same sex as student A. Transitive since if student A is the same sex as student B, e.g., both boys, and student B is the same sex as student C, then C must be a boy. Hence A "is the same sex as" C. The equivalence classes are the *boys* and the *girls*.
5. Call the relation Ⓡ. For a, b, and c integers: a Ⓡ a because $a - a = 0 = 0 \cdot 4$; hence Ⓡ is reflexive. a Ⓡ b means $a - b = k \cdot 4$ for some integer k; then $b - a = (-k)4$; hence b Ⓡ a. Ⓡ is symmetric. a Ⓡ b means $a - b = k \cdot 4$ and b Ⓡ c means $b - c = m \cdot 4$; then $(a - b) + (b - c) = k \cdot 4 + m \cdot 4$ or $a - c = (k + m)4$; but $k + m$ is an integer; hence a Ⓡ c. Ⓡ is transitive. It is an equivalence relation. The equivalence classes are those integers related to 0, 1, 2, and 3, respectively.
7. Inclusion: Set A "is included in" set B if every element of A is an element of B. It is reflexive, is not symmetric, and is transitive. It is not an

equivalence relation. "Is the daughter of": The criterion is inherent in the relation. It is not reflexive, not symmetric, and not transitive. It is not an equivalence relation. "Is a classmate of": It is reflexive, symmetric, and transitive. It is an equivalence relation, and the equivalence classes are the classes such as freshmen, sophomore, junior, and senior.

EXERCISE 3.13

1. $\{1, 2, 3, 4, 5, 6, 8\}$
3. ϕ
5. $\{1, 2, 3, 4, 5, 6, 7\}$
7. $\{8\}$
9. $\{1, 2, 3, 4, 5, 6, 8\}$
11. $\{2, 4, 5\}$
13. ϕ
15. $\{5\}$
17. 10
19. 12
21. 20
23. 0
25. $16 = 10 + 12 - 6$
27. 100
29. 56
31. 24

EXERCISE 3.14

1. (a) If A and B have exactly the same elements. (c) If $a = c$ and $b = d$
4. One cut and the other choose first.

EXERCISE 3.16

2. When the ordered pairs of f have no two second components the same.
4. (*b*) is a function of x and has domain $\{2, 3, 4\}$ and range $\{2, 3, 4\}$; (*d*) is a function of x and has domain $\{1, 2, 3, 4\}$ and range $\{1, 3\}$; (*a*) is a function of y and has domain $\{1, 2, 3, 4\}$ and range $\{4\}$; (*b*) is a function of y and has domain $\{2, 3, 4\}$ and range $\{2, 3, 4\}$.

EXERCISE 4.2

1. $1 \cdot 10^6 + 0 \cdot 10^5 + 2 \cdot 10^4 + 0 \cdot 10^3 + 3 \cdot 10^2 + 0 \cdot 10^1 + 4 \cdot 10^0$
3. $1 \cdot 10^1 + 0 \cdot 10^0$
5. $3 \cdot 10^2$; $3 \cdot 10^1$; $3 \cdot 10^0$
6. (a) 2^9 (c) a^8 (e) m^2 (g) $1/x^4 = x^{-4}$
7. (a) 100,000 (c) $8 - 1 = 7$ (e) 625 (g) 1/8

EXERCISE 4.4

1. (a) $1 \cdot 10^1 + 2 \cdot 10^0$ (c) $3 \cdot 10^2 + 0 \cdot 10^1 + 2 \cdot 10^0$
   (e) $1 \cdot 10^4 + 0 \cdot 10^3 + 0 \cdot 10^2 + 0 \cdot 10^1 + 0 \cdot 10^0$ (g) $1 \cdot 10^1 + 1 \cdot 10^0$
2. (a) 10^5; 100,000 (c) 10^{10}; 10,000,000,000 (e) 2^7; 128 (g) 2^1; 2
3. (12) (a) XII; (b) ∩|| ; (c) $\iota\beta$. (302) (a) CCCII; (b) ϱϱϱ||; (c) $\tau\beta$.
   (10,000) (a) $\overline{\text{X}}$; (b) ʃ ; (c) M. (11) (a) XI; (b) ∩| ; (c) $\iota\alpha$.
5. 13
6. (a) $6 \cdot 10^{12}$ (c) $18 \cdot 10^5 = 1.8 \cdot 10^6$
7. (a) $6.5 \cdot 10^{-6}$ (c) $8 \cdot 10^{-9}$ (e) $6 \cdot 10^{12}$
8. (a) 8,700,000,000 (c) 0.000000087 (e) 0.000000005
9. (a) 10^2; 100 (c) 10^0; 1
   (e) $(7.25)(2.16)(10^{-3}) = 15.66(10^{-3}) = 1.566(10^{-2}) = 0.01566$

EXERCISE 4.7

1. 1, 2, 3, 4, 10, 11, 12, 13, 14, 20, 21, 22, 23, 24, 30, 31, 32, 33, 34, 40, 41, 42, 43, 44, 100, 101, 102, 103, 104, 110, 111, 112, 113, 114, 120, 121, 122, 123, 124, 130, 131, 132, 133, 134, 140, 141, 142, 143, 144, 200.
2. (a) $3 \cdot 5^2 + 2 \cdot 5^1 + 0 \cdot 5^0 = 85$ (c) $2 \cdot 5^2 + 0 \cdot 5^1 + 3 \cdot 5^0 = 53$
3. (a) $24)_5$ (c) $2302)_5$
4. (a) Two dens, four qens, one fen, and one sen. (c) Four mens, three dens, two qens, one fen, and two sens.

EXERCISE 4.8

1. (a) $2342)_5 = 347)_{10}$ (c) $101101)_2 = 45)_{10}$
2. (a) $1 \cdot 5^2 + 2 \cdot 5^1 + 4 \cdot 5^0$ (c) $1 \cdot 7^2 + 4 \cdot 7^1 + 6 \cdot 7^0$
3. (a) $125)_{10} = 64 + 32 + 16 + 8 + 4 + 1 = 1 \cdot 2^6 + 1 \cdot 2^5 + 1 \cdot 2^4 + 1 \cdot 2^3 + 1 \cdot 2^2 + 0 \cdot 2^1 + 1 \cdot 2^0 = 1111101)_2$
   (c) $32 = 2^5$ $32)_{10} = 100000)_2$
5. In each system the counting number representing the base is symbolized 10. Multiples of the base (other than two) are 20, 30, etc.

EXERCISE 4.9a

2. (a) 1144 (c) 22010
3. (a) 13131 (c) 1130011
4. (a) 132 (c) 302
5. (a) 232 (c) 20432
7. (a) 1202; 1110 (c) 20211; 122120021
8. 4 weights: 1 oz, 3 oz, 9 oz, and 27 oz. Use weights in both pans as needed.

EXERCISE 4.9b

2. (a) 1100 (c) 11101 (e) 1001110
3. (a) 1001101 (c) 101011111 (e) 1001

EXERCISE 4.9c

1. Fewer symbols; fewer elementary facts; and adaptable to yes-no or on-off type problems.
3. Unfavorable for first mover; choose to move second.
5. (a) 123 (c) 935E8 (e) 526 (g) 13096 (i) 4646 (k) 13T0874 (m) 49 (o) 239—15 rem.

EXERCISE 5.2

1. (a) A 1–1 correspondence can be established between the set A and the set $\{1, 2, 3\}$. (c) A set is finite if it can be placed in a 1–1 correspondence with the set $\{1, 2, 3, \ldots, n\}$ for n a natural number.
3. Transitive
5. (a) $\{1, 2, 3, 4\}$ (c) $\{1, 2, 3, 4, 8, 9\}$

EXERCISE 5.4

3. $1 \in N$ implies $1 + 1 = 2 \in N$; $2 \in N$ implies $2 + 1 = 3 \in N$; and so on to $9 \in N$ implies $9 + 1 = 10 \in N$. Could do the same for 1,000,000,000 but it would take a long time.

5.

...	−12,	−6,	0,	6,	12,	18,	...
...	−11,	−5,	1,	7,	13,	19,	...
...	−10,	−4,	2,	8,	14,	20,	...
...	−9,	−3,	3,	9,	15,	21,	...
...	−8,	−2,	4,	10,	16,	22,	...
...	−7,	−1,	5,	11,	17,	23,	...

EXERCISE 5.5

1. (a) Let $2k$ and $2m$ represent arbitrary even numbers where k and m are whole numbers. Then $2k + 2m = 2(k + m)$. But $(k + m)$ is a whole number, so $2(k + m)$ is an even number. Hence the set of even numbers is closed with respect to addition. (c) Let $2k + 1$ and $2m + 1$ represent arbitrary odd numbers, where k and m are whole numbers. Then $(2k + 1)(2m + 1) = 2km + 2k + 2m + 1 = 2(km + k + m) + 1$. But $(km + k + m)$ is a whole number. Hence the set of odd numbers is closed with respect to multiplication.
2. (a) $1 \odot 3 = 5$; $1 \odot 5 = 7$; $3 \odot 7 = 11$; $5 \odot 7 = 13$ (c) Let $2k - 1$ and $2m - 1$ be arbitrary odd numbers where k and m are natural numbers. Then $(2k - 1) \odot (2m - 1) = (2k - 1) + (2m - 1) + 1 = 2(k + m - 1) + 1$. But $(k + m - 1)$ is a natural number, hence $2(k + m - 1) + 1$ is an odd number. Hence the set of odd numbers is closed with respect to the operation $\odot$.

3. The set W is closed with respect to the operation $\odot$ as defined since if m and n are whole numbers, m^n is a whole number.
5. The set W is *not* closed with respect to the operation as defined. One counterexample is sufficient to show this, e.g., let $m = 5$ and $n = 7$; then $m \odot n = 5 - 7 = -2$, and -2 is not in W.
8. Substitution principle.

EXERCISE 5.6

1. Commutative Law
3. Commutative Law
5. Commutative Law
7. Associative Law
9. Zero is used as the cardinal number of the empty set. As an element of a number system zero is the additive identity.

EXERCISE 5.7

1. (a) Commutative Law (c) Commutative Law (e) Associative Law
3. (a) Commutative Law of Addition (c) Commutative Law of Multiplication (e) Commutative Law of Multiplication (g) Associative Law of Addition
4. (a) The operation of problem 2 is associative; the operation of problem 3 is not associative. (b) The operation of problem 2 is commutative; the operation of problem 3 is not commutative.
5.

$(a \cdot b)^2 = (a \cdot b)(a \cdot b)$	by the definition of exponent
$= a \cdot (b \cdot a) \cdot b$	by the Assoc. Law of Mult.
$= a \cdot (a \cdot b) \cdot b$	by the Com. Law of Mult.
$= (a \cdot a)(b \cdot b)$	by the Assoc. Law of Mult.
$= a^2 \cdot b^2$	by the definition of exponent

EXERCISE 5.8

1. $ab + a \cdot 2$ or $ab + 2a$
3. $23 \cdot 2 + 23 \cdot 1 = 69$
5. $(30 + 2)10$
7. $ac + bc + ad + bd$
9. $xy + x \cdot 2$
11. $(2a + 3)x$
13. $(3 \cdot 10 + 2)10$
15. $(2xb + 1)a$
17. $a \triangle b = b \triangle a$
19. $(a \triangle b) \triangle c = a \triangle (b \triangle c)$
21. $a \triangle (b \oplus c) = (a \triangle b) \oplus (a \triangle c)$

EXERCISE 5.10

1. Let 1 represent the multiplicative identity and suppose there is another, cal it $1'$. Then $1 \cdot 1' = 1'$ because 1 is the multiplicative identity; also $1 \cdot 1' = 1$ since we are supposing $1'$ is another multiplicative identity. Then $1' = 1$ by the transitive property of equals. Hence the multiplicative identity is unique.

3. $5 + 10m = 5 \cdot 1 + 5(2m) = 5(1 + 2m)$ or $(1 + 2m)5$.

4. (a) No

5. (a) Yes, 5 "divides" 0 because $0 = 5 \cdot 0$.

8. $(a + b)(c + d) = a(c + d) + b(c + d) = ac + ad + bc + bd$ by two applications of the Distributive Law.

9.
$$\begin{aligned}
(a + b)^2 &= (a + b)(a + b) && \text{by defn. of exponents}\\
&= a(a + b) + b(a + b) && \text{by the Distributive Law}\\
&= a^2 + ab + ba + b^2 && \text{by the Distributive Law}\\
&= a^2 + ab + ab + b^2 && \text{by the Com. Law of Mult.}\\
&= a^2 + (ab + ab) + b^2 && \text{by the Assoc. Law of Mult.}\\
&= a^2 + (1 \cdot ab + 1 \cdot ab) + b^2 && \text{1 is the Mult. Identity}\\
&= a^2 + (1 + 1)ab + b^2 && \text{by the Dist. Law}\\
&= a^2 + 2ab + b^2 && \text{by the Tables of Elem. Facts}
\end{aligned}$$

EXERCISE 5.11

1. (a)
$$\begin{aligned}
27 + 9 &= (2 \cdot 10^1 + 7 \cdot 10^0) + 9 \cdot 10^0 && \text{Sys. of Num.}\\
&= 2 \cdot 10^1 + (7 \cdot 10^0 + 9 \cdot 10^0) && \text{Assoc. Law Add.}\\
&= 2 \cdot 10^1 + (7 + 9)10^0 && \text{Dist. Law}\\
&= 2 \cdot 10^1 + 16 \cdot 10^0 && \text{Tables}\\
&= 2 \cdot 10^1 + (1 \cdot 10^1 + 6 \cdot 10^0)10^0 && \text{Sys. of Num.}\\
&= 2 \cdot 10^1 + (1 \cdot 10^1)10^0 + (6 \cdot 10^0)10^0 && \text{Dist. Law}\\
&= 2 \cdot 10^1 + 1(10^1 \cdot 10^0) + 6(10^0 \cdot 10^0) && \text{Assoc. Law of Mult.}\\
&= 2 \cdot 10^1 + 1 \cdot 10^1 + 6 \cdot 10^0 && \text{Law of Exponents}\\
&= (2 \cdot 10^1 + 1 \cdot 10^1) + 6 \cdot 10^0 && \text{Assoc. Law of Add.}\\
&= (2 + 1)10^1 + 6 \cdot 10^0 && \text{Dist. Law}\\
&= 3 \cdot 10^1 + 6 \cdot 10^0 && \text{Tables}\\
&= 36 && \text{Sys. of Num.}\\
27 + 9 &= 36 && \text{Trans. Prop of} =
\end{aligned}$$

2. (a) $9E7 + T = (9 \cdot 10^2 + E \cdot 10^1 + 7 \cdot 10^0) + T \cdot 10^0$ Sys. of Numeration

Note that the base has the same symbol but $10)_{12} = 12)_{10}$.

$$\begin{aligned}
&= 9 \cdot 10^2 + E \cdot 10^1 + (7 \cdot 10^0 + T \cdot 10^0) && \text{Assoc. Law Add.}\\
&= 9 \cdot 10^2 + E \cdot 10^1 + (7 + T)10^0 && \text{Distributive Law}\\
&= 9 \cdot 10^2 + E \cdot 10^1 + 15 \cdot 10^0 && \text{Tables}\\
&= 9 \cdot 10^2 + E \cdot 10^1 + (1 \cdot 10^1 + 5 \cdot 10^0)10^0 && \text{Sys. of Numeration}\\
&= 9 \cdot 10^2 + E \cdot 10^1 + (1 \cdot 10^1)10^0 + (5 \cdot 10^0)10^0 && \text{Distributive Law}\\
&= 9 \cdot 10^2 + E \cdot 10^1 + 1(10^1 \cdot 10^0) + 5(10^0 \cdot 10^0) && \text{Assoc. Law Mult.}
\end{aligned}$$

$= 9\cdot10^2 + E\cdot10^1 + 1\cdot10^1 + 5\cdot10^0$	Law of Exponents
$= 9\cdot10^2 + (E\cdot10^1 + 1\cdot10^1) + 5\cdot10^0$	Assoc. Law Add.
$= 9\cdot10^2 + (E + 1)10^1 + 5\cdot10^0$	Distributive Law
$= 9\cdot10^2 + 10\cdot10^1 + 5\cdot10^0$	Tables
$= 9\cdot10^2 + (1\cdot10^1 + 0\cdot10^0)10^1 + 5\cdot10^0$	Sys. of Numeration
$= 9\cdot10^2 + (1\cdot10^1)10^1 + (0\cdot10^0)10^1 + 5\cdot10^0$	Distributive Law
$= 9\cdot10^2 + 1(10^1\cdot10^1) + 0(10^0\cdot10^1) + 5\cdot10^0$	Assoc. Law Mult.
$= 9\cdot10^2 + 1\cdot10^2 + 0\cdot10^1 + 5\cdot10^0$	Law of Exponents
$= (9\cdot10^2 + 1\cdot10^2) + 0\cdot10^1 + 5\cdot10^0$	Assoc. Law Add.
$= (9 + 1)10^2 + 0\cdot10^1 + 5\cdot10^0$	Distributive Law
$= T\cdot10^2 + 0\cdot10^1 + 5\cdot10^0$	Tables
$= T05$	Sys. of Numeration
$9E7 + T = T05$	Trans. Prop. of =

3. (a)

$(EE)(9) = (E\cdot10^1 + E\cdot10^0)(9\cdot10^0)$	Sys. of Numeration
$= (E\cdot10^1)(9\cdot10^0) + (E\cdot10^0)(9\cdot10^0)$	Distributive Law
$= E(10^1\cdot9)10^0 + E(10^0\cdot9)10^0$	Assoc. Law Mult.
$= E(9\cdot10^1)10^0 + E(9\cdot10^0)10^0$	Com. Law Mult.
$= (E\cdot9)(10^1\cdot10^0) + (E\cdot9)(10^0\cdot10^0)$	Assoc. Law Mult.
$= (E\cdot9)10^1 + (E\cdot9)10^0$	Law of Exponents
$= 83\cdot10^1 + 83\cdot10^0$	Tables
$= (8\cdot10^1 + 3\cdot10^0)10^1 + (8\cdot10^1 + 3\cdot10^0)10^0$	Sys. of Numeration
$= (8\cdot10^1)10^1 + (3\cdot10^0)10^1 + (8\cdot10^1)10^0 + (3\cdot10^0)10^0$	Distributive Law
$= 8(10^1\cdot10^1) + 3(10^0\cdot10^1) + 8(10^1\cdot10^0) + 3(10^0\cdot10^0)$	Assoc. Law Mult.
$= 8\cdot10^2 + 3\cdot10^1 + 8\cdot10^1 + 3\cdot10^0$	Law of Exponents
$= 8\cdot10^2 + (3\cdot10^1 + 8\cdot10^1) + 3\cdot10^0$	Assoc. Law Add.
$= 8\cdot10^2 + (3 + 8)10^1 + 3\cdot10^0$	Distributive Law
$= 8\cdot10^2 + E\cdot10^1 + 3\cdot10^0$	Tables
$= 8E3$	Sys. of Numeration
$(EE)(9) = 8E3$	Trans. Prop. of =

7. (a)

$379 + 96 = (3\cdot10^2 + 7\cdot10 + 9) + (9\cdot10 + 6)$	Sys. of Numeration
$= 3\cdot10^2 + (7\cdot10 + 9\cdot10) + (9 + 6)$	Assoc., Com. Add.
$= 3\cdot10^2 + (7 + 9)10 + (9 + 6)$	Distributive Law
$= 3\cdot10^2 + 16\cdot10 + 15$	Tables
$= 3\cdot10^2 + (1\cdot10 + 6)10 + (1\cdot10 + 5)$	Sys. of Numeration
$= (3\cdot10^2 + 1\cdot10^2) + (6\cdot10 + 1\cdot10) + 5$	Dist., Assoc., Com.
$= (3 + 1)10^2 + (6 + 1)10 + 5$	Distributive Law
$= 4\cdot10^2 + 7\cdot10 + 5$	Tables
$= 475$	Sys. of Numeration

8. (a)

$(36)(9) = (3\cdot 10 + 6)(9)$	Sys. of Numeration
$= (3\cdot 10)9 + (6)9$	Distributive Law
$= (3\cdot 9)10 + 6\cdot 9$	Assoc. and Com. Mult.
$= 27\cdot 10 + 54$	Tables
$= (2\cdot 10 + 7)10 + (5\cdot 10 + 4)$	Sys. of Numeration
$= 2\cdot 10^2 + (7\cdot 10 + 5\cdot 10) + 4$	Dist. Law; Assoc. Mult. and Add. Law of Exponents
$= 2\cdot 10^2 + (7 + 5)10 + 4$	Distributive Law
$= 2\cdot 10^2 + 12\cdot 10 + 4$	Tables
$= 2\cdot 10^2 + (1\cdot 10 + 2)10 + 4$	Sys. of Numeration
$= (2\cdot 10^2 + 1\cdot 10^2) + 2\cdot 10 + 4$	Dist. Law; Assoc. Mult. Law of Exponents
$= (2 + 1)10^2 + 2\cdot 10 + 4$	Distributive Law
$= 3\cdot 10^2 + 2\cdot 10 + 4$	Tables
$= 324$	Sys. of Numeration

9. (a) Moves the reference point one place to the right.
(b) 3420 (c) TET70

EXERCISE 5.12

1. (a) $A = \{4, 5, 6, 7, 8, 9, 10, 11\}$; l.u.b. 11; g.l.b. 4 (b) $B = \{1, 2, 3\}$; e.g., 3 and 4

3. $A \cap B = \phi$

5. $C = \{6, 7, 8, 9, 10, 11, 12\}$; l.u.b. is 12; $\{1, 2, 3, 6, 7, 8, 9, 10, 11, 12\}$

7. (a) $\{n|0 \leqq n < 7\}$ (b) $\{n|0 \leqq n < 4\}$ (c) $\{n|0 \leqq n < 4\}$

9. $3n < 5n$ for $n > 0$

13. $ac = ac$ and $a = b$ implies $ac = bc$ by the substitution principle.

15. In problem 8, none. In problem 9, n must be positive.

17.

$(x + 3) + (y + 2) = x + (3 + y) + 2$	Assoc. Law of Add.
$= x + (y + 3) + 2$	Com. Law of Add.
$= (x + y) + (3 + 2)$	Assoc. Law of Add.
$= (3 + 2) + (x + y)$	Com. Law of Add.
$= (2 + 3) + (x + y)$	Com. Law of Add.
$(x + 3) + (y + 2) = (2 + 3) + (x + y)$	Trans. Prop. of =

19.

$(3b)^2 = (3b)(3b)$	Defn. of Exponent
$= 3(b3)b$	Assoc. Law Mult.
$= 3(3b)b$	Com. Law Mult.
$= (3\cdot 3)(bb)$	Assoc. Law Mult.
$= 9b^2$	Defn. of exponent and tables.
$(3b)^2 = 9b^2$	Trans. Prop. of =

21.

$3\cdot 10^0 + 4\cdot 10^0 = (3 + 4)10^0$	Distributive Law
$= 7\cdot 10^0$	Tables

23.
$$\begin{aligned} 13\cdot 10^2 &= (1\cdot 10^1 + 3\cdot 10^0)10^2 && \text{Sys. of Numeration}\\ &= (1\cdot 10^1)10^2 + (3\cdot 10^0)10^2 && \text{Distributive Law}\\ &= 1(10^1\cdot 10^2) + 3(10^0\cdot 10^2) && \text{Assoc. Law Mult.}\\ &= 1\cdot 10^3 + 3\cdot 10^2 && \text{Law of Exponents}\\ 13\cdot 10^2 &= 1\cdot 10^3 + 3\cdot 10^2 && \text{Trans. Prop. of } = \end{aligned}$$

25.
$$\begin{aligned} (3+x)(2+y) &= 3(2+y) + x(2+y) && \text{Distributive Law}\\ &= 3\cdot 2 + 3y + x\cdot 2 + xy && \text{Distributive Law}\\ &= 6 + 3y + x\cdot 2 + xy && \text{Tables}\\ &= 6 + 3y + 2x + xy && \text{Com. Law Mult.} \end{aligned}$$

EXERCISE 6.3

1. No. Zero is neither positive nor negative.

3. Yes. $0 + {}^{-}0 = 0$ by the property of the additive inverse. $0 + {}^{-}0 = {}^{-}0$ by the property of the additive identity. Hence $0 = {}^{-}0$ by the transitive property of equals.

5. ${}^{-}m + m = 0$ by the property of the additive inverse. ${}^{-}m + {}^{-}({}^{-}m) = 0$ by the property of the additive inverse. Then ${}^{-}({}^{-}m) = m$ by the uniqueness of the inverse.

7. ${}^{-}(m + n)$ is the additive inverse of $(m + n)$; also ${}^{-}(m + n) = {}^{-}m + {}^{-}n$.

9. ${}^{-}({}^{-}m) = m$

EXERCISE 6.4a

1.
$$\begin{aligned} 9 + {}^{-}3 &= (6+3) + {}^{-}3 && \text{Tables}\\ &= 6 + (3 + {}^{-}3) && \text{Assoc. Law Add.}\\ &= 6 + 0 && \text{Additive Inverse}\\ &= 6 && \text{Additive Identity} \end{aligned}$$

2.
$$\begin{aligned} {}^{-}7 + 4 &= {}^{-}(3+4) + 4 && \text{Tables}\\ &= ({}^{-}3 + {}^{-}4) + 4 && \text{A-1}\\ &= {}^{-}3 + ({}^{-}4 + 4) && \text{Assoc. Law Add.}\\ &= {}^{-}3 + 0 && \text{Additive Inverse}\\ &= {}^{-}3 && \text{Additive Identity} \end{aligned}$$

4.
$$\begin{aligned} (m+n) + {}^{-}(m+n) &= 0 && \text{Additive Inverse}\\ (m+n) + ({}^{-}m + {}^{-}n) &= m + (n + {}^{-}m) + {}^{-}n && \text{Assoc. Law Add.}\\ &= m + ({}^{-}m + n) + {}^{-}n && \text{Com. Law Add.}\\ &= (m + {}^{-}m) + (n + {}^{-}n) && \text{Assoc. Law Add.}\\ &= 0 + 0 && \text{Additive Inverse}\\ &= 0 && \text{Additive Identity} \end{aligned}$$

Hence ${}^{-}(m + n) = ({}^{-}m + {}^{-}n)$ since the additive inverse is unique.

5. (a) ${}^{-}12$ (c) 3 (e) 0 (g) a (i) ${}^{-}({}^{-}2 + a) = 2 + {}^{-}a$
(k) ${}^{-}({}^{-}3 + 3) = 3 + {}^{-}3 = 0$ (m) $a + b + {}^{-}2$ (o) $a + {}^{-}b + {}^{-}3$

6. (a) ${}^{-}8$ (c) $a + {}^{-}4$ (e) ${}^{-}22$ (g) 8

7. (a)

$3 + n = 10$	Given
$^-3 + 3 + n = {}^-3 + 10$	Uniqueness of Sums
$(^-3 + 3) + n = {}^-3 + 10$	Assoc. Law Add.
$0 + n = {}^-3 + 10$	Additive Inverse
$n = {}^-3 + 10$	Additive Identity
$n = 7$	Addition of Integers

7. (c)

$a + x = b$	Given
$^-a + a + x = {}^-a + b$	Uniqueness of Sums
$(^-a + a) + x = {}^-a + b$	Assoc. Law Add.
$0 + x = {}^-a + b$	Additive Inverse
$x = {}^-a + b$	Additive Identity
$x = b + {}^-a$	Com. Law Add.
$x = b - a$	Defn. of Sub.

9.

$372 - 176 = 372 + {}^-176$	Defn. of Sub.
$= (196 + 176) + {}^-176$	Substitution Prin.
$= 196 + (176 + {}^-176)$	Assoc. Law Add.
$= 196 + 0$	Additive Inverse
$= 196$	Additive Identity
$372 + 176 = 196$	Trans. Prop. of =

11. At 9 in. or 27 in.

13. No. $(12 - 5) - 2 = 7 - 2 = 5; 12 - (5 - 2) = 12 - 3 = 9$

14.

$0 + 0 = 0$	Additive Identity
$m(0 + 0) = m \cdot 0$	Uniqueness of Products
$m \cdot 0 + m \cdot 0 = m \cdot 0$	Distributive Law
$m \cdot 0 + m \cdot 0 + {}^-m \cdot 0 = m \cdot 0 + {}^-m \cdot 0$	Uniqueness of Sums
$m \cdot 0 + (m \cdot 0 + {}^-m \cdot 0) = (m \cdot 0 + {}^-m \cdot 0)$	Assoc. Law Add.
$m \cdot 0 + 0 = 0$	Additive Inverse
$m \cdot 0 = 0$	Additive Identity

EXERCISE 6.4b

3. $(-2)(-3) = (2)(3)$ by M-2

5.

$(-2)(-3)(-4) = [(-2)(-3)](-4)$	Assoc. Law Mult.
$= [(2)(3)](-4)$	M-2
$= (6)(-4)$	Tables
$= -(6)(4)$	M-1
$= -24$	Tables

7.

$(^-3)(^-4 + {}^-5) = (^-3)(^-4) + (^-3)(^-5)$	Distributive Law
$= (3)(4) + (3)(5)$	M-2
$= 12 + 15$	Tables
$= 27$	Addition Algorithm

or

$(^-3)(^-4 + {}^-5) = (^-3)[^-(4 + 5)]$	A-1
$= (^-3)(^-9)$	Tables
$= (3)(9)$	M-2
$= 27$	Tables

8.
$$\begin{aligned} 8(7-3) &= (8)(7+{}^-3) && \text{Defn. of Subtraction}\\ &= (8)(7)+(8)({}^-3) && \text{Distributive Law}\\ &= (8)(7)+{}^-(8)(3) && \text{M-1}\\ &= 56+{}^-24 && \text{Tables}\\ &= (32+24)+{}^-24 && \text{Substitution}\\ &= 32+(24+{}^-24) && \text{Assoc. Law Add.}\\ &= 32+0 && \text{Additive Inverse}\\ &= 32 && \text{Additive Identity} \end{aligned}$$

or

$$\begin{aligned} 8(7-3) &= 8(7+{}^-3) && \text{Defn. of Subtraction}\\ &= 8[(4+3)+{}^-3] && \text{Tables and Substitution}\\ &= 8[4+(3+{}^-3)] && \text{Assoc. Law Add.}\\ &= 8(4+0) && \text{Additive Inverse}\\ &= 8(4) && \text{Additive Identity}\\ &= 32 && \text{Tables} \end{aligned}$$

11.
$$\begin{aligned} {}^-(m-n) &= {}^-(m+{}^-n) && \text{Defn. of Subtraction}\\ &= {}^-m+{}^-({}^-n) && \text{A-1}\\ &= {}^-m+n && \text{I-1}\\ &= n+{}^-m && \text{Com. Law Add.}\\ &= n-m && \text{A-2} \end{aligned}$$

13. M-1
15. See Problem 14, 6.4a

EXERCISE 6.5

1. Either $x = 3$ or $x = 7$. The product $(x - 3)(x - 7) = 0$ if and only if $(x - 3) = 0$, in which case $x = 3$, or $(x - 7) = 0$, in which case $x = 7$.
3. $x \neq 1$. If $x = 1$ is substituted into the expression, we would have $y = \frac{8}{0}$. If the expression $\frac{8}{0}$ is interpreted as division, it would be undefined.
5. Additive Identity; Additive Inverse; Substitution; Associative Law of Addition; Distributive Law; Additive Inverse; $0 \cdot m = 0$ for any m; and Additive Identity.
7. ${}^-({}^-a)$ is the additive inverse of ${}^-a$; ${}^-({}^-a) = a$
9. Yes, if $m \neq 0$
11. Uniqueness of Sums; Associative Law of Addition; Additive Inverse; and Additive Identity.
13. If $a \cdot x = a \cdot y$ and $a \neq 0$, then $x = y$.

EXERCISE 6.6

1. 2, 3, 5, 7, 11, 13, 17, 19, 23, 29, 31, 37, 41, 47
3. 1, 2, 13, 26, 52; primes 2, 13
5. 1, 3, 13, 39; primes 3, 13
7. See section 6.7
9. (a) $2^3 \cdot 3^2$ (b) $2^2 \cdot 89$ (c) 2^9 (d) $2^3 \cdot 5^3$

EXERCISE 6.7

1. 1, 2, 3, 4, 6, 8, 9, 12, 18, 24, 36, 72
3. (a) $2^2 \cdot 3 \cdot 7$ (c) $3 \cdot 5^2 \cdot 13$ (e) $3^4 \cdot 5 \cdot 11$
5. 1, 3, −1, −3
7. $2^3 \cdot 19 \cdot 29$
9. (a) None (c) 2 and 4

EXERCISE 6.9a

1. 6; 18
3. 12; 48
5. 18
7. 3
9. If $n = 0$ then g.c.d. $(p, n) = |p|$. If n is a multiple of p then g.c.d. $(p, n) = |p|$. If $n \neq 0$ and not a multiple of p then g.c.d. $(p, n) = 1$.

EXERCISE 6.9b

1. (a) 6 (c) 18
2. (a) 2 (b) 42
3. (a) Yes (b) Yes (c) Yes
5. (a) 9 (c) 9
7. 1

EXERCISE 6.10

1. (a) 160 (c) 504
2. (a) 252 (c) 672
3. (a) 1 (c) 6 (e) 6 (g) 13 (i) 62 (k) 216
4. (a) 144 (c) 210 (e) 630 (g) 12,220 (i) 14,508 (k) 43,200
5. (a) Yes (b) Yes (c) Yes

EXERCISE 6.11

1. (a) The set A consists of the integers −2, −1, 0, 1, 2, 3, 4, 5. (c) The set C is the set of negative integers. (e) The set 0 is the singleton set $\{0\}$.
2. (a) $\{n | 0 \leqq n \leqq 5\}$ (c) $\{n | -3 < n < 0\}$
3. {(0, 0), (0, 1), (0, 2), (0, 3), (0, 4), (0, 5), (0, 6), (0, 7), (1, 0), (1, 1), (1, 2), (1, 3), (1, 4), (1, 5), (1, 6), (1, 7), (2, 0), (2, 1), (2, 2), (2, 3), (2, 4), (2, 5), (2, 6), (2, 7), (3, 0), (3, 1), (3, 2), (3, 3), (3, 4), (3, 5), (3, 6), (3, 7), (4, 0), (4, 1), (4, 2), (4, 3), (4, 4), (4, 5), (4, 6), (4, 7), (5, 0), (5, 1), (5, 2), (5, 3), (5, 4), (5, 5), (5, 6), (5, 7), (6, 0), (6, 1), (6, 2), (6, 3), (6, 4), (6, 5), (6, 6), (6, 7), (7, 0), (7, 1), (7, 2), (7, 3), (7, 4), (7, 5), (7, 6), (7, 7)}

7	⊙	⊙	⊙	⊙	⊙	⊙	⊙	⊙
6	⊙	⊙	⊙	⊙	⊙	⊙	⊙	⊙
5	⊙	⊙	⊙	⊙	⊙	⊙	⊙	⊙
4	⊙	⊙	⊙	⊙	⊙	⊙	⊙	⊙
3	⊙	⊙	⊙	⊙	⊙	⊙	⊙	⊙
2	⊙	⊙	⊙	⊙	⊙	⊙	⊙	⊙
1	⊙	⊙	⊙	⊙	⊙	⊙	⊙	⊙
0	⊙	⊙	⊙	⊙	⊙	⊙	⊙	⊙
	0	1	2	3	4	5	6	7

5. $N \times N = \{(m, n) | m > 0 \text{ and } n > 0\}$. $N \times N$ is the set of all ordered positive integers.

7. No; Yes, 1

9. Yes, -1

11. $a < b$ if and only if $b - a > 0$. We must use this fact to show that $(b + c) - (a + c) > 0$ or that $a + c < b + c$. But $(b + c) - (a + c) = b + c + {}^-a + {}^-c = b + {}^-a + c + {}^-c = b + {}^-a + 0 = b + {}^-a = b - a > 0$. That is, $(b + c) - (a + c) > 0$, so $a + c < b + c$.

13. If $a < b$ then $b - a > 0$. If $c < 0$ then $0 - c = -c > 0$. $-c(b - a) > 0$ since the product of two positive integers is positive. But $-c(b - a) = {}^-c(b + {}^-a) = -cb + ca = ca - cb > 0$, which means $ca > cb$.

15. 15

17. $\dfrac{10 \cdot 11}{2} = 55$

19. $\dfrac{50 \cdot 51}{2} = 1275$

21. 9

23. 25

25. Each is the square of the number of terms in the indicated sum, and each differs from the next by the $(n + 1)st$ term of the sum.

27. $11^2 = 121$

28. $1 + 3 + 5 + 7 + \ldots + (2n - 1) = n^2$, where n is the number of terms in the sum.

EXERCISE 6.12

1. (a) $-4, -3, -2, -1, 0, 1, 2, 3, 4$ (c) $-1, 0, 1, 2, 3, 4$

2. (a)

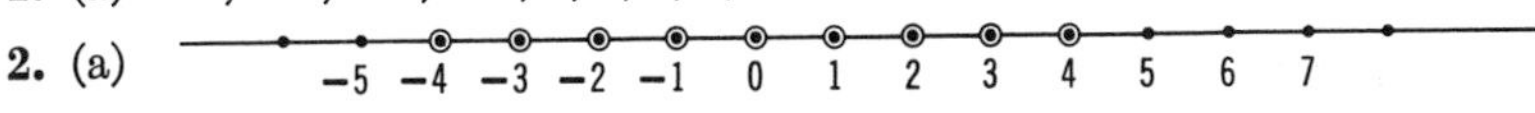

(c)

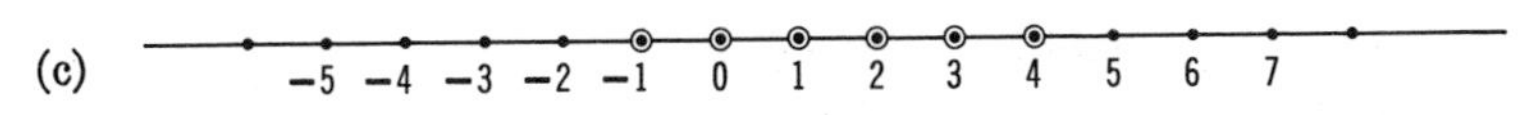

3. (a) $-3, -2, -1, 0, 1, 2, 3$ (c) $-1, 0, 1$ (e) 4, 8

4. (a) −5 −4 −3 −2 −1 0 1 2 3 4 5 6

(c) −5 −4 −3 −2 −1 0 1 2 3 4 5 6

(e) −5 −4 −3 −2 −1 0 1 2 3 4 5 6 7 8 9

5. (a) $|3 - 9|$
6. (a) $|4 - n|$
7. 4; 10
9. Not necessarily

EXERCISE 6.13

1. (a) 6:00 A.M. (c) 8:00 A.M.
2. (a) 2 (c) 11
3. (a) 7:00 A.M. (c) 11:00 A.M.

EXERCISE 6.14a

2. (a) [4] (c) [4] (e) [6]

EXERCISE 6.14c

3. Not in general; $[4]\cdot[x] = [3]$ has no solution.
4. (a) $[x] = [0]$ or $[x] = [6]$ (c) $[x] = [1]$ or $[5]$ or $[9]$
5. No, e.g., $[3]\cdot[4] = [0]$

7.

+	[0]	[1]	[2]
[0]	[0]	[1]	[2]
[1]	[1]	[2]	[0]
[2]	[2]	[0]	[1]

·	[1]	[2]
[1]	[1]	[2]
[2]	[2]	[1]

9. [1]
11. 210; 87,780
13. $a - b = 0$; cannot divide by 0

EXERCISE 7.2

1. (a) ordinal (b) cardinal (c) ordinal
3. 0 is the additive identity, i.e., $0 + a = a$
1 is the multiplicative identity, i.e., $1\cdot a = a$

EXERCISE 7.4

1. (a) $\frac{-2}{-3}, \frac{-4}{-6}, \frac{-6}{-9}, \frac{2}{3}, \frac{4}{6}, \frac{6}{9}$, etc. (c) $\frac{-2}{-2}, \frac{-1}{-1}, \frac{1}{1}, \frac{2}{2}, \frac{3}{3}$, etc.

   (e) $\frac{-34}{38}, \frac{-17}{19}, \frac{34}{-38}, \frac{51}{-57}, \frac{68}{-76}$, etc. (g) $\frac{-18}{-2}, \frac{-9}{-1}, \frac{18}{2}, \frac{27}{3}, \frac{36}{4}$, etc.

   (i) $\frac{-9}{-12}, \frac{-6}{-8}, \frac{-3}{-4}, \frac{6}{8}, \frac{9}{12}$, etc. (k) $\frac{-8}{12}, \frac{-4}{6}, \frac{8}{-12}, \frac{12}{-18}, \frac{16}{-24}$, etc.

2. First and third; fourth and fifth

3. $\frac{33}{29} \doteq \frac{2\cdot 33}{2\cdot 29}$

4. (a) $(-2)(-3) = (2)(3)$ (c) $(-5)(-6) = -(5)(6) = -30$; $(3)(10) = 30$
   (e) $(0)(6) = 0$; $(7)(0) = 0$ (g) $(0)(1) = 0$; $(-1)(0) = 0$

5. (a) $\frac{1982}{43{,}629}$ (c) $\frac{2}{7}$

6. (a) What number multiplied by 3 and added to 1 yields a sum of 7?
   (c) What is the number which when multiplied by 3 and added to 1 gives 10?

7.

$$\begin{array}{cccccccc}
\ldots, & -39, & -26, & -13, & 0, & 13, & 26, & \ldots \\
\ldots, & -38, & -25, & -12, & 1, & 14, & 27, & \ldots \\
\ldots, & -37, & -24, & -11, & 2, & 15, & 28, & \ldots \\
\ldots, & -36, & -23, & -10, & 3, & 16, & 29, & \ldots \\
\ldots, & -35, & -22, & -9, & 4, & 17, & 30, & \ldots \\
\ldots, & -34, & -21, & -8, & 5, & 18, & 31, & \ldots \\
\ldots, & -33, & -20, & -7, & 6, & 19, & 32, & \ldots \\
\ldots, & -32, & -19, & -6, & 7, & 20, & 33, & \ldots \\
\ldots, & -31, & -18, & -5, & 8, & 21, & 34, & \ldots \\
\ldots, & -30, & -17, & -4, & 9, & 22, & 35, & \ldots \\
\ldots, & -29, & -16, & -3, & 10, & 23, & 36, & \ldots \\
\ldots, & -28, & -15, & -2, & 11, & 24, & 37, & \ldots \\
\ldots, & -27, & -14, & -1, & 12, & 25, & 38, & \ldots
\end{array}$$

EXERCISE 7.5

1. If $a/b \doteq c/d$, then $ad = bc$; but if $ad = bc$, then $bc = ad$ by the symmetric property of equals and $cb = da$ by the Commutative Law of multiplication; then $cb = da$ implies $c/d \doteq a/b$ by the definition of $\doteq$.

3. (a) $\left[\frac{2}{3}\right]$ (c) $\left[\frac{19}{2}\right]$ (e) $\left[\frac{0}{1}\right]$

4. (a) $\left[\frac{-1}{2}\right]$ (c) $\left[\frac{-2}{3}\right]$ (e) $\left[\frac{0}{1}\right]$ (g) $\left[\frac{-2}{3}\right]$ (i) $\left[\frac{4}{5}\right]$ (k) $\left[\frac{-4}{1}\right]$

5. (a) $\frac{2}{3} \doteq \frac{2\cdot 2}{2\cdot 3}$ since $2(2\cdot 3) = 2\cdot 6 = 12$ and $3(2\cdot 2) = 3\cdot 4 = 12$

(c) $\frac{m}{n} \doteq \frac{2m}{2n}$ since $m(2n) = (m\cdot 2)n = (2m)n = 2(mn)$ and $n(2m) = (n\cdot 2)m = (2n)m = 2(nm) = 2(mn)$

7. The two classes are equal (set equality).

9. The class to which 6/6 belongs is the same class as the one to which $-3/-3$ belongs.

EXERCISE 7.7

1. a, b, c, and d are integers; $ad + bc$ is an integer since the system of integers is closed under addition and multiplication; bd is also an integer; $bd \neq 0$ since $b \neq 0$ and $d \neq 0$; hence $(ad + bc)/bd$ is an ordered pair of integers.

3. $\frac{-3}{-4} + \frac{1}{6} = \frac{-18 - 4}{-24} = \frac{-22}{-24} = \frac{(-2)(11)}{(-2)(12)} \doteq \frac{11}{12}$

5. The class of $\frac{3}{4} + \frac{1}{6}$ is the same as the class of $\frac{3\cdot 6 + 4\cdot 1}{4\cdot 6}$.

6. (a) $\frac{2}{3}$ (c) $\frac{0}{1}$

7. (a) $\frac{131}{72}$

9. $\left[\frac{m}{1}\right] + \left[\frac{n}{1}\right] = \left[\frac{m+n}{1}\right]$; $\frac{m+n}{1}$ corresponds to the integer $m + n$.

EXERCISE 7.8

1. $\frac{14}{27}$

3. $\frac{1}{1}$

5. (a) $\left(\frac{7}{7}\right)\left(\frac{5}{7}\right)$ (b) $\left(\frac{3}{3}\right)\left(\frac{11}{13}\right)$

7. $\left[\frac{m}{1}\right] \cdot \left[\frac{n}{1}\right] = \left[\frac{m\cdot n}{1\cdot 1}\right] = \left[\frac{m\cdot n}{1}\right]$ which corresponds to $m\cdot n$

8. (a) $\frac{80}{63}$ (c) $\frac{4}{3}$ (e) $\frac{7}{1}$ (g) $\frac{0}{1}$ (i) $\frac{4}{9}$ (k) $\frac{355{,}630{,}706{,}103}{4{,}031{,}419{,}203{,}605}$

9. (a) $\frac{4}{5}$ (c) $\frac{1}{1}$ (e) $\frac{7}{6}$ (g) $\frac{8}{1}$ (i) $\frac{7}{1}$ (k) $\frac{1{,}167{,}543{,}234}{4{,}031{,}419{,}203{,}605}$

10. (a) Any member of the class containing $\frac{6}{8}$ added to any member of the class containing $\frac{4}{8}$ gives a sum which is in the class $\frac{5}{4}$.

11. (a) Any member from the class containing $\frac{9}{18}$ multiplied by any member from the class containing $\frac{6}{3}$ gives a product which is a member of the class containing $\frac{1}{1}$.

12. (a) e.g., $\frac{2}{3} + \frac{2}{5} = \frac{2\cdot5 + 3\cdot2}{3\cdot5} = \frac{10+6}{15} = \frac{16}{15}$;

$$\frac{2}{5} + \frac{2}{3} = \frac{2\cdot3 + 5\cdot2}{5\cdot3} = \frac{6+10}{15} = \frac{16}{15}; \text{ hence } \frac{2}{3} + \frac{2}{5} = \frac{2}{5} + \frac{2}{3}.$$

13. (a) e.g., $\frac{2}{3} \cdot \frac{3}{5} = \frac{2\cdot3}{3\cdot5} = \frac{6}{15}; \frac{3}{5} \cdot \frac{2}{3} = \frac{3\cdot2}{5\cdot3} = \frac{6}{15}$; hence $\frac{2}{3} \cdot \frac{3}{5} = \frac{3}{5} \cdot \frac{2}{3}$.

14. (a) $\left[\frac{395}{84}\right]$

15. (a) $\left[\frac{64}{15}\right]$

16. (a) $\left[\frac{1}{1}\right]$

17. (a) $\frac{30{,}150{,}837{,}407{,}444}{5{,}954{,}621{,}431{,}472}$

EXERCISE 7.9

1. $\frac{1}{2}$

3. $\frac{40{,}816}{688{,}527}$

5. $\frac{81}{104}$

7. $\frac{13}{18}$

9. $-\frac{2}{3}$

11. $\frac{0}{1}$

EXERCISE 7.10

3. (a) $\frac{29}{10}$ (c) $\frac{275}{68}$ (e) $\frac{8}{1}$

6. (a) $\frac{0}{1}$ (c) $\frac{1}{5}$

EXERCISE 7.10a

3. Yes

4. (a) $\frac{a}{b} + \frac{c}{d} = \frac{a \cdot d + b \cdot c}{b \cdot d}$ Defn. of Add. for Ratl. Nos.

$= \frac{d \cdot a + c \cdot b}{d \cdot b}$ Com. Law for Mult. of Integers

$= \frac{c \cdot b + d \cdot a}{d \cdot b}$ Com. Law for Add. of Integers

$= \frac{c}{d} + \frac{a}{b}$ Defn. of Add. for Ratl. Nos.

$\frac{a}{b} + \frac{c}{d} = \frac{c}{d} + \frac{a}{b}$ Transitive Prop. of Equals

(b) $\frac{a}{b} \cdot \frac{c}{d} = \frac{a \cdot c}{b \cdot d}$ Defn. of Mult. for Ratl. Nos.

$= \frac{c \cdot a}{d \cdot b}$ Com. Law for Mult. of Integers

$= \frac{c}{d} \cdot \frac{a}{b}$ Defn. of Mult. for Ratl. Nos.

$\frac{a}{b} \cdot \frac{c}{d} = \frac{c}{d} \cdot \frac{a}{b}$ Transitive Prop. of Equals

(c) $\frac{a}{b} \cdot \left(\frac{c}{d} + \frac{e}{f}\right) = \frac{a}{b} \cdot \left(\frac{cf + de}{df}\right)$ Defn. of Add.

$= \frac{a(cf + de)}{b(df)}$ Defn. of Mult.

$= \frac{a(cf) + a(de)}{b(df)}$ Dist. Law for Integers

$= \frac{a(cf) + a(de)}{b(df)} \cdot \frac{b}{b}$ Mult. by the Identity

$= \frac{[a(cf) + a(de)] \cdot b}{[b(df)] \cdot b}$ Defn. of Mult.

$= \frac{[a(cf)] \cdot b + [a(de)] \cdot b}{[b(df)] \cdot b}$ Dist. Law for Integers

$= \frac{(ac)(bf) + (bd)(ae)}{(bd)(bf)}$ Assoc. and Com. Laws for Mult. of Integers

$= \frac{ac}{bd} + \frac{ae}{bf}$ Defn. of Add.

$= \frac{a}{b} \cdot \frac{c}{d} + \frac{a}{b} \cdot \frac{e}{f}$ Defn. of Mult.

$\frac{a}{b} \cdot \left(\frac{c}{d} + \frac{e}{f}\right) = \frac{a}{b} \cdot \frac{c}{d} + \frac{a}{b} \cdot \frac{e}{f}$ Trans. Prop. of Equals

6. Cancellation Law for multiplication of rational numbers:

If $\frac{a}{b} \cdot \frac{c}{d} = \frac{a}{b} \cdot \frac{e}{f}$, then $\frac{c}{d} = \frac{e}{f}$.

Proof:

$\frac{a}{b} \cdot \frac{c}{d} = \frac{a}{b} \cdot \frac{e}{f}$	Hypothesis
$\frac{b}{a} \cdot \left(\frac{a}{b} \cdot \frac{c}{d}\right) = \frac{b}{a} \cdot \left(\frac{a}{b} \cdot \frac{e}{f}\right)$	Uniqueness of Products
$\left(\frac{b}{a} \cdot \frac{a}{b}\right) \cdot \frac{c}{d} = \left(\frac{b}{a} \cdot \frac{a}{b}\right) \cdot \frac{e}{f}$	Assoc. Law Mult.
$\frac{1}{1} \cdot \frac{c}{d} = \frac{1}{1} \cdot \frac{e}{f}$	Multiplicative Inverse
$\frac{c}{d} = \frac{e}{f}$	Multiplicative Identity

EXERCISE 7.11b

1. (a) $\frac{8}{9}$ (c) $\frac{10}{3}$
2. (a) $\frac{10}{9}$ (c) $\frac{49}{16}$
3. (a) $\frac{3}{2}$ (c) $\frac{5}{1}$ (e) $\frac{1}{31}$
4. (a) $-\frac{4}{5}$ (c) $-\frac{3}{4} - \frac{2}{3} = -\frac{1}{12}$
6. (a) $\frac{2}{49}$ (c) $\frac{1}{1}$ (e) $\frac{1}{10}$
7. (a) $\frac{14}{9}$ (c) $\frac{2}{5}$

EXERCISE 7.11c

2. (a) $\frac{17}{12}$ or $1\frac{5}{12}$ (c) $\frac{87}{40}$ or $2\frac{7}{40}$
6. (a) $\frac{85}{161}$ (c) $\frac{34}{39}$ (e) $\frac{8}{23}$
7. $\frac{76}{63}$
8. (a) $\frac{1827}{50}$
9. (a) $\frac{5}{3}$ (c) $\frac{7}{2}$ (e) $\frac{29}{16}$

EXERCISE 7.11d

4. 15
5. $2000
7. 40 ft
9. 40 ft

EXERCISE 7.11e

1. (a) 32% (c) 75% (e) 16% (g) 24%
2. (a) $\frac{1}{4}$ (c) $\frac{2}{5}$ (e) $\frac{5}{4}$ (g) $\frac{4}{1}$
3. (a) 12 (c) 12.5% (e) 400

EXERCISE 7.12a

1. (a) $\dfrac{32}{51} - \dfrac{3}{5} = \dfrac{32\cdot 5 - 51\cdot 3}{5\cdot 51} = \dfrac{160 - 153}{255} = \dfrac{7}{255} > 0$; hence $\dfrac{3}{5} < \dfrac{32}{51}$.

2. (a) $\dfrac{2}{3} - \dfrac{-2}{3} = \dfrac{2\cdot 3 - 3(-2)}{3\cdot 3} = \dfrac{6 + 6}{9} = \dfrac{12}{9} > 0$; hence $\dfrac{-2}{3} < \dfrac{2}{3}$.

3. $\dfrac{1}{a} > \dfrac{1}{b}$

5. (a) $-2, -1, 0, 1, 2, 3, 4, 5$ (c) $-4 < x \leqq 3$

EXERCISE 7.12b

1. (a) $-3, -2, -1, 0, 1, 2, 3$ (c) $-8, -7, -6, -5, -4, -3, -2$
2. (a) 1

EXERCISE 7.12c

4. No. The rational numbers are dense.
6. Yes
8. $1/2^{n+1}$
10. No
12. -6
14. $\frac{7}{1}$
17. (a) 10 (c) 0

EXERCISE 8.2

1. $\frac{6449}{4560} \cong 1.4142$; $(2 - \frac{57}{40})^2 \cong 0.0306$; $(2 - \frac{6449}{4560})^2 \cong 0.000115$
3. 1st approx. 17; 2nd approx. 17.32; 3rd approx. 17.320508
5. 1st approx. 1.4; 2nd approx. 1.414; 3rd approx. 1.4142136

EXERCISE 8.2a

1. Assume $5 + \sqrt{2} = p/q$, where p/q is a rational number. Then $\sqrt{2} = p/q - 5 = (p - 5q)/q$. But $(p - 5q)/q$ is a rational number and $\sqrt{2}$ is not rational. Hence the assumption is false and $5 + \sqrt{2}$ is irrational.
3. $2; -1$
5. (a) e.g., 17, 20, 25 (c) e.g., 2, 10, $\sqrt{2}$
7. Circle with radius $\sqrt{2}$ or $\sqrt{5}$, etc.

EXERCISE 8.4

1. (a) $\frac{32}{100}$ (c) $\frac{79}{1000}$
2. (a) 0.32 (c) 0.079
3. (a) $7\cdot10^2 + 0\cdot10^1 + 0\cdot10^0 + 1\cdot10^{-1} + 2\cdot10^{-2} + 5\cdot10^{-3}$
   (c) $1\cdot10^4 + 0\cdot10^3 + 0\cdot10^2 + 0\cdot10^1 + 0\cdot10^0 + 0\cdot10^{-1}$
   $+ 0\cdot10^{-2} + 0\cdot10^{-3} + 1\cdot10^{-4}$
   (e) $3\cdot10^0 + 1\cdot10^{-1} + 4\cdot10^{-2} + 1\cdot10^{-3} + 6\cdot10^{-4}$
4. (a) 55.731984 (c) 0.1771 (e) 200,202.04 or 200,000 to one significant digit.
5. (a) $(2.99776)(1.673)(10^{-14}) \cong (5.015)(10^{-14})$
   (c) $(6.0228)(1.673)(10^{-1}) \cong 1.008$ (e) $(6.45 \div 2.4)(10^{-8}) \cong (2.7)(10^{-8})$
7. π units
8. (*Hint:* $\widehat{AB} = \widehat{AB'}$, hence $\angle BOA = \angle B'O'A$. Since $OB \| C'O'$, $\angle BOA = \angle AO'C$. $\angle B'O'C' = 2(\angle AOB)$.)

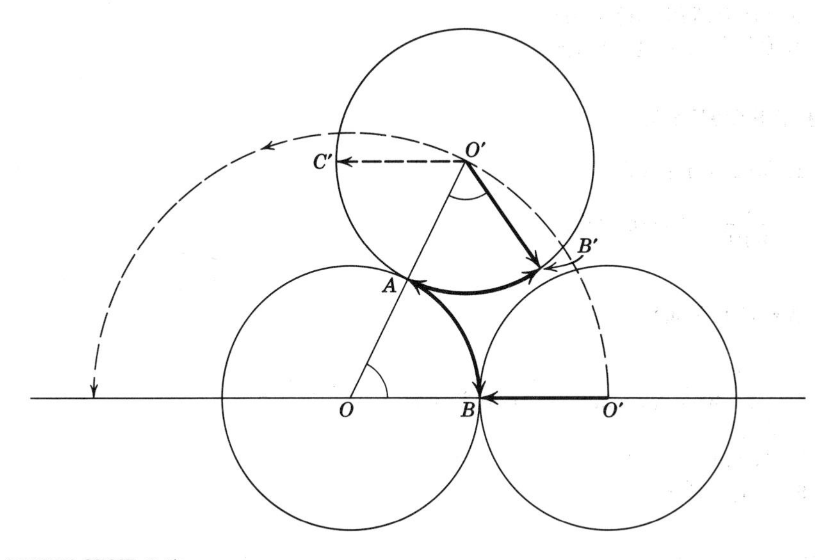

EXERCISE 8.5

1 $\frac{1}{2} = 0.5$; $\frac{1}{4} = 0.25$; $\frac{1}{8} = 0.125$; $\frac{1}{16} = 0.0625$; $\frac{1}{5} = 0.2$; $\frac{2}{5} = 0.4$; $\frac{3}{5} = 0.6$; $\frac{4}{5} = 0.8$; $\frac{5}{5} = 1.0$; $\frac{1}{10} = 0.1$; etc.
3. (a) 1,006,764 (b) 1,007,578.06 (c) 814.06
5. Use more subdivisions.

EXERCISE 8.6

1. $3.33
3. 6
5. 0.1428571429; 0.0909090909

EXERCISE 8.8

1. 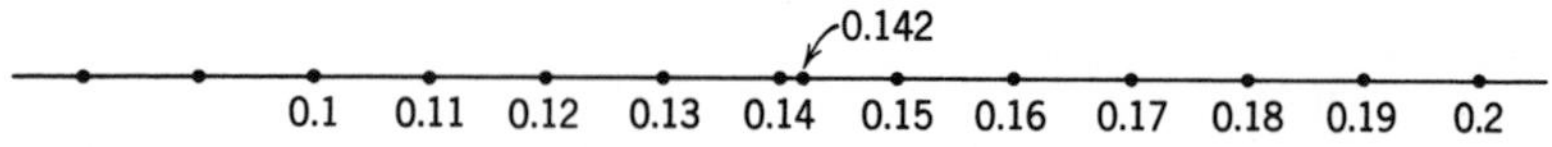

3. 1.41425; (table) 1.41421
5. $3.141\overline{60}\ldots$; $3.141\overline{6}\ldots$; $3.141\overline{592}\ldots$; table value of π to 15 places: $3.141592653589793\ldots$

EXERCISE 8.11

1. (a) $\{0, 1, 2, 3, 4, 5, 6, 7, 8, 9, 10\}$ (c) $0.\overline{18}\ldots$
2. (a) 12 (c) $0.1\overline{6}\ldots$
3. (a) 13 (c) $0.\overline{153846}\ldots$
4. (a) $\frac{1772}{9999}$ (c) $\frac{2906}{9900} = \frac{1453}{4950}$
5. (a) 0.1772 (c) 0.2935
6. (a) 5 (c) $\frac{9}{999}$ or $\frac{1}{111}$

EXERCISE 8.13

1. $3.14 = \pi \pm 0.01$
3. $\dfrac{1}{3 \cdot 10^7}$ or $0.00000003\ldots$

EXERCISE 8.14

1. Yes
3. sum: $2\sqrt{a}$; product: $a - b$; difference: $2\sqrt{b}$
5. 0.7071
7. 0.5720
9. 1; 1; 5.8284

EXERCISE 8.14a

1. 22.412
3. 31.6228
5. 0.7087

EXERCISE 8.14b

1. 1.7320508
3. 54.772256
5. 7.0710678
7. 1.843909

EXERCISE 9.2

1. $l_2 = AC + CB$; $l_4 = AD + DC + CE + EB$; $AC \leqq AD + DC$ and $CB \leqq CE + EB$ by the triangular inequality. Hence $AC + CB \leqq AD + DC + CE + EB$ and $l_2 \leqq l_4$.
2. $l_{2^n} = 2^n \cdot AC$, where AC is the length of $\overline{AC}$, one of the equal line segments of the polygonal path of length l_{2^n}. Let B denote the midpoint of $\widehat{AC}$. Then $AC \leqq AB + BC$ by the triangular inequality. Hence $2^n \cdot AC \leqq 2^n(AB + BC)$. But $l_{2^{n+1}} = 2^{n+1}(AB) = 2^n[2(ab)] = 2^n(AB + BC)$. Hence $l_{2^n} \leqq l_{2^{n+1}}$.
3. 4.59 (Compare with arc length of approx. 4.71, using $\frac{22}{7}$ as an approximation to π.)
6. $\dfrac{3\pi}{2}$

EXERCISE 9.3

1. (a) 10 sq in. (c) 28 sq yd (e) 65 sq ft
2. (a) 12 sq ft (c) 80 sq cm (e) 105 sq cm
3. (a) 15,000 sq ft (c) 11,250 sq ft
5. (a) 20 sq in. (c) 30 sq ft
6. $(1.414)(1.732) \cong 2.449$

EXERCISE 9.4

1. (a) 240 cu in.; 256 sq in. (c) 22.5 cu ft; 54 sq ft
2. (a) 114 sq in.; 84 sq in.; 72 cu in. (c) 96 sq ft; 60 sq ft; 48 cu ft (e) 156 sq units; 126 sq units; 84 cu units
3. (a) $\frac{792}{7}$ sq in.; $\frac{792}{7}$ cu in. (c) 2464 sq in.; $\frac{34496}{3}$ cu in.

EXERCISE 9.5

1. 37.5 ft
3. $166\frac{2}{3}$ yds
5. 2
7. ab

EXERCISE 9.6

1. (a) 2 sq in.
2. (a) $150\sqrt{3}$ sq in.
3. (a) $75\sqrt{3}$ sq in.
4. (a) 160 sq units
5. (a) 162 sq units

EXERCISE 9.7

3. $b \cong 0.195$; $\pi \cong 16(0.195) = 3.12$
5. Third approximation to π: 3.1056

EXERCISE 9.8

1. $J \times J = \{(m, n) | m \text{ and } n \text{ are integers.}\}$

3. (a)

4. (a)

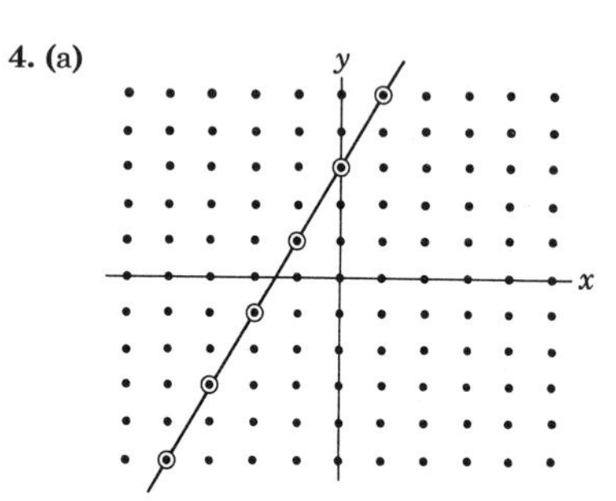

4. (c)

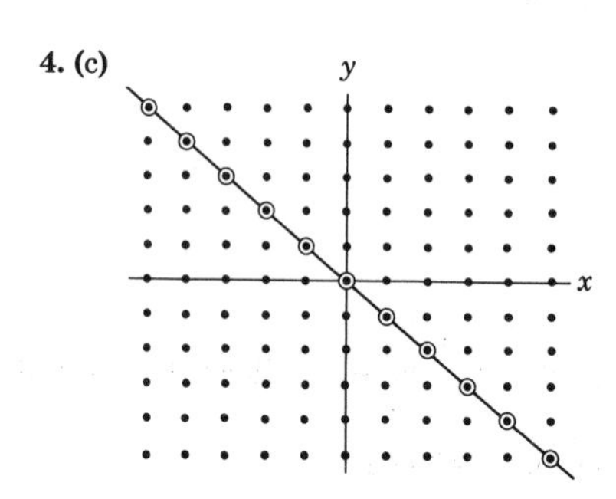

5. (a)

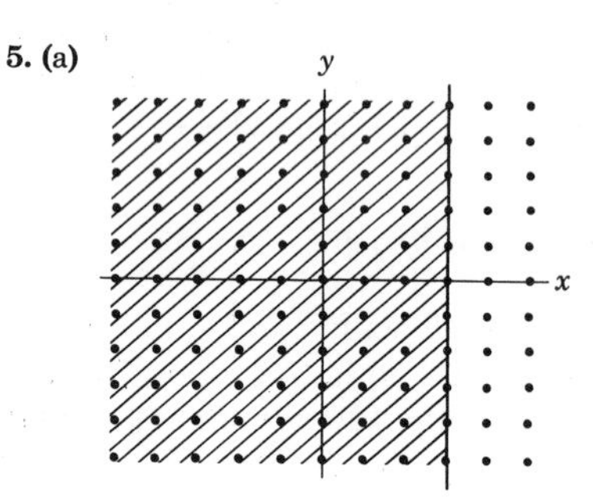

5. (c)

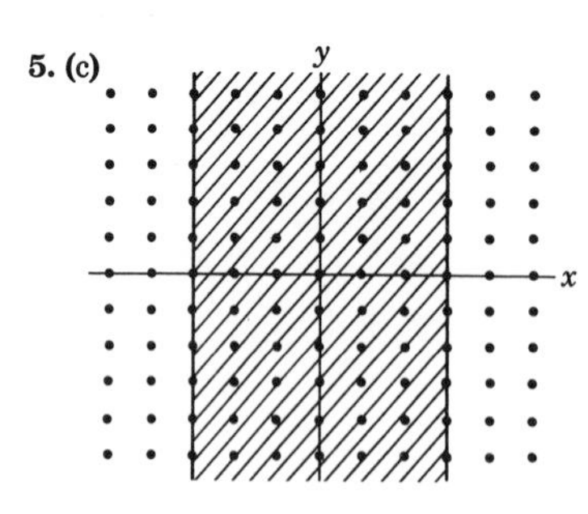

(e)

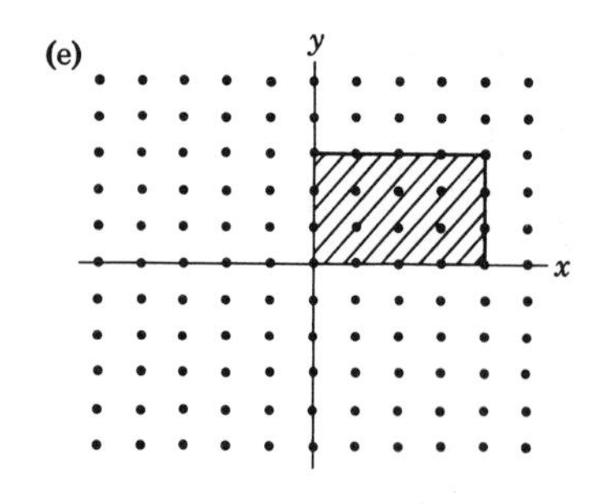

EXERCISE 9.8b

1. (a) 13 (b) 13 (d) $x^2 + y^2 = 13^2$
2. (a) $x^2 + y^2 = r^2$
3. (a) 7 (b) $|x| + |y|$

Index

Abacists, 18
Abacus, 14
Absolute value, 140, 186, 219
Addition:
  as a binary operation, 86
  in J_{12}, 145
  in J_2, 149
  of decimal fractions, 202
  of integers, 116
  of rational numbers, 159
  of whole numbers, 89
Additive:
  identity, 90, 98, 116, 147, 166, 171
  inverse, 114, 116, 147, 167, 172
  principle, 4
  systems, 4
Algorists, 18
Algorithm, 18, 100
  addition, 101
  multiplication, 103
  square root, 220
Allowable error, 206
Apothem, 258
Approximations, 195, 223
  denseness, 189
  using decimal fractions, 206, 208
Area, 231
  properties of, 232
Arithmetic mean, 195
Associative Law, 91
  addition, 91, 99, 116, 171
  multiplication, 94, 99, 116, 171
Average, 195, 223

Babylonian system, 12
Barn, 193
Base, 3, 59
  changing, 66
  computation in other bases, 69
  counting in other bases, 68
  other bases, 12, 13, 64, 66
  percent, 182
Between-ness, 139, 187
Binary number system, 68
Binary operation, 86
  addition, 86
  definition, 87
  multiplication, 92
Bound:
  greatest lower, 108, 200, 229
  least upper, 108, 200, 208, 229
  lower, 108, 200, 208
  on errors, 217
  upper, 108, 200, 208

Cancellation laws, 122
Cardinal number, 50, 82
Cardinal use, 82

Carry, in addition, 101, 102
Cartesian product, 32, 39, 53
  pictorial representation, 34
  relations as, 55
Chinese-Japanese system, 10
Classes, equivalence, 47
  (mod 12), 145
  ordered pairs of integers, 157
Clock arithmetic, 142
Closure Law, 88
  property of positive integers, 115
  system of integers, 116
  system of rational numbers, 171
  system of whole numbers, 99
Columnwise addition, 101, 104
Common divisor, 127
Commutative law, 90
  of addition, 90, 116, 171
  of multiplication, 93, 116, 171
Complement, 31
Completeness, 194, 211, 229
  definition of, 200
Complex numbers, 154, 220
Component of ordered pairs, 33
Composite number, 125
Computation, 87
  decimal fraction, 202
  in other bases, 69
Cone, 242
Congruence relation, 143
  definition of, 144
  (mod 12), 145
  (mod 2), 148
Coordinate geometry, 264
Correspondence:
  many-to-many, 181
  one-to-one, 45, 49, 50, 107, 187
Counter, 14
Counting, 49
  finger, 64
  other bases for, 64
Counting board, 14
Cylinder, 242

Decimal:
  fractions, 201
  point, 11, 61, 201
  system of numeration, 10
Decimal approximations, 206
  of irrational numbers, 216
  of rational numbers, 208
Decimals:
  infinite, 209
  repeating, 212
  rounding off, 215
  terminating, 212
Denominator, 154, 177
Denseness, 188, 194
  of decimal fractions, 210
Difference, 119
Digital computer, 18
Digits, 10
  Hindu-Arabic, 60
Disjoint, 26, 29
Distance, 140, 187
  in the plane, 267
  number line, 139
  properties of, 140
Distributive Law, 96, 98, 101, 103
  in the system of integers, 116
  in the system of rational numbers, 171
  in the system of whole numbers, 100
Divide and average method of approximating square roots, 223
Divides relation, 43, 56
  definition of, 43
Divisibility, 126
Division:
  in base *5*, 72
  in base *2*, 75
  of decimal fractions, 204
  of fractions, 174
Division algorithm, 128, 130
Division interpretation of number pairs, 151, 174
Divisor, 124
  common, 127
  proper, 124
Domain, 53
Doubling and summing, 105
Duo-decimal, 68, 78

Egyptian hieroglyphic, 4
Elementary facts, 70
  base *12*, 78, 79
  of addition, 89
  of multiplication, 93
Element:
  of a mathematical system, 151
  of J_{12}, 146
  of sets, 21
Empty set, 26

Equals, 22, 52
 as subset of Cartesian product, 55
 for numbers, 86, 87
 for ordered pairs, 33
 for rational numbers, 155
 for sets, 41, 42
Equivalence classes, 47, 81
 of ordered pairs of integers, 157
 of the congruence relation, 145, 148
Equivalence relation, 46, 47, 81, 156
 congruence relation, 144
 for ordered pairs of integers, 155
Equivalent rate pairs, 181
Equivalent sets, 46
Error, 206, 208, 215, 217
Estimates, 195
Euclidean algorithm, 131
Euclidean plane, 265
Expanded form, 61, 62, 65
Exponents, 59

Factor, 124
 proper factor, 124
Finger counting, 64
Finite, set, 50, 82
 decimal, 212
Fraction, 151, 176
Function, 54
Fundamental Theorem of Arithmetic, 126

Geometry, 226
Greatest common divisor, 128, 164
 as a binary operation, 132
 properties of, 132
 using division algorithm, 130
 using prime factorization, 129
Greatest lower bound, 108, 200, 229

Halving and doubling, 106
Hieroglyphic, 4
Hindu-Arabic, 11, 60

Identities:
 additive identity, 90, 98, 116, 147, 166, 171
 multiplicative identity, 93, 98, 116, 148, 167, 172
Inclusion, 25, 38
Incommensurable quantities, 190, 194

Indent, 104
Inductive property, 84
Inequalities, 54
 in the integers, 136
 in the rationals, 184
 in the whole numbers, 107
 properties of, 137
Infinite, set, 50, 82
 decimal, 209, 214
Integers:
 as a subsystem of rational numbers, 172
 negative, 114
 properties of, 114
 set of, 113, 114
 system of, 112
Interpretation of number pairs, 151, 173
Intersection of sets, 29
Inverses:
 additive, 114, 116, 147, 167, 172
 multiplicative, 148, 169, 172
 of a relation, 53
Ionic-Greek, 8
Irrationality of $\sqrt{2}$, 191
Irrational numbers, 189
 as infinite nonrepeating decimals, 214
Iterative process, 223

Least common denominator, 159
Least common multiple, 124
 as a binary operation, 135
Least upper bound, 108, 200, 229
Leibnitz, Gottfried Wilhelm, 223
Length, 226
Less than, 107, 136, 185
Lower bound, 108

Many-to-many correspondence, 181
Matching relation, 46, 81
Mayan, 12
Measure, 193, 227, 232
Measurements, 193
Megaton, 193
Multiple of, 148
Multiplication:
 algorithm, 103
 in J_{12}, 147
 of decimal fractions, 203
 of integers, 120
 of rational numbers, 162
 of whole numbers, 92

Multiplicative:
identity, 93, 98, 116, 148, 167, 172
inverse, 148, 169, 172
principle, 7
systems, 9

Names of sets, 154
Natural numbers, 81, 82, 114
set of, 23, 43, 84
Negative:
integers, 114
rational numbers, 185
real numbers, 211
Newton, Sir Isaac, 223
Newton's method, 223
Nim, 75
Nonnumber, 193
Number, 1, 49, 81, 84, 91, 94
Number blindness, 81
Number line, 138, 187, 194, 209
Number pairs, 151
Number systems, 85
Numeral 1, 81
Numerator, 154, 177

One, special properties of, 98
One-to-one correspondence, 45, 49, 50, 107, 187
Operations, 85
binary, 86
Order, 54
in the integers, 136
in the rational numbers, 184
in the real numbers, 210
in the whole numbers, 107
Ordered pairs, 33
operations on, 86, 87, 89, 93
rational numbers as, 153, 154, 155, 157
relations as, 53
Ordering, 7
Ordinal, 82

Pairing, 25, 52, 53
Parallelepiped, 240
Parallelogram, 234
Partition of a set, 48
Percent, 182
Perfect squares, 218
Periods, 62
Permutation, 45
Pi, 256, 257
calculation of, 258
Pi, chronology of, 262
existence of, 256
Place, 64, 220
Place-value systems of numeration, 10, 60
Point sets in the plane, 267
Polygons, regular, 236
Polyhedra, regular, 243
Positive:
integers, 114, 115
rational numbers, 184, 185
reals, 211
Power, of the base, 59
Prime, 125
divisors, 124
factorization, 125, 129, 134
numbers, 124
Prism, 240
Properties of:
absolute value, 140
area, 232
congruence relation, 144
denseness, 187
distance, 140
equals, 87
greatest common divisor, 132
inequalities, 137
positive integers, 115
positive rationals, 185
sameness relation, 42
relations, 37
Pyramid, 242
Pythagorean theorem, 190, 250

Quinary, 64
Quinary arithmetic, 69

Range of a relation, 53
Rate pair, 151
percent, 182
ratio, 180
Ratio, 180
Rational numbers, 151
set of, 171
Real line, 209
Real numbers, 209
Reciprocal, 169
Reduced form, 164
Reducing fractions, 164
Reflexive property, 39, 44, 46, 56, 144, 156

Regular, polyhedra, 243
 polygon, 236
Relation, *see* Equals, 37
 as a set, 52
 definition of, 53
 divides, 43
 equivalence, 46
 inclusion, 38
 inverse of, 53
 matching, 46
 order, 54
 sameness, 40
Repetitive:
 principle, 3
 process, 223
Right section, 240
Roman:
 abacus, 16
 counting board, 13
 numerals, 6
 system of numeration, 6
Rounding off, 213
R, S, T properties, 44

Sameness relation, 40, 42
Scientific notation, 62
Separatrix, 201
Set builder notation, 23
Set of:
 integers, 114
 natural numbers, 23, 43, 84
 rational numbers, 171
 real numbers, 209
Sets, 20
Single-valued relations, 54
Significant digits, 216
Stevin, Simon, 201
Solvability of equations, 173
Soroban, 17
Sphere, 245
Square root algorithm, 220
Square roots, 217
Suan pan, 17
Subsets, 24
 counting, 26
Substitution property of equals, 87
Subtraction as a binary operation, 119
Subtractive principle, 37
Surface area, 238
Symbols, xiii, 2
 Babylonian, 13
Symbols, Chinese-Japanese, 10
 Egyptian, 4
 Hindu-Arabic, 2, 5
 Ionic Greek, 8
 Mayan, 12
 Roman, 6
Symmetric property, 43, 44, 46, 144, 156
System of:
 integers, 115, 116
 rational numbers, 166, 171
 real numbers, 211
 whole numbers, 99
System of numeration and number systems, 84
Systems of numeration:
 additive, 4
 multiplicative, 9
 place-value, 10

Terminating decimals, 212
Torus, 245
Transitive property, 40, 44, 46, 54, 144, 156
Trapezoid, 235
Triangles, area of, 233
Triangular inequality, 141
Trichotomy Law, 108, 115
 in the integers, 137
 in the rationals, 184

Union of sets, 29
Unit, 61
Unit of:
 area, 232
 length, 227
 volume, 239
Universal set, 26
Unreasonable number, 194
Upper bound, 108

Venn diagram, 29
Volumes, 238

Weak inequality, 136
Whole numbers, 81
 set of, 84

Zero, 2, 84
 in addition, 90
 in division, 100, 153, 154
 special properties of, 98
Zero divisors, 122, 148